2011
Yearbook of
Astronomy

2011 Yearbook of Astronomy

edited by
Patrick Moore

and
John Mason

MACMILLAN

First published 2010 by Macmillan
an imprint of Pan Macmillan, a division of Macmillan Publishers Limited
Pan Macmillan, 20 New Wharf Road, London N1 9RR
Basingstoke and Oxford
Associated companies throughout the world
www.panmacmillan.com

ISBN 978-0-230-75209-2

9 8 7 6 5 4 3 2 1

A CIP catalogue record for this book is available from
the British Library.

Typeset by Ellipsis Books Limited, Glasgow
Printed in the UK by CPI Mackays, Chatham, Kent ME5 8TD

Visit **www.panmacmillan.com** to read more about all our books
and to buy them. You will also find features, author interviews and
news of any author events, and you can sign up for e-newsletters
so that you're always first to hear about our new releases.

Contents

Part III
Miscellaneous

Editors' Foreword

The *2011 Yearbook* follows the usual pattern, but with some important refinements. Wil Tirion has once again produced all of the line diagrams showing the positions and movements of the planets to accompany the Monthly Notes, and the sections outlining the observing prospects for eclipses, comets and minor planets, provided by Martin Mobberley, have been improved. Nick James has again produced the data for the phases of the Moon, longitudes of the Sun, Moon and planets, and details of lunar occultations. As always, John Isles and Bob Argyle have provided the information on variable stars and double stars, respectively.

We have a fine selection of longer articles, many from our regular contributors and some from writers who are new to the *Yearbook* this year. As usual, we have done our best to give you a wide range, both of subject and of technical level. For example, David Harland examines the evidence that has been acquired, from a wide range of sources, for the existence of water ice on the Moon. Richard Baum looks back to the eighteenth century and the work of Johann Hieronymus Schröter in establishing, beyond doubt, the existence of an atmosphere around Venus. Martin Mobberley investigates the remarkable achievements of the Japanese patrollers – amateur astronomers with an incredible record for discovering comets, novae and supernovae. Fred Watson explains how astronomers – taking on the rôle of galactic archaeologists – have unravelled the mysteries of the structure of our Galaxy. For the more practically minded amateur astronomer, Paul Abel describes the techniques required to make useful visual observations of the elusive libration areas of the Moon; and for those looking for an interesting place to visit, Jack Wickings describes the Norman Lockyer Observatory near Sidmouth in Devon.

PATRICK MOORE
JOHN MASON
Selsey, August 2010

Preface

New readers will find that all the information in this *Yearbook* is given in diagrammatic or descriptive form; the positions of the planets may easily be found from the specially designed star charts, while the Monthly Notes describe the movements of the planets and give details of other astronomical phenomena visible in both in the Northern and Southern Hemispheres. Two sets of star charts are provided. The **Northern Charts** (pp. 17 to 41) are designed for use at latitude 52°N, but may be used without alteration throughout the British Isles, and (except in the case of eclipses and occultations) in other countries of similar northerly latitude. The **Southern Charts** (pp. 43 to 67) are drawn for latitude 35°S, and are suitable for use in South Africa, Australia and New Zealand, and other locations in approximately the same southerly latitude. The reader who needs more detailed information will find *Norton's Star Atlas* an invaluable guide, while more precise positions of the planets and their satellites, together with predictions of occultations, meteor showers and periodic comets, may be found in the *Handbook of the British Astronomical Association*. Readers will also find details of forthcoming events given in the American monthly magazine *Sky & Telescope* and the British periodicals *The Sky at Night*, *Astronomy Now* and *Astronomy and Space*.

Important note
The times given on the star charts and in the Monthly Notes are generally given as local times, using the 24-hour clock, the day beginning at midnight. All the dates, and the times of a few events (e.g. eclipses) are given in Greenwich Mean Time (GMT), which is related to local time by the formula:

Local Mean Time = GMT − west longitude

In practice, small differences in longitude are ignored, and the observer will use local clock time, which will be the appropriate Standard (or Zone) Time. As the formula indicates, places in west longitude will have a Standard Time slow on GMT, while places in east longitude will have a Standard Time fast on GMT. As examples we have:

Standard Time in

New Zealand	GMT + 12 hours
Victoria, NSW	GMT + 10 hours
Western Australia	GMT + 8 hours
South Africa	GMT + 2 hours
British Isles	GMT
Eastern ST	GMT − 5 hours
Central ST	GMT − 6 hours, etc.

If Summer Time is in use, the clocks will have been advanced by one hour, and this hour must be subtracted from the clock time to give Standard Time.

Part I

Monthly Charts and Astronomical Phenomena

Notes on the Star Charts

The stars, together with the Sun, Moon and planets, seem to be set on the surface of the celestial sphere, which appears to rotate about the Earth from east to west. Since it is impossible to represent a curved surface accurately on a plane, any kind of star map is bound to contain some form of distortion.

Most of the monthly star charts which appear in the various journals and some national newspapers are drawn in circular form. This is perfectly accurate, but it can make the charts awkward to use. For the star charts in this volume, we have preferred to give two hemispherical maps for each month of the year, one showing the northern aspect of the sky and the other showing the southern aspect. Two sets of monthly charts are provided, one for observers in the Northern Hemisphere and one for those in the Southern Hemisphere.

Unfortunately, the constellations near the overhead point (the zenith) on these hemispherical charts can be rather distorted. This would be a serious drawback for precision charts, but what we have done is to give maps which are best suited to star recognition. We have also refrained from putting in too many stars, so that the main patterns stand out clearly. To help observers with any distortions near the zenith, and the lack of overlap between the charts of each pair, we have also included two circular maps, one showing all the constellations in the northern half of the sky and the other showing those in the southern half. Incidentally, there is a curious illusion that stars at an altitude of 60° or more are actually overhead, and beginners may often feel that they are leaning over backwards in trying to see them.

The charts show all stars down to the fourth magnitude, together with a number of fainter stars which are necessary to define the shapes of constellations. There is no standard system for representing the outlines of the constellations, and triangles and other simple figures have been used to give outlines which are easy to trace with the naked eye. The names of the constellations are given, together with the proper names of the brighter stars. The apparent magnitudes of the stars are indicated roughly by using different sizes of dot, the larger dots representing the brighter stars.

The two sets of star charts – one each for Northern and Southern Hemisphere observers – are similar in design. At each opening there is a single circular chart which shows all the constellations in that hemisphere of the sky. (These two charts are centred on the North and South Celestial Poles, respectively.) Then there are twelve double-page spreads, showing the northern and southern aspects for each month of the year for observers in that hemisphere. In the **Northern Charts** (drawn for latitude 52°N) the left-hand chart of each spread shows the northern half of the sky (lettered 1N, 2N, 3N…12N), and the corresponding right-hand chart shows the southern half of the sky (lettered 1S, 2S, 3S…12S). The arrangement and lettering of the charts is exactly the same for the **Southern Charts** (drawn for latitude 35°S).

Because the sidereal day is shorter than the solar day, the stars appear to rise and set about four minutes earlier each day, and this amounts to two hours in a month. Hence the twelve pairs of charts in each set are sufficient to give the appearance of the sky throughout the day at intervals of two hours, or at the same time of night at monthly intervals throughout the year. For example, charts 1N and 1S here are drawn for 23 hours on 6 January. The view will also be the same on 6 October at 05 hours; 6 November at 03 hours; 6 December at 01 hours; and 6 February at 21 hours. The actual range of dates and times when the stars on the charts are visible is indicated on each page. Each pair of charts is numbered in bold type, and the number to be used for any given month and time may be found from the following table:

Local Time	18h	20h	22h	0h	2h	4h	6h
January	11	12	1	2	3	4	5
February	12	1	2	3	4	5	6
March	1	2	3	4	5	6	7
April	2	3	4	5	6	7	8
May	3	4	5	6	7	8	9
June	4	5	6	7	8	9	10
July	5	6	7	8	9	10	11
August	6	7	8	9	10	11	12
September	7	8	9	10	11	12	1

Local Time	18h	20h	22h	0h	2h	4h	6h
October	8	9	10	11	12	1	2
November	9	10	11	12	1	2	3
December	10	11	12	1	2	3	4

On these charts, the ecliptic is drawn as a broken line on which longitude is marked every 10°. The positions of the planets are then easily found by reference to the table on p. 74. It will be noticed that on the **Southern Charts** the ecliptic may reach an altitude in excess of 62.5° on the star charts showing the northern aspect (5N to 9N). The continuations of the broken line will be found on the corresponding charts for the southern aspect (5S, 6S, 8S and 9S).

Northern Star Charts

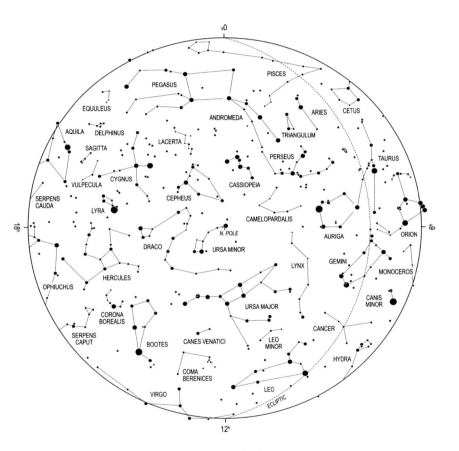

Northern Hemisphere

Note that the markers at 0ʰ, 6ʰ, 12ʰ and 18ʰ
indicate hours of Right Ascension.

1N

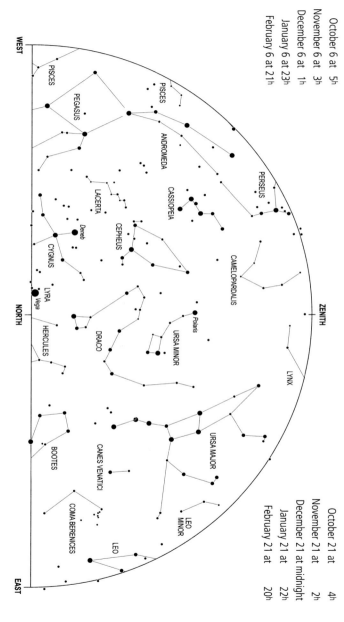

October 6 at 5h
November 6 at 3h
December 6 at 1h
January 6 at 23h
February 6 at 21h

WEST

PISCES
PEGASUS
PISCES
ANDROMEDA
LACERTA
CASSIOPEIA
PERSEUS
Deneb
CEPHEUS
CYGNUS
CAMELOPARDALIS
LYRA
Vega
Polaris
URSA MINOR
HERCULES
DRACO
LYNX
BOOTES
CANES VENATICI
URSA MAJOR
COMA BERENICES
LEO MINOR
LEO

NORTH

ZENITH

EAST

October 21 at 4h
November 21 at 2h
December 21 at midnight
January 21 at 22h
February 21 at 20h

1S

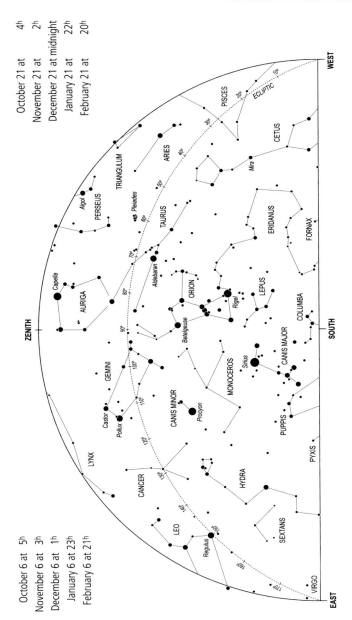

2N

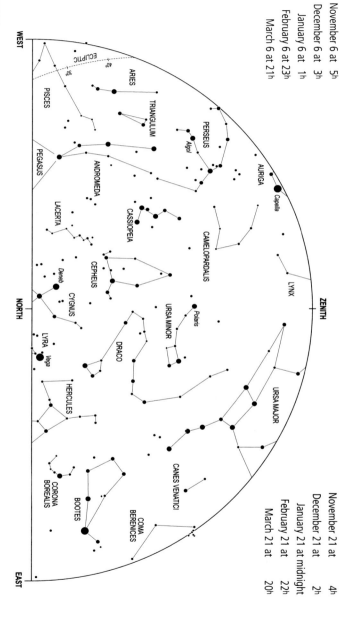

November 6 at 5h
December 6 at 3h
January 6 at 1h
February 6 at 23h
March 6 at 21h

November 21 at 4h
December 21 at 2h
January 21 at midnight
February 21 at 22h
March 21 at 20h

November 21 at 4h
December 21 at 2h
January 21 at midnight
February 21 at 22h
March 21 at 20h

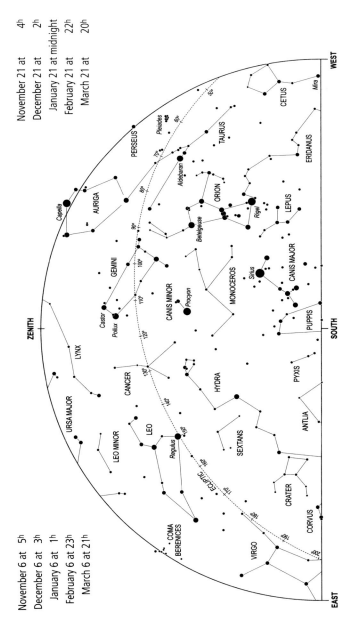

November 6 at 5h
December 6 at 3h
January 6 at 1h
February 6 at 23h
March 6 at 21h

3N

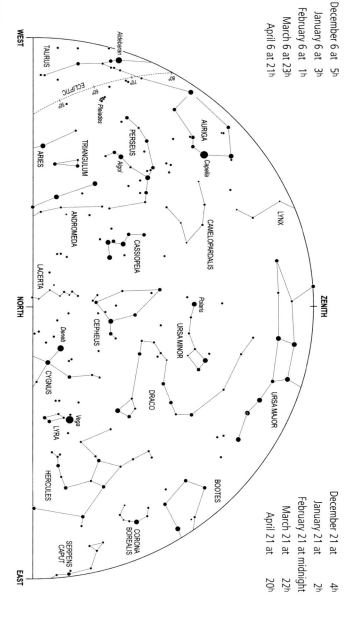

December 6 at 5h
January 6 at 3h
February 6 at 1h
March 6 at 23h
April 6 at 21h

December 21 at 4h
January 21 at 2h
February 21 at midnight
March 21 at 22h
April 21 at 20h

WEST

TAURUS
Aldebaran
ECLIPTIC
70°
80°
60°
Pleiades
50°
ARIES
TRIANGULUM
PERSEUS
Algol
AURIGA
Capella
LYNX
ANDROMEDA
CAMELOPARDALIS
CASSIOPEIA
LACERTA
ZENITH
CEPHEUS
Polaris
URSA MINOR
NORTH
Deneb
CYGNUS
DRACO
URSA MAJOR
Vega
LYRA
HERCULES
BOOTES
CORONA BOREALIS
SERPENS CAPUT
EAST

3S

December 21 at 4h
January 21 at 2h
February 21 at midnight
March 21 at 22h
April 21 at 20h

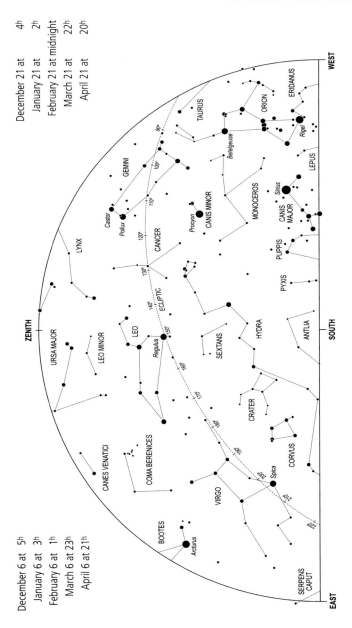

December 6 at 5h
January 6 at 3h
February 6 at 1h
March 6 at 23h
April 6 at 21h

4N

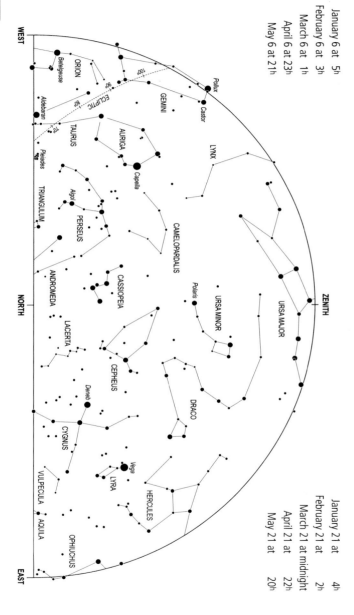

January 6 at 5h
February 6 at 3h
March 6 at 1h
April 6 at 23h
May 6 at 21h

January 21 at 4h
February 21 at 2h
March 21 at midnight
April 21 at 22h
May 21 at 20h

4S

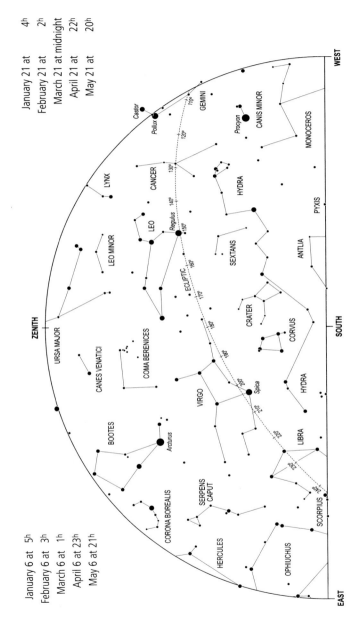

January 21 at   4ʰ
February 21 at   2ʰ
March 21 at midnight
April 21 at   22ʰ
May 21 at   20ʰ

WEST

ZENITH

SOUTH

EAST

January 6 at   5ʰ
February 6 at 3ʰ
March 6 at   1ʰ
April 6 at   23ʰ
May 6 at   21ʰ

Castor
Pollux
GEMINI
CANIS MINOR
Procyon
MONOCEROS
LYNX
CANCER
HYDRA
PYXIS
LEO MINOR
LEO
Regulus
SEXTANS
ANTLIA
ECLIPTIC
CRATER
URSA MAJOR
CANES VENATICI
COMA BERENICES
CORVUS
HYDRA
BOOTES
VIRGO
Spica
Arcturus
LIBRA
CORONA BOREALIS
SERPENS CAPUT
SCORPIUS
HERCULES
OPHIUCHUS

5N

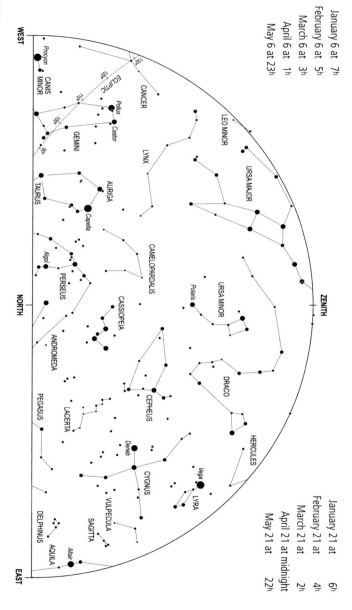

January 6 at 7h
February 6 at 5h
March 6 at 3h
April 6 at 1h
May 6 at 23h

January 21 at 6h
February 21 at 4h
March 21 at 2h
April 21 at midnight
May 21 at 22h

5S

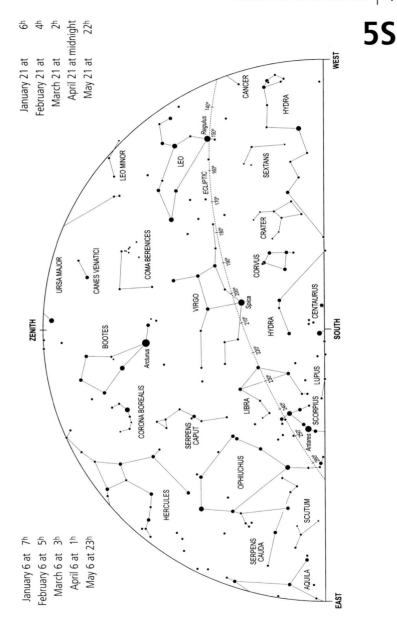

January 21 at 6ʰ
February 21 at 4ʰ
March 21 at 2ʰ
April 21 at midnight
May 21 at 22ʰ

January 6 at 7ʰ
February 6 at 5ʰ
March 6 at 3ʰ
April 6 at 1ʰ
May 6 at 23ʰ

6N

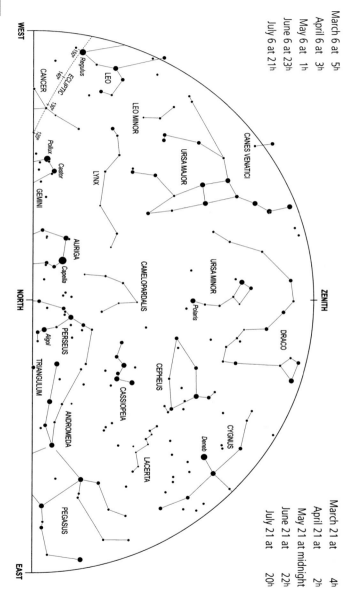

March 6 at 5h
April 6 at 3h
May 6 at 1h
June 6 at 23h
July 6 at 21h

WEST

ZENITH

NORTH

EAST

March 21 at 4h
April 21 at 2h
May 21 at midnight
June 21 at 22h
July 21 at 20h

LEO

CANCER

ECLIPTIC

Regulus

Pollux
Castor

GEMINI

LEO MINOR

LYNX

URSA MAJOR

CANES VENATICI

URSA MINOR

Polaris

DRACO

AURIGA

Capella

CAMELOPARDALIS

PERSEUS

Algol

TRIANGULUM

CEPHEUS

CASSIOPEIA

ANDROMEDA

CYGNUS

Deneb

LACERTA

PEGASUS

6S

March 21 at   4h
April 21 at   2h
May 21 at midnight
June 21 at   22h
July 21 at   20h

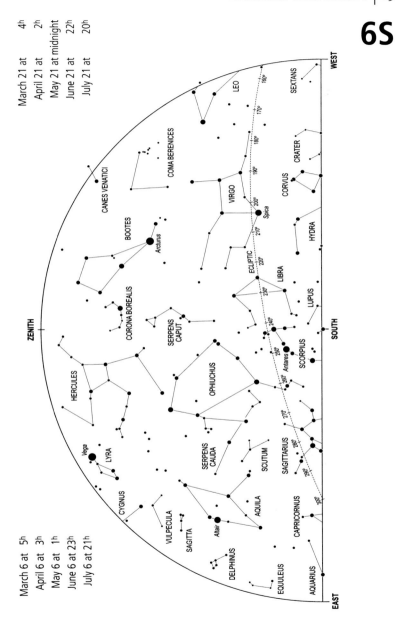

March 6 at   5h
April 6 at   3h
May 6 at   1h
June 6 at 23h
July 6 at 21h

ZENITH

WEST

SEXTANS

LEO

160°
170°

COMA BERENICES

CRATER

CORVUS

VIRGO

190°
180°

CANES VENATICI

200°
Spica

BOOTES

210°
Arcturus

HYDRA

ECLIPTIC
220°

LIBRA

CORONA BOREALIS

230°

LUPUS

SERPENS
CAPUT

240°

SOUTH

HERCULES

OPHIUCHUS

250°
Antares
SCORPIUS
260°

270°

LYRA
Vega

SERPENS
CAUDA

SCUTUM

SAGITTARIUS

280°

CYGNUS

290°

VULPECULA

AQUILA

CAPRICORNUS

300°

SAGITTA

Altair

DELPHINUS

EQUULEUS

AQUARIUS

EAST

7N

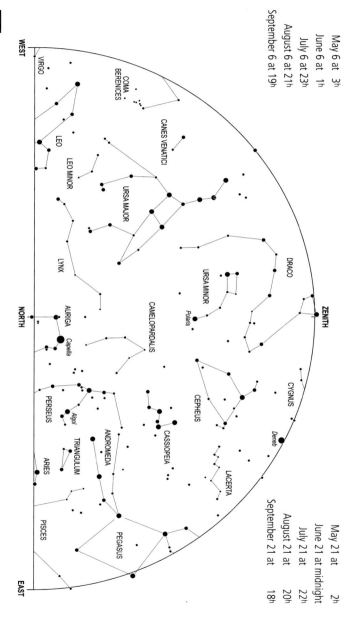

May 6 at   3ʰ
June 6 at   1ʰ
July 6 at 23ʰ
September 6 at 19ʰ

May 21 at   2ʰ
June 21 at midnight
July 21 at   22ʰ
August 21 at   20ʰ
September 21 at   18ʰ

WEST

NORTH

EAST

ZENITH

VIRGO
COMA BERENICES
CANES VENATICI
LEO
LEO MINOR
URSA MAJOR
LYNX
AURIGA
Capella
CAMELOPARDALIS
URSA MINOR
Polaris
DRACO
CYGNUS
Deneb
CEPHEUS
CASSIOPEIA
LACERTA
PERSEUS
Algol
TRIANGULUM
ANDROMEDA
ARIES
PISCES
PEGASUS

7S

May 21 at 2h
June 21 at midnight
July 21 at 22h
August 21 at 20h
September 21 at 18h

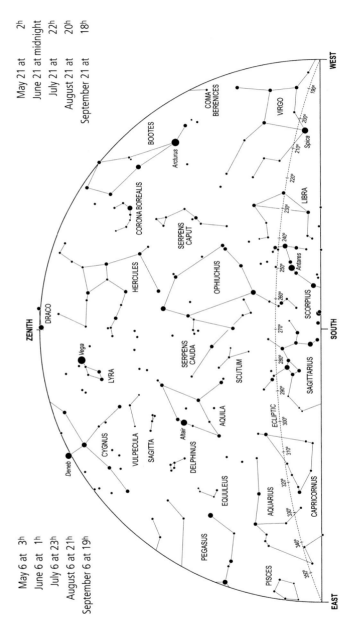

May 6 at 3h
June 6 at 1h
July 6 at 23h
August 6 at 21h
September 6 at 19h

8N

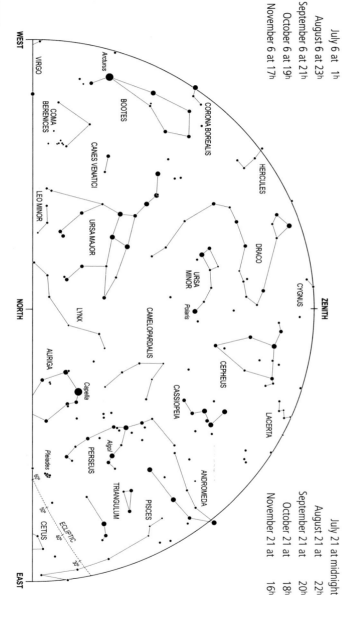

July 6 at 1h
August 6 at 23h
September 6 at 21h
October 6 at 19h
November 6 at 17h

July 21 at midnight
August 21 at 22h
September 21 at 20h
October 21 at 18h
November 21 at 16h

WEST

ZENITH

NORTH

EAST

VIRGO
Arcturus
COMA BERENICES
BOOTES
CORONA BOREALIS
HERCULES
CANES VENATICI
LEO MINOR
URSA MAJOR
DRACO
CYGNUS
URSA MINOR
Polaris
LYNX
CAMELOPARDALIS
CEPHEUS
LACERTA
AURIGA
CASSIOPEIA
Capella
Algol
PERSEUS
Pleiades
ANDROMEDA
TRIANGULUM
PISCES
ECLIPTIC
CETUS
60°
50°
40°
30°

July 21 at midnight   22ʰ
August 21 at   20ʰ
September 21 at   20ʰ
October 21 at   18ʰ
November 21 at   16ʰ

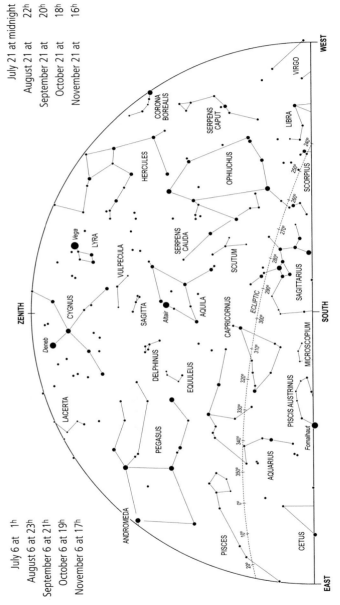

July 6 at   1ʰ
August 6 at 23ʰ
September 6 at 21ʰ
October 6 at 19ʰ
November 6 at 17ʰ

9N

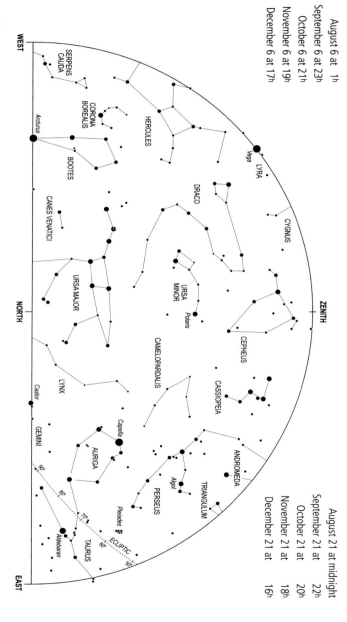

August 6 at 1h
September 6 at 23h
October 6 at 21h
November 6 at 19h
December 6 at 17h

August 21 at midnight
September 21 at 22h
October 21 at 20h
November 21 at 18h
December 21 at 16h

WEST

NORTH

EAST

ZENITH

SERPENS CAUDA
CORONA BOREALIS
HERCULES
BOOTES
Arcturus
CANES VENATICI
URSA MAJOR
LYNX
Castor
GEMINI
AURIGA
Capella
DRACO
URSA MINOR
Polaris
CAMELOPARDALIS
Vega
LYRA
CYGNUS
CEPHEUS
CASSIOPEIA
ANDROMEDA
TRIANGULUM
Algol
PERSEUS
Pleiades
ECLIPTIC
Aldebaran
TAURUS

90°
80°
70°
60°
50°

9S

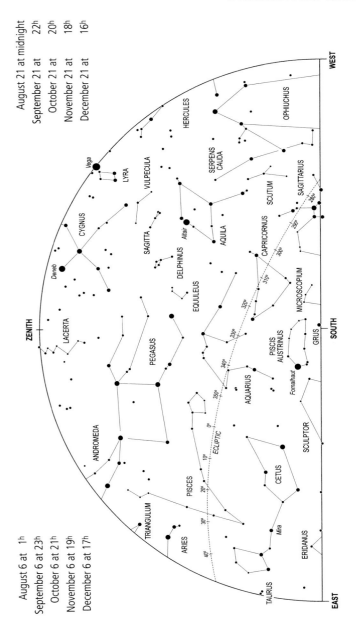

August 21 at midnight
September 21 at 22ʰ
October 21 at 20ʰ
November 21 at 18ʰ
December 21 at 16ʰ

August 6 at 1ʰ
September 6 at 23ʰ
October 6 at 21ʰ
November 6 at 19ʰ
December 6 at 17ʰ

WEST

HERCULES
OPHIUCHUS
SERPENS CAUDA
SAGITTARIUS
280°
Vega
LYRA
VULPECULA
SCUTUM
290°
CYGNUS
SAGITTA
AQUILA
CAPRICORNUS
Altair
300°
Deneb
DELPHINUS
310°
MICROSCOPIUM
EQUULEUS
320°
ZENITH
LACERTA
330°
PISCIS AUSTRINUS
GRUS
SOUTH
PEGASUS
340°
AQUARIUS
Fomalhaut
350°
ANDROMEDA
SCULPTOR
0°
ECLIPTIC
10°
PISCES
20°
CETUS
TRIANGULUM
30°
Mira
ERIDANUS
ARIES
40°
TAURUS
EAST

10N

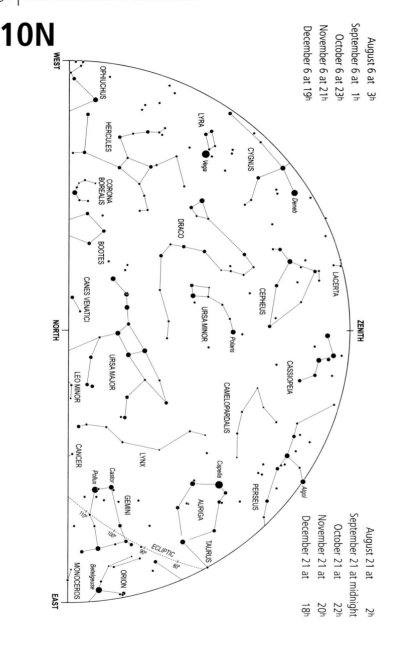

August 6 at 3h
September 6 at 1h
October 6 at 23h
November 6 at 21h
December 6 at 19h

August 21 at 2h
September 21 at midnight
October 21 at 22h
November 21 at 20h
December 21 at 18h

10S

August 21 at 2ʰ
September 21 at midnight
October 21 at 22ʰ
November 21 at 20ʰ
December 21 at 18ʰ

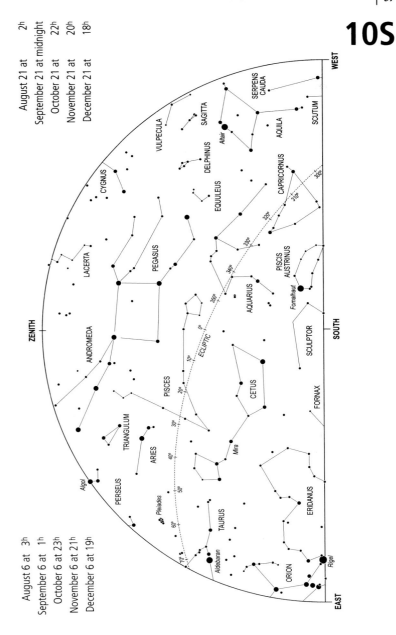

August 6 at 3ʰ
September 6 at 1ʰ
October 6 at 23ʰ
November 6 at 21ʰ
December 6 at 19ʰ

11N

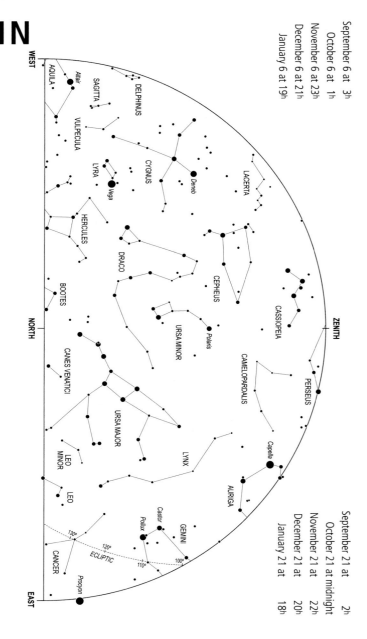

September 6 at 3ʰ
October 6 at 1ʰ
November 6 at 23ʰ
December 6 at 21ʰ
January 6 at 19ʰ

September 21 at   2ʰ
October 21 at midnight
November 21 at 22ʰ
December 21 at 20ʰ
January 21 at 18ʰ

11S

September 21 at 2h
October 21 at midnight
November 21 at 22h
December 21 at 20h
January 21 at 18h

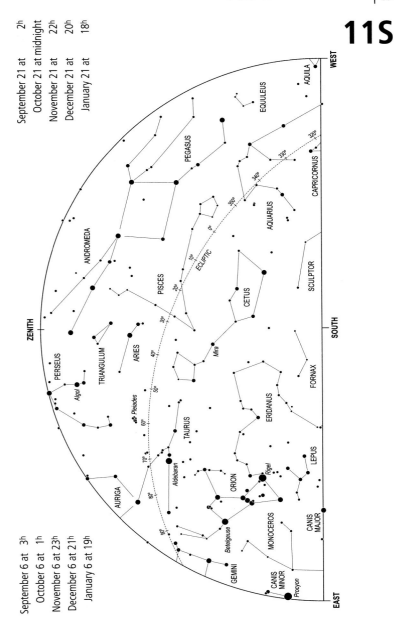

September 6 at 3h
October 6 at 1h
November 6 at 23h
December 6 at 21h
January 6 at 19h

12N

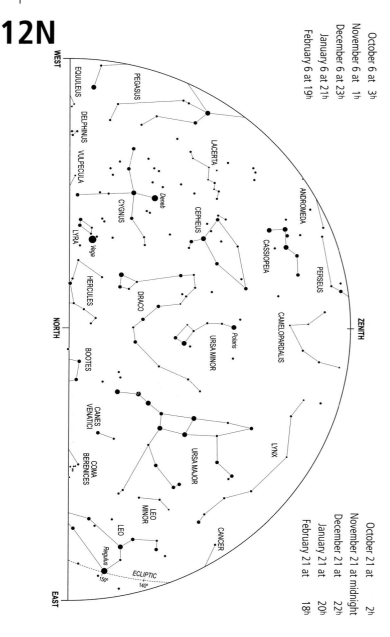

October 6 at 3h
November 6 at 1h
December 6 at 23h
January 6 at 21h
February 6 at 19h

October 21 at 2h
November 21 at midnight
December 21 at 22h
January 21 at 20h
February 21 at 18h

WEST

NORTH

EAST

ZENITH

EQUULEUS
DELPHINUS
VULPECULA
PEGASUS
LACERTA
CYGNUS
Deneb
LYRA
Vega
HERCULES
CEPHEUS
ANDROMEDA
CASSIOPEIA
PERSEUS
DRACO
CAMELOPARDALIS
Polaris
URSA MINOR
BOOTES
CANES VENATICI
COMA BERENICES
URSA MAJOR
LYNX
LEO MINOR
LEO
Regulus
CANCER
ECLIPTIC
150°
140°

12S

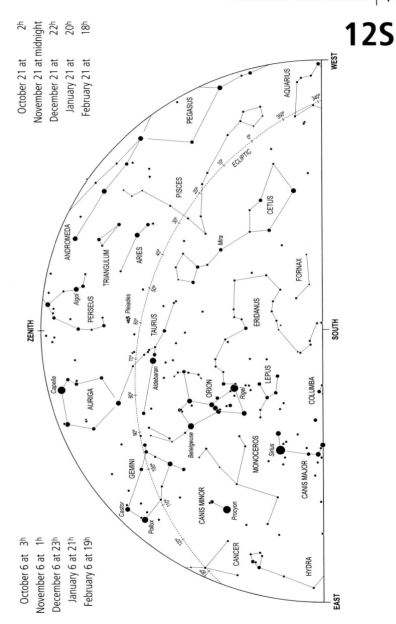

WEST

AQUARIUS

PEGASUS

340°

350°

0°

ECLIPTIC

10°

PISCES

20°

CETUS

30°

ANDROMEDA

Mira

40°

FORNAX

TRIANGULUM

ARIES

SOUTH

50°

Algol

PERSEUS

Pleiades

60°

TAURUS

ERIDANUS

ZENITH

70°

Capella

Aldebaran

AURIGA

80°

ORION

LEPUS

Rigel

Betelgeuse

90°

COLUMBA

MONOCEROS

Sirius

100°

GEMINI

CANIS MAJOR

Castor

110°

Pollux

CANIS MINOR

Procyon

120°

CANCER

HYDRA

130°

EAST

Southern Star Charts

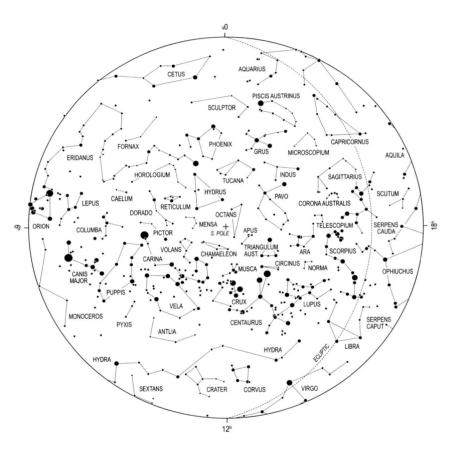

Southern Hemisphere

Note that the markers at 0ʰ, 6ʰ, 12ʰ and 18ʰ
indicate hours of Right Ascension.

1N

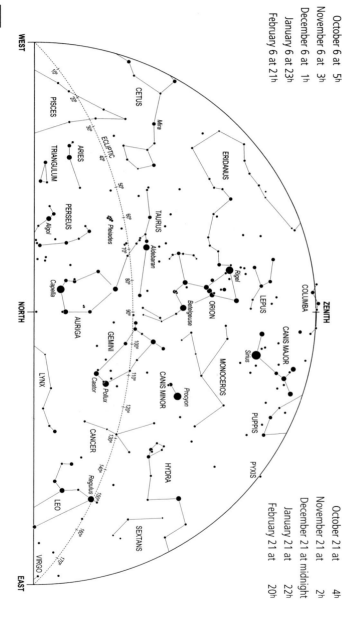

WEST

ZENITH

NORTH

EAST

CETUS
PISCES
Mira
ECLIPTIC
TRIANGULUM
ARIES
ERIDANUS
PERSEUS
Algol
TAURUS
Pleiades
Aldebaran
Capella
AURIGA
Rigel
LEPUS
COLUMBA
Betelgeuse
ORION
CANIS MAJOR
Sirius
GEMINI
MONOCEROS
LYNX
Castor
Pollux
CANIS MINOR
Procyon
PUPPIS
CANCER
HYDRA
PYXIS
LEO
Regulus
SEXTANS
VIRGO

10°
20°
30°
40°
50°
60°
70°
80°
90°
100°
110°
120°
130°
140°
150°
160°
170°

1S

October 21 at 4h
November 21 at 2h
December 21 at midnight
January 21 at 22h
February 21 at 20h

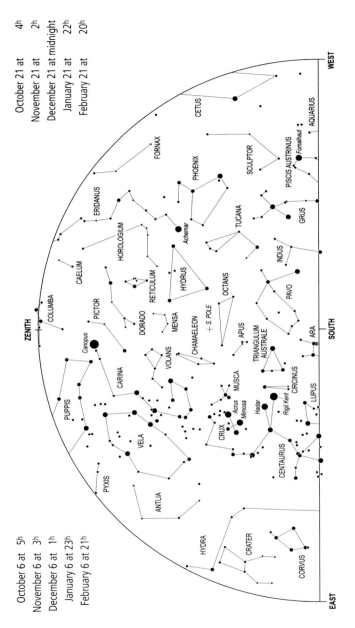

October 6 at 5h
November 6 at 3h
December 6 at 1h
January 6 at 23h
February 6 at 21h

2N

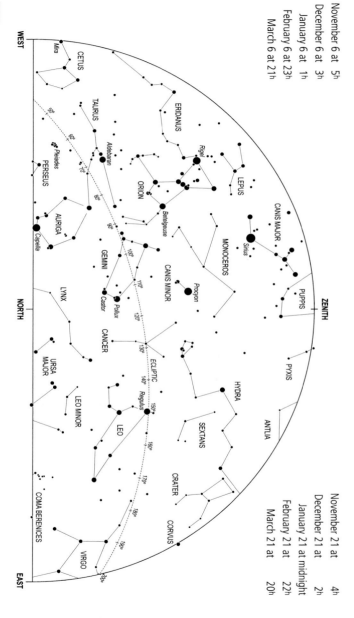

November 6 at 5ʰ
December 6 at 3ʰ
January 6 at 1ʰ
February 6 at 23ʰ
March 6 at 21ʰ

November 21 at 4ʰ
December 21 at 2ʰ
January 21 at midnight
February 21 at 22ʰ
March 21 at 20ʰ

WEST

NORTH

EAST

ZENITH

CETUS
Mira
TAURUS
ERIDANUS
Aldebaran
Pleiades
PERSEUS
ORION
Rigel
LEPUS
Betelgeuse
CANIS MAJOR
Sirius
AURIGA
Capella
GEMINI
MONOCEROS
PUPPIS
Castor
Pollux
CANIS MINOR
Procyon
LYNX
CANCER
PYXIS
URSA MAJOR
ECLIPTIC
HYDRA
ANTLIA
LEO MINOR
LEO
Regulus
SEXTANS
COMA BERENICES
CRATER
VIRGO
CORVUS

50°
60°
70°
80°
90°
100°
110°
120°
130°
140°
150°
160°
170°
180°
190°
200°

2S

November 21 at 4h
December 21 at 2h
January 21 at midnight
February 21 at 22h
March 21 at 20h

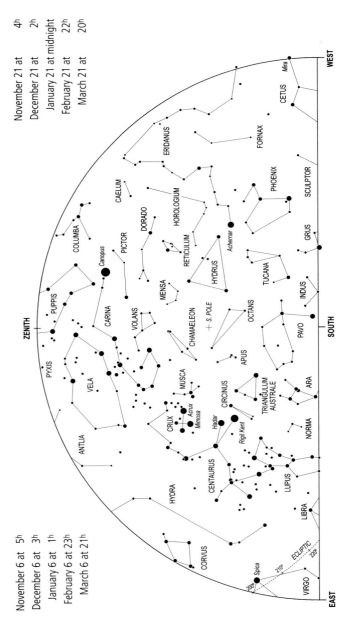

November 6 at 5h
December 6 at 3h
January 6 at 1h
February 6 at 23h
March 6 at 21h

WEST

ZENITH

SOUTH

EAST

Mira
CETUS
ERIDANUS
FORNAX
CAELUM
PHOENIX
SCULPTOR
DORADO
HOROLOGIUM
COLUMBA
PICTOR
RETICULUM
Achernar
GRUS
Canopus
HYDRUS
PUPPIS
CARINA
MENSA
TUCANA
INDUS
VOLANS
CHAMAELEON
S. POLE
OCTANS
PYXIS
PAVO
VELA
MUSCA
APUS
ANTLIA
CRUX
CIRCINUS
TRIANGULUM AUSTRALE
ARA
Acrux
Mimosa
Hadar
Rigil Kent
NORMA
HYDRA
CENTAURUS
LUPUS
LIBRA
CORVUS
Spica
200°
210°
ECLIPTIC
220°
VIRGO

3N

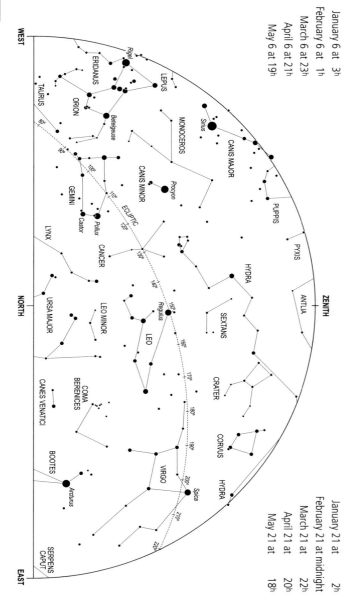

3S

January 21 at 2ʰ
February 21 at midnight
March 21 at 22ʰ
April 21 at 20ʰ
May 21 at 18ʰ

January 6 at 3ʰ
February 6 at 1ʰ
March 6 at 23ʰ
April 6 at 21ʰ
May 6 at 19ʰ

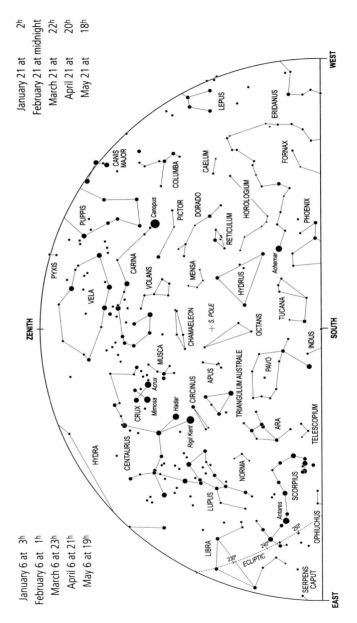

WEST

ZENITH

SOUTH

EAST

LEPUS
ERIDANUS
CANIS MAJOR
COLUMBA
CAELUM
FORNAX
PUPPIS
Canopus
PICTOR
DORADO
HOROLOGIUM
PHOENIX
PYXIS
CARINA
RETICULUM
VOLANS
MENSA
HYDRUS
Achernar
VELA
CHAMAELEON
OCTANS
TUCANA
+ S. POLE
MUSCA
APUS
INDUS
Actrux
CRUX
CIRCINUS
TRIANGULUM AUSTRALE
PAVO
Mimosa
Hadar
Rigil Kent
CENTAURUS
ARA
HYDRA
NORMA
TELESCOPIUM
SCORPIUS
LUPUS
Antares
250°
240°
230°
LIBRA
OPHIUCHUS
ECLIPTIC
SERPENS CAPUT

4N

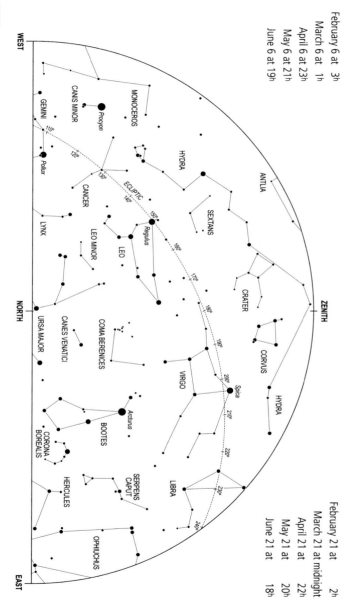

4S

February 21 at 2ʰ
March 21 at midnight
April 21 at 22ʰ
May 21 at 20ʰ
June 21 at 18ʰ

February 6 at 3ʰ
March 6 at 1ʰ
April 6 at 23ʰ
May 6 at 21ʰ
June 6 at 19ʰ

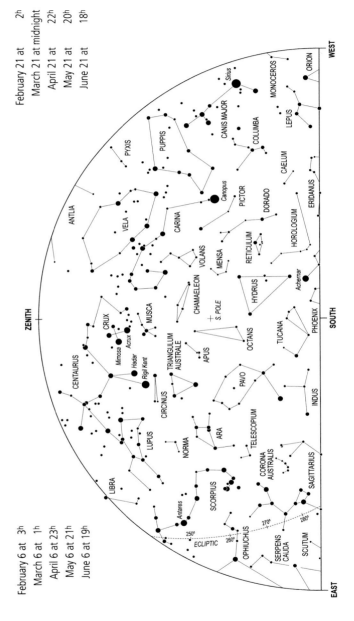

WEST

ZENITH

SOUTH

EAST

ORION
MONOCEROS
Sirius
CANIS MAJOR
COLUMBA
LEPUS
CAELUM
PYXIS
PUPPIS
ERIDANUS
PICTOR
Canopus
DORADO
CARINA
ANTLIA
VELA
HOROLOGIUM
RETICULUM
MENSA
VOLANS
Achernar
CHAMAELEON
HYDRUS
PHOENIX
CRUX
MUSCA
S. POLE
Acrux
Mimosa
Hadar
TRIANGULUM
AUSTRALE
OCTANS
TUCANA
CENTAURUS
Rigil Kent
APUS
CIRCINUS
PAVO
INDUS
LUPUS
NORMA
ARA
TELESCOPIUM
LIBRA
CORONA
AUSTRALIS
SAGITTARIUS
SCORPIUS
Antares
250°
260°
270°
280°
OPHIUCHUS
ECLIPTIC
SERPENS
CAUDA
SCUTUM

5N

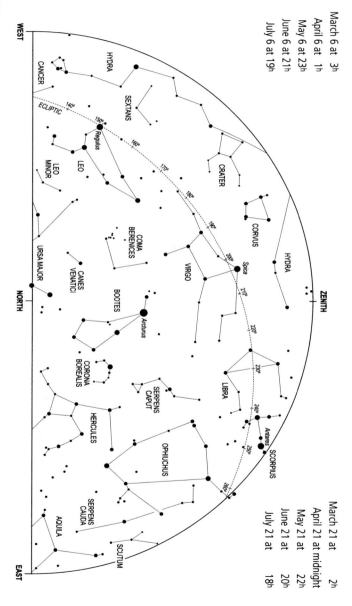

March 6 at 3h
April 6 at 1h
May 6 at 23h
June 6 at 21h
July 6 at 19h

March 21 at 2h
April 21 at midnight
May 21 at 22h
June 21 at 20h
July 21 at 18h

5S

March 21 at 2ʰ
April 21 at midnight
May 21 at 22ʰ
June 21 at 20ʰ
July 21 at 18ʰ

March 6 at 3ʰ
April 6 at 1ʰ
May 6 at 23ʰ
June 6 at 21ʰ
July 6 at 19ʰ

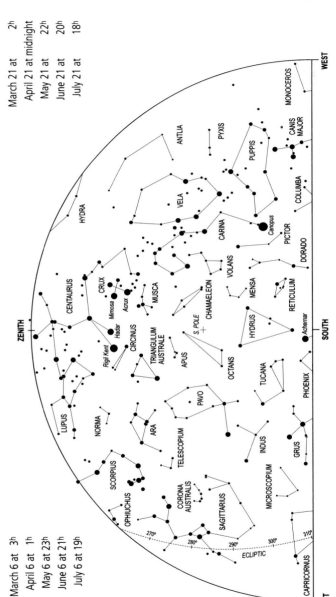

6N

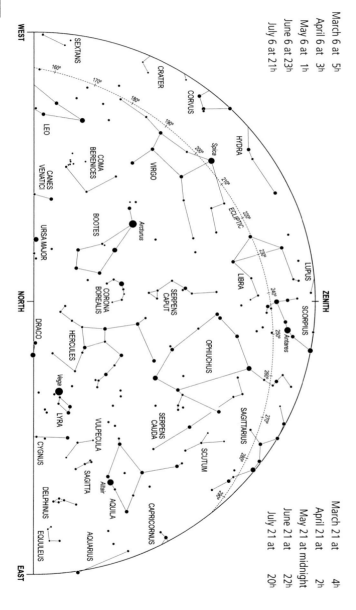

March 6 at 5h
April 6 at 3h
May 6 at 1h
June 6 at 23h
July 6 at 21h

March 21 at 4h
April 21 at 2h
May 21 at midnight
June 21 at 22h
July 21 at 20h

WEST

SEXTANS
CRATER
CORVUS
LEO
COMA BERENICES
HYDRA
Spica
VIRGO
CANES VENATICI
BOOTES
Arcturus
LIBRA
ECLIPTIC
LUPUS
ZENITH
SCORPIUS
Antares
SERPENS CAPUT
CORONA BOREALIS
URSA MAJOR
OPHIUCHUS
HERCULES
Vega
LYRA
SERPENS CAUDA
SAGITTARIUS
DRACO
NORTH
VULPECULA
SCUTUM
CYGNUS
SAGITTA
Altair
AQUILA
CAPRICORNUS
DELPHINUS
AQUARIUS
EQUULEUS
EAST

6S

March 21 at 4ʰ
April 21 at 2ʰ
May 21 at midnight
June 21 at 22ʰ
July 21 at 20ʰ

March 6 at 5ʰ
April 6 at 3ʰ
May 6 at 1ʰ
June 6 at 23ʰ
July 6 at 21ʰ

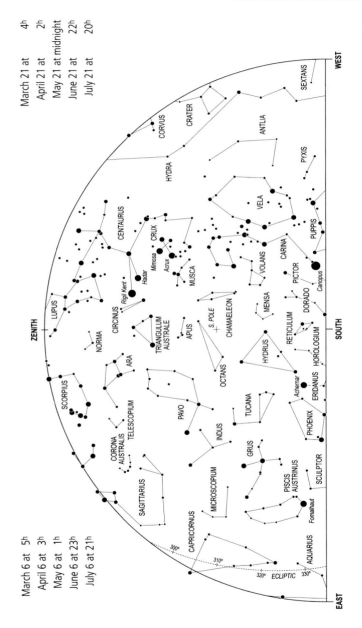

7N

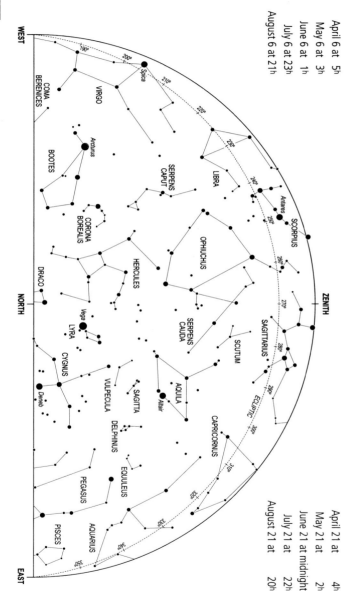

WEST

April 6 at 5h
May 6 at 3h
June 6 at 1h
July 6 at 23h
August 6 at 21h

COMA BERENICES
VIRGO
Spica
190°
200°
210°
220°
BOOTES
Arcturus
SERPENS CAPUT
LIBRA
230°
240°
Antares
250°
SCORPIUS
CORONA BOREALIS
HERCULES
OPHIUCHUS
260°
DRACO
NORTH
SERPENS CAUDA
270°
ZENITH
SAGITTARIUS
280°
Vega
LYRA
SCUTUM
290°
ECLIPTIC
CYGNUS
VULPECULA
SAGITTA
AQUILA
Altair
CAPRICORNUS
300°
Deneb
DELPHINUS
EQUULEUS
310°
PEGASUS
320°
330°
AQUARIUS
340°
PISCES
350°
EAST

April 21 at 4h
May 21 at 2h
June 21 at midnight
July 21 at 22h
August 21 at 20h

7S

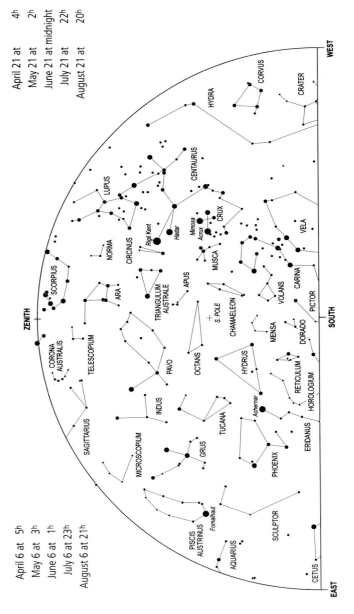

April 21 at 4ʰ
May 21 at 2ʰ
June 21 at midnight
July 21 at 22ʰ
August 21 at 20ʰ

April 6 at 5ʰ
May 6 at 3ʰ
June 6 at 1ʰ
July 6 at 23ʰ
August 6 at 21ʰ

WEST

EAST

SOUTH

ZENITH

S. POLE

CORVUS
CRATER
HYDRA
CENTAURUS
LUPUS
Rigil Kent
Hadar
Mimosa
Acrux
CRUX
VELA
MUSCA
NORMA
CIRCINUS
CARINA
SCORPIUS
ARA
APUS
VOLANS
TRIANGULUM AUSTRALE
PICTOR
CHAMAELEON
CORONA AUSTRALIS
TELESCOPIUM
PAVO
OCTANS
HYDRUS
MENSA
DORADO
RETICULUM
SAGITTARIUS
INDUS
TUCANA
Achernar
HOROLOGIUM
MICROSCOPIUM
GRUS
PHOENIX
ERIDANUS
PISCIS AUSTRINUS
Fomalhaut
SCULPTOR
AQUARIUS
CETUS

8N

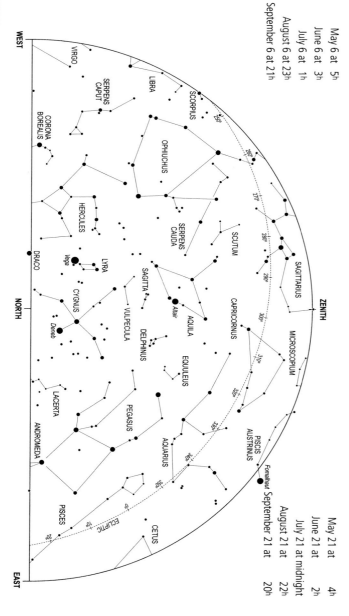

May 6 at 5h
June 6 at 3h
July 6 at 1h
August 6 at 23h
September 6 at 21h

May 21 at 4h
June 21 at 2h
July 21 at midnight
August 21 at 22h
September 21 at 20h

8S

May 21 at 4h
June 21 at 2h
July 21 at midnight
August 21 at 22h
September 21 at 20h

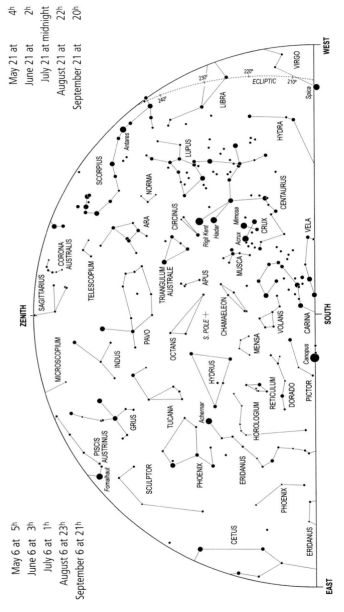

May 6 at 5h
June 6 at 3h
July 6 at 1h
August 6 at 23h
September 6 at 21h

9N

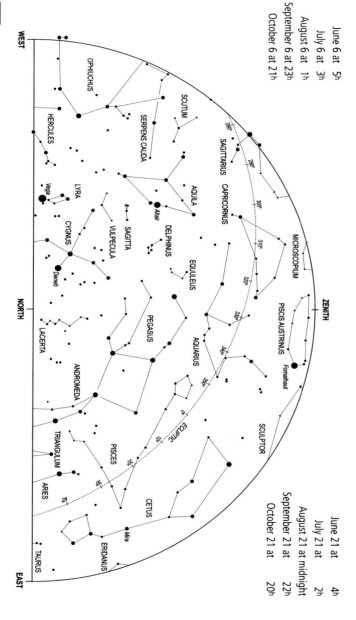

WEST

June 6 at 5h
July 6 at 3h
August 6 at 1h
September 6 at 23h
October 6 at 21h

NORTH

EAST

June 21 at 4h
July 21 at 2h
August 21 at midnight
September 21 at 22h
October 21 at 20h

ZENITH

9S

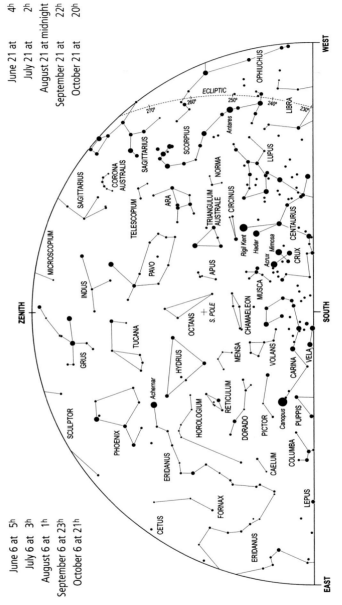

June 21 at 4h
July 21 at 2h
August 21 at midnight
September 21 at 22h
October 21 at 20h

June 6 at 5h
July 6 at 3h
August 6 at 1h
September 6 at 23h
October 6 at 21h

WEST

ZENITH

SOUTH

EAST

OPHIUCHUS

ECLIPTIC

270° 260° 250° 240° 230°

LIBRA

Antares

SCORPIUS

SAGITTARIUS

LUPUS

CORONA AUSTRALIS

SAGITTARIUS

NORMA

TRIANGULUM AUSTRALE

CIRCINUS

CENTAURUS

ARA

TELESCOPIUM

MICROSCOPIUM

PAVO

APUS

Rigil Kent

Hadar

Mimosa

Acrux

CRUX

MUSCA

INDUS

OCTANS

S. POLE

CHAMAELEON

TUCANA

MENSA

VOLANS

CARINA

VELA

GRUS

HYDRUS

RETICULUM

Achernar

HOROLOGIUM

DORADO

PICTOR

Canopus

PUPPIS

SCULPTOR

PHOENIX

ERIDANUS

CAELUM

COLUMBA

LEPUS

CETUS

FORNAX

ERIDANUS

10N

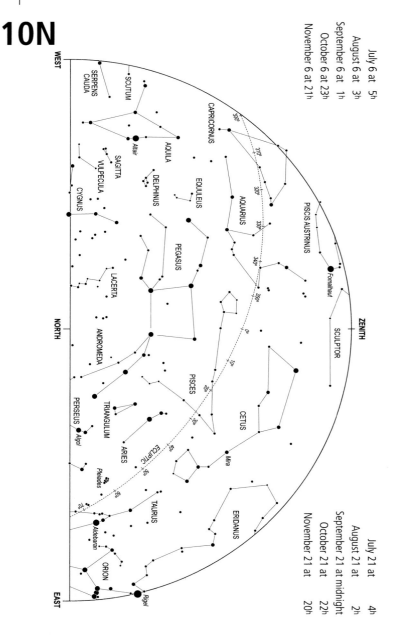

July 6 at 5h
August 6 at 3h
September 6 at 1h
October 6 at 23h
November 6 at 21h

July 21 at 4h
August 21 at 2h
September 21 at midnight
October 21 at 22h
November 21 at 20h

WEST

NORTH

EAST

ZENITH

SERPENS CAUDA
SCUTUM
Altair
AQUILA
SAGITTA
VULPECULA
DELPHINUS
CYGNUS
CAPRICORNUS
EQUULEUS
AQUARIUS
PISCIS AUSTRINUS
Fomalhaut
SCULPTOR
PEGASUS
LACERTA
ANDROMEDA
PISCES
CETUS
PERSEUS
Algol
TRIANGULUM
ARIES
Mira
ECLIPTIC
Pleiades
TAURUS
Aldebaran
ERIDANUS
ORION
Rigel

300°
310°
320°
330°
340°
350°
0°
10°
20°
30°
40°
50°
60°
70°

10S

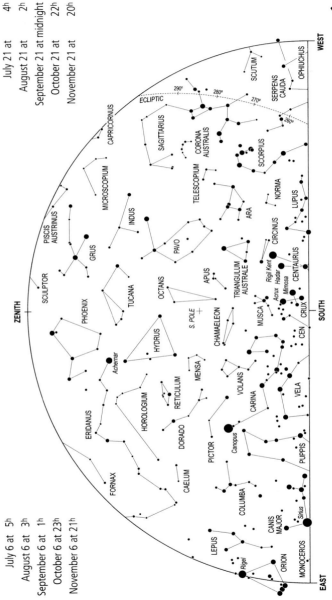

July 21 at 4h
August 21 at 2h
September 21 at midnight
October 21 at 22h
November 21 at 20h

July 6 at 5h
August 6 at 3h
September 6 at 1h
October 6 at 23h
November 6 at 21h

WEST

ZENITH

SOUTH

EAST

ECLIPTIC

290° 280° 270° 260°

OPHIUCHUS
SCUTUM
SERPENS CAUDA
CAPRICORNUS
SAGITTARIUS
CORONA AUSTRALIS
SCORPIUS
MICROSCOPIUM
TELESCOPIUM
NORMA
INDUS
ARA
LUPUS
PISCIS AUSTRINUS
PAVO
CIRCINUS
GRUS
Rigil Kent
Hadar
CENTAURUS
SCULPTOR
APUS
TRIANGULUM AUSTRALE
Acrux
Mimosa
PHOENIX
TUCANA
OCTANS
MUSCA
CRUX
CEN
S. POLE
CHAMAELEON
HYDRUS
Achernar
MENSA
VOLANS
VELA
ERIDANUS
HOROLOGIUM
RETICULUM
CARINA
DORADO
PICTOR
FORNAX
CAELUM
Canopus
PUPPIS
LEPUS
COLUMBA
CANIS MAJOR
Sirius
Rigel
ORION
MONOCEROS

11N

August 6 at 5h
September 6 at 3h
October 6 at 1h
November 6 at 23h
December 6 at 21h

August 21 at 4h
September 21 at 2h
October 21 at midnight
November 21 at 22h
December 21 at 20h

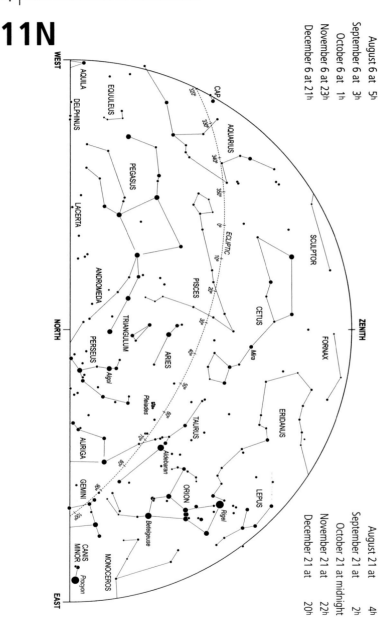

August 21 at 4h
September 21 at 2h
October 21 at midnight
November 21 at 22h
December 21 at 20h

August 6 at 5h
September 6 at 3h
October 6 at 1h
November 6 at 23h
December 6 at 21h

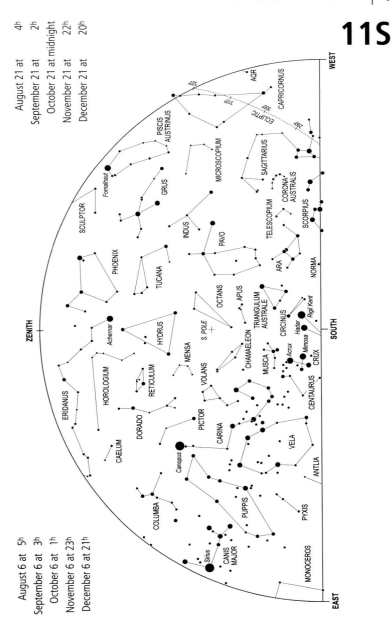

WEST

AQR

PISCIS AUSTRINUS

CAPRICORNUS

320°

310°

300°

ECLIPTIC

290°

SAGITTARIUS

MICROSCOPIUM

Fomalhaut

GRUS

CORONA AUSTRALIS

SCORPIUS

SCULPTOR

INDUS

PAVO

TELESCOPIUM

ARA

NORMA

PHOENIX

TUCANA

OCTANS

APUS

TRIANGULUM AUSTRALE

CIRCINUS

Rigil Kent

Hadar

Mimosa

Achernar

ZENITH

S. POLE

CHAMAELEON

Acrux

CRUX

HYDRUS

MENSA

MUSCA

SOUTH

ERIDANUS

HOROLOGIUM

RETICULUM

VOLANS

CENTAURUS

CAELUM

DORADO

PICTOR

CARINA

VELA

ANTLIA

Canopus

COLUMBA

PUPPIS

PYXIS

Sirius

CANIS MAJOR

MONOCEROS

EAST

12N

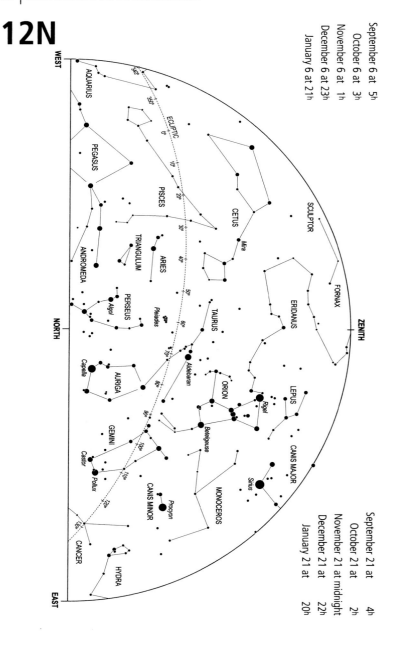

September 6 at 5h
October 6 at 3h
November 6 at 1h
December 6 at 23h
January 6 at 21h

September 21 at 4h
October 21 at 2h
November 21 at midnight
December 21 at 22h
January 21 at 20h

12S

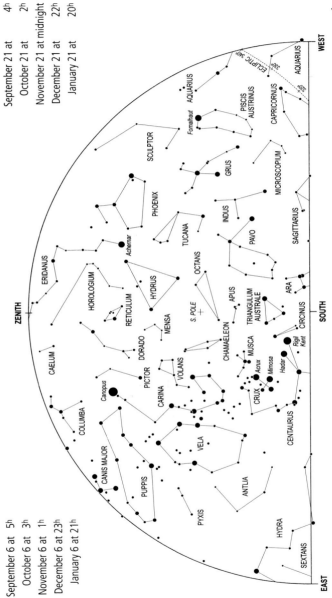

September 21 at 4h
October 21 at 2h
November 21 at midnight
December 21 at 22h
January 21 at 20h

September 6 at 5h
October 6 at 3h
November 6 at 1h
December 6 at 23h
January 6 at 21h

WEST

ZENITH

SOUTH

EAST

AQUARIUS
PISCIS AUSTRINUS
CAPRICORNUS
Fomalhaut
GRUS
MICROSCOPIUM
SCULPTOR
INDUS
SAGITTARIUS
PHOENIX
TUCANA
PAVO
Achernar
ERIDANUS
OCTANS
ARA
HOROLOGIUM
HYDRUS
APUS
CIRCINUS
RETICULUM
MENSA
TRIANGULUM AUSTRALE
Rigil Kent
CAELUM
DORADO
S. POLE
CHAMAELEON
MUSCA
Mimosa
VOLANS
Acrux
Hadar
PICTOR
CRUX
Canopus
CARINA
CENTAURUS
COLUMBA
VELA
CANIS MAJOR
ANTLIA
PUPPIS
PYXIS
HYDRA
SEXTANS

ECLIPTIC 340°
350°
360°

The Planets and the Ecliptic

The paths of the planets about the Sun all lie close to the plane of the ecliptic, which is marked for us in the sky by the apparent path of the Sun among the stars, and is shown on the star charts by a broken line. The Moon and planets will always be found close to this line, never departing from it by more than about 7°. Thus the planets are most favourably placed for observation when the ecliptic is well displayed, and this means that it should be as high in the sky as possible. This avoids the difficulty of finding a clear horizon, and also overcomes the problem of atmospheric absorption, which greatly reduces the light of the stars. Thus a star at an altitude of 10° suffers a loss of 60 per cent of its light, which corresponds to a whole magnitude; at an altitude of only 4°, the loss may amount to two magnitudes.

The position of the ecliptic in the sky is therefore of great importance, and since it is tilted at about 23.5° to the Equator, it is only at certain times of the day or year that it is displayed to best advantage. It will be realized that the Sun (and therefore the ecliptic) is at its highest in the sky at noon in midsummer, and at its lowest at noon in midwinter. Allowing for the daily motion of the sky, it follows that the ecliptic is highest at midnight in winter, at sunset in the spring, at noon in summer and at sunrise in the autumn. Hence these are the best times to see the planets. Thus, if Venus is an evening object in the western sky after sunset, it will be seen to best advantage if this occurs in the spring, when the ecliptic is high in the sky and slopes down steeply to the horizon. This means that the planet is not only higher in the sky, but will remain for a much longer period above the horizon. For similar reasons, a morning object will be seen at its best on autumn mornings before sunrise, when the ecliptic is high in the east. The outer planets, which can come to opposition (i.e. opposite the Sun), are best seen when opposition occurs in the winter months, when the ecliptic is high in the sky at midnight.

The seasons are reversed in the Southern Hemisphere, spring beginning at the September Equinox, when the Sun crosses the Equator on its way south, summer beginning at the December Solstice, when the

Sun is highest in the southern sky, and so on. Thus, the times when the ecliptic is highest in the sky, and therefore best placed for observing the planets, may be summarized as follows:

	Midnight	Sunrise	Noon	Sunset
Northern latitudes	December	September	June	March
Southern latitudes	June	March	December	September

In addition to the daily rotation of the celestial sphere from east to west, the planets have a motion of their own among the stars. The apparent movement is generally *direct*, i.e. to the east, in the direction of increasing longitude, but for a certain period (which depends on the distance of the planet) this apparent motion is reversed. With the outer planets this *retrograde* motion occurs about the time of opposition. Owing to the different inclination of the orbits of these planets, the actual effect is to cause the apparent path to form a loop, or sometimes an S-shaped curve. The same effect is present in the motion of the inferior planets, Mercury and Venus, but it is not so obvious, since it always occurs at the time of inferior conjunction.

The *inferior planets*, Mercury and Venus, move in smaller orbits than that of the Earth, and so are always seen near the Sun. They are most obvious at the times of greatest angular distance from the Sun (greatest elongation), which may reach 28° for Mercury and 47° for Venus. They are seen as evening objects in the western sky after sunset (at eastern elongations) or as morning objects in the eastern sky before sunrise (at western elongations). The succession of phenomena, conjunctions and elongations always follows the same order, but the intervals between them are not equal. Thus, if either planet is moving round the far side of its orbit its motion will be to the east, in the same direction in which the Sun appears to be moving. It therefore takes much longer for the planet to overtake the Sun – that is, to come to superior conjunction – than it does when moving round to inferior conjunction, between Sun and Earth. The intervals given in the table at the top of p.70 are average values; they remain fairly constant in the case of Venus, which travels in an almost circular orbit. In the case of Mercury, however, conditions vary widely because of the great eccentricity and inclination of the planet's orbit.

		Mercury	Venus
Inferior Conjunction	to Elongation West	22 days	72 days
Elongation West	to Superior Conjunction	36 days	220 days
Superior Conjunction	to Elongation East	35 days	220 days
Elongation East	to Inferior Conjunction	22 days	72 days

The greatest brilliancy of Venus always occurs about 36 days before or after inferior conjunction. This will be about a month after greatest eastern elongation (as an evening object), or a month before greatest western elongation (as a morning object). No such rule can be given for Mercury, because its distances from the Earth and the Sun can vary over a wide range.

Mercury is not likely to be seen unless a clear horizon is available. It is seldom as much as 10° above the horizon in the twilight sky in northern temperate latitudes, but this figure is often exceeded in the Southern Hemisphere. This favourable condition arises because the maximum elongation of 28° can occur only when the planet is at aphelion (farthest from the Sun), and it then lies well south of the Equator. Northern observers must be content with smaller elongations, which may be as little as 18° at perihelion. In general, it may be said that the most favourable times for seeing Mercury as an evening object will be in spring, some days before greatest eastern elongation; in autumn, it may be seen as a morning object some days after greatest western elongation.

Venus is the brightest of the planets and may be seen on occasions in broad daylight. Like Mercury, it is alternately a morning and an evening object, and it will be highest in the sky when it is a morning object in autumn or an evening object in spring. Venus is to be seen at its best as an evening object in northern latitudes when eastern elongation occurs in June. The planet is then well north of the Sun in the preceding spring months, and is a brilliant object in the evening sky over a long period. In the Southern Hemisphere a November elongation is best. For similar reasons, Venus gives a prolonged display as a morning object in the months following western elongation in October (in northern latitudes) or in June (in the Southern Hemisphere).

The *superior planets*, which travel in orbits larger than that of the Earth, differ from Mercury and Venus in that they can be seen opposite the Sun in the sky. The superior planets are morning objects after conjunction with the Sun, rising earlier each day until they come to opposition. They will then be nearest to the Earth (and therefore at their brightest), and will be on the meridian at midnight, due south in northern latitudes, but due north in the Southern Hemisphere. After opposition they are evening objects, setting earlier each evening until they set in the west with the Sun at the next conjunction. The difference in brightness from one opposition to another is most noticeable in the case of Mars, whose distance from Earth can vary considerably and rapidly. The other superior planets are at such great distances that there is very little change in brightness from one opposition to the next. The effect of altitude is, however, of some importance, for at a December opposition in northern latitudes the planets will be among the stars of Taurus or Gemini, and can then be at an altitude of more than 60° in southern England. At a summer opposition, when the planet is in Sagittarius, it may only rise to about 15° above the southern horizon, and so makes a less impressive appearance. In the Southern Hemisphere the reverse conditions apply, a June opposition being the best, with the planet in Sagittarius at an altitude which can reach 80° above the northern horizon for observers in South Africa.

Mars, whose orbit is appreciably eccentric, comes nearest to the Earth at oppositions at the end of August. It may then be brighter even than Jupiter, but rather low in the sky in Aquarius for northern observers, though very well placed for those in southern latitudes. These favourable oppositions occur every fifteen or seventeen years (e.g. in 1988, 2003 and 2018). In the Northern Hemisphere the planet is probably better seen at oppositions in the autumn or winter months, when it is higher in the sky – such as in 2005 when opposition was in early November. Oppositions of Mars occur at an average interval of 780 days, and during this time the planet makes a complete circuit of the sky.

Jupiter is always a bright planet, and comes to opposition a month later each year, having moved, roughly speaking, from one Zodiacal constellation to the next.

Saturn moves much more slowly than Jupiter, and may remain in the same constellation for several years. The brightness of Saturn depends on the aspects of its rings, as well as on the distance from Earth and Sun. The Earth passed through the plane of Saturn's rings in 1995 and 1996, when they appeared edge-on; we saw them at maximum opening, and Saturn at its brightest, in 2002. The rings last appeared edge-on in 2009.

Uranus and *Neptune* are both visible with binoculars or a small telescope, but you will need a finder chart to help locate them (such as those reproduced in this *Yearbook* on pages 122 and 128). *Pluto* (now officially classified as a 'dwarf planet') is hardly likely to attract the attention of observers without adequate telescopes.

Phases of the Moon in 2011

NICK JAMES

New Moon				First Quarter				Full Moon				Last Quarter			
	d	h	m		d	h	m		d	h	m		d	h	m
Jan	4	09	03	Jan	12	11	31	Jan	19	21	21	Jan	26	12	57
Feb	3	02	31	Feb	11	07	18	Feb	18	08	36	Feb	24	23	26
Mar	4	20	46	Mar	12	23	45	Mar	19	18	10	Mar	26	12	07
Apr	3	14	32	Apr	11	12	05	Apr	18	02	44	Apr	25	02	47
May	3	06	51	May	10	20	33	May	17	11	09	May	24	18	52
June	1	21	03	June	9	02	11	June	15	20	14	June	23	11	48
July	1	08	54	July	8	06	29	July	15	06	40	July	23	05	02
July	30	18	40	Aug	6	11	08	Aug	13	18	58	Aug	21	21	55
Aug	29	03	04	Sept	4	17	39	Sept	12	09	27	Sept	20	13	39
Sept	27	11	09	Oct	4	03	15	Oct	12	02	06	Oct	20	03	30
Oct	26	19	56	Nov	2	16	38	Nov	10	20	16	Nov	18	15	09
Nov	25	06	10	Dec	2	09	52	Dec	10	14	36	Dec	18	00	48
Dec	24	18	06	Jan	1	06	15								

All times are UTC (GMT)

Longitudes of the Sun, Moon and Planets in 2011

NICK JAMES

Date		Sun °	Moon °	Venus °	Mars °	Jupiter °	Saturn °	Uranus °	Neptune °
Jan	6	285	304	238	292	357	197	357	327
	21	301	136	254	304	0	197	358	327
Feb	6	317	349	272	317	3	197	358	328
	21	332	189	289	328	6	197	359	329
Mar	6	345	357	305	339	9	196	0	329
	21	0	198	322	350	12	195	1	330
Apr	6	16	42	342	3	16	194	1	330
	21	31	250	0	15	20	193	2	330
May	6	45	76	18	26	23	192	3	331
	21	60	286	36	37	27	191	4	331
June	6	75	125	56	49	30	190	4	331
	21	89	332	74	60	33	190	4	331
July	6	104	163	92	71	36	191	5	331
	21	118	4	111	81	38	192	5	330
Aug	6	133	217	130	92	39	193	4	330
	21	148	48	149	102	40	194	4	330
Sept	6	163	269	169	112	40	196	3	329
	21	178	93	187	121	40	197	3	329
Oct	6	192	305	206	130	38	199	2	328
	21	207	128	225	139	36	201	2	328
Nov	6	223	351	245	147	34	203	1	328
	21	238	179	263	155	32	205	1	328
Dec	6	253	23	282	161	31	206	1	328
	21	269	218	300	167	30	208	1	329

Moon: Longitude of the ascending node: Jan 1: 272°   Dec 31: 253°

Mercury moves so quickly among the stars that it is not possible to indicate its position on the star charts at convenient intervals. The Monthly Notes should be consulted for the best times at which the planet may be seen.

The positions of the Sun, Moon and planets other than Mercury are given in the table on p. 74. These objects move along paths which remain close to the ecliptic and this list shows the apparent ecliptic longitude for each object on dates which correspond to those of the star charts. This information can be used to plot the position of the desired object on the selected chart.

EXAMPLES

A bright planet is seen due south at around 10 p.m. in late November. What is it?

> The northern star chart 11S shows the southern sky for 21 November at 22h. The ecliptic longitude corresponding to due south is around 30°. The table of longitudes on p. 74 for 21 November shows that only one planet, Jupiter (at 32°), has an ecliptic longitude consistent with this observation. The bright planet is therefore Jupiter near to opposition on the Aries/Pisces border.

The positions of the Sun and Moon can be plotted on the star maps in the same manner as for the planets. The average daily motion of the Sun is 1°, and of the Moon 13°. For the Moon an indication of its position relative to the ecliptic may be obtained from a consideration of its longitude relative to that of the ascending node. The latter changes only slowly during the year, as will be seen from the values given on p. 74. Let us denote by d the difference in longitude between the Moon and its ascending node. Then if $d = 0°$, 180° or 360°, the Moon is on the ecliptic. If $d = 90°$ the Moon is 5° north of the ecliptic, and if $d = 270°$ the Moon is 5° south of the ecliptic.

On 6 November, the Moon's longitude is given in the table on p. 74 as 351° and the longitude of the ascending node is found by interpolation to be about 256°. Thus $d = 95°$ and the Moon is about 5° north of the ecliptic. Its position may be plotted on northern star charts 7S, 8S and 9S and on southern star charts 8N and 9N.

Some Events in 2011

Jan   3   *Earth* at Perihelion
      4   New Moon
      4   Partial Eclipse of the Sun
      8   *Venus* at Greatest Western Elongation (47°)
      9   *Mercury* at Greatest Western Elongation (23°)
   10   Moon at Apogee (404,980 km)
   19   Full Moon
   22   Moon at Perigee (362,790 km)

Feb   3   New Moon
      4   *Mars* in Conjunction with Sun
      6   Moon at Apogee (405,920 km)
   17   *Neptune* in Conjunction with Sun
   18   Full Moon
   19   Moon at Perigee (358,250 km)
   25   *Mercury* in Superior Conjunction

Mar   4   New Moon
      6   Moon at Apogee (406,580 km)
   19   Full Moon
   19   Moon at Perigee (356,575 km)
   20   Equinox (Spring Equinox in Northern Hemisphere)
   21   *Uranus* in Conjunction with Sun
   23   *Mercury* at Greatest Eastern Elongation (19°)
   27   Summer Time Begins in the UK

Apr   2   Moon at Apogee (406,655 km)
      3   *Saturn* at Opposition in Virgo
      3   New Moon
      6   *Jupiter* in Conjunction with Sun
      9   *Mercury* in Inferior Conjunction
   17   Moon at Perigee (358,090 km)
   18   Full Moon
   29   Moon at Apogee (406,040 km)

May   3   New Moon
       7   *Mercury* at Greatest Western Elongation (27°)
     15   Moon at Perigee (362,135 km)
     17   Full Moon
     27   Moon at Apogee (405,005 km)

June   1   New Moon
      1   Partial Eclipse of the Sun
     12   Moon at Perigee (367,190 km)
     12   *Mercury* in Superior Conjunction
     15   Full Moon
     15   Total Eclipse of the Moon
     21   Solstice (Summer Solstice in Northern Hemisphere)
     24   Moon at Apogee (404,270 km)
     28   *Pluto* at Opposition in Sagittarius

July   1   New Moon
      1   Partial Eclipse of the Sun
      4   *Earth* at Aphelion
      7   Moon at Perigee (369,570 km)
     15   Full Moon
     20   *Mercury* at Greatest Eastern Elongation (27°)
     21   Moon at Apogee (404,355 km)
     30   New Moon

Aug   2   Moon at Perigee (365,760 km)
     13   Full Moon
     16   *Venus* in Superior Conjunction
     17   *Mercury* in Inferior Conjunction
     18   Moon at Apogee (405,160 km)
     22   *Neptune* at Opposition in Aquarius
     29   New Moon
     30   Moon at Perigee (360,860 km)

Sept   3   *Mercury* at Greatest Western Elongation (18°)
     12   Full Moon
     15   Moon at Apogee (406,065 km)
     23   Equinox (Autumn Equinox in Northern Hemisphere)
     26   *Uranus* at Opposition in Pisces

27   New Moon
28   *Mercury* in Superior Conjunction
28   Moon at Perigee (357,560 km)

Oct 12   Full Moon
12   Moon at Apogee (406,435 km)
13   *Saturn* in Conjunction with Sun
26   Moon at Perigee (357,050 km)
26   New Moon
29   *Jupiter* at Opposition in Aries
30   Summer Time Ends in the UK

Nov   8   Moon at Apogee (406,180 km)
10   Full Moon
14   *Mercury* at Greatest Eastern Elongation (23°)
23   Moon at Perigee (359,690 km)
25   New Moon
25   Partial Eclipse of the Sun

Dec   4   *Mercury* in Inferior Conjunction
6   Moon at Apogee (405,415 km)
10   Full Moon
10   Total Eclipse of the Moon
22   Moon at Perigee (364,800 km)
22   Solstice (Winter Solstice in Northern Hemisphere)
23   *Mercury* at Greatest Western Elongation (22°)
24   New Moon

Monthly Notes 2011

January

EARTH is at perihelion (nearest to the Sun) on 3 January at a distance of 147 million kilometres (91.3 million miles).

MERCURY passed through inferior conjunction on 20 December 2010 and, having moved rapidly west of the Sun, reaches greatest western elongation (23°) on 9 January. For a few days before and after this date the planet should be visible from northern temperate latitudes low above the south-eastern horizon at the beginning of morning civil twilight. For observers in equatorial and southern latitudes the period of visibility will extend to the end of the month and the planet will be rather higher above the east-south-eastern horizon at the same time. The magnitude of Mercury increases from +0.2 to −0.3 during January.

VENUS is a brilliant object in the south-eastern sky before dawn, reaching greatest western elongation (47°) on 8 January. In northern temperate latitudes the planet rises four hours before the Sun at the beginning of the month; from the southern hemisphere the planet rises almost three hours before the Sun. The planet is in Libra and it fades very slightly from magnitude −4.5 to −4.3 during January. Over the same period the phase of the planet increases from 47 per cent to 60 per cent; that is, from just less than half phase to gibbous. On 30 January the waning crescent will pass close to Venus and the pair will make a pleasing spectacle in the dawn twilight sky.

MARS passes through superior conjunction in early February. Consequently, the planet lies too close to the Sun in the sky to be visible this month.

JUPITER is a splendid object visible in the south-western sky during the early evening, but setting an hour or so before midnight. The planet

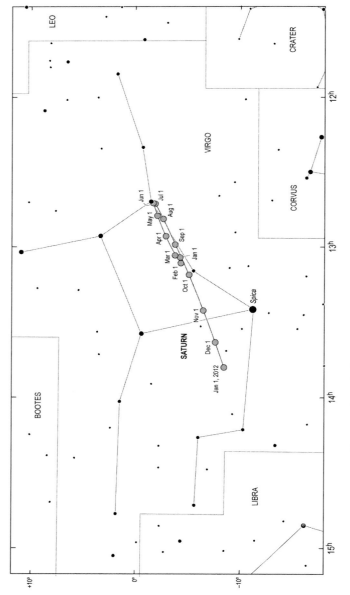

Figure 1. The path of Saturn against the background stars of Virgo during 2011.

is moving direct in Pisces and on 2 January it will pass only about 0.5°S of the planet Uranus (magnitude +5.9) and will be a useful guide to locating the fainter planet. Jupiter fades very slightly from magnitude −2.3 to −2.2 in the course of the month.

SATURN rises a little before midnight, brightening from magnitude +0.8 to +0.6 during the month. The planet is in Virgo and, after reaching a stationary point on 27 January, its motion is retrograde. Figure 1 shows the path of Saturn against the background stars during 2011. Following the ring-plane crossing in September 2009, the rings are now opening nicely again and are displayed at an angle of 10.1° as viewed from the Earth at the beginning of January, so the planet is once again a fine sight even in a small telescope.

Lepus. The winter skies are so dominated by Orion, the Hunter – particularly during the evening – that the lesser constellations are too often ignored. One of these is Lepus, the Hare. It is one of Ptolemy's original constellations, but there are no definite mythological legends attached to it. It is said that Orion was particularly fond of hunting hares, and so one was placed below him in the sky, but whether this proximity was appreciated by the hare must be regarded as questionable!

Lepus has no star of the first magnitude, but its pattern is quite distinctive, located to the south of Beta and Kappa Orionis and west of Beta Canis Majoris (Figure 2). There are eight stars above the fourth magnitude; the brightest are Alpha (Arneb), magnitude 2.6, and Beta (Nihal), magnitude 2.8. Arneb is an F-type supergiant, over 7,000 times as luminous as the Sun and almost 1,000 light years away. It is also worth locating M79 (NGC 1904), an easily found globular cluster with an integrated magnitude of 8 not far from the third-magnitude Epsilon. The position is RA 05h 24.5m, Dec −24° 33′.

M79 was discovered by Pierre Méchain in 1780. His friend and colleague, Charles Messier, determined its position and included it in his catalogue later that year. It was first resolved into stars and recognized as a globular cluster by William Herschel in about 1784. M79 is in a somewhat unusual location in the sky; in the hemisphere opposite to the galactic centre, most globulars being grouped around the galactic centre. It is little over 40,000 light years from us, but about 60,000 light years from the galactic centre. M79 may be a relative newcomer to the globular cluster system of our Milky Way. Some astronomers think

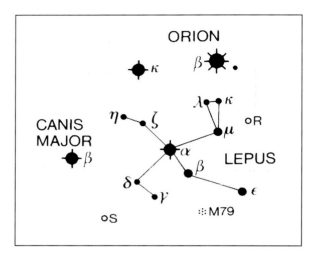

Figure 2. The small but distinctive pattern of Lepus, the Hare, may be found below the bright stars of Orion during January evenings.

that it may come from, or still be a member of, the remnant globular cluster system of the Canis Major dwarf spheroidal galaxy which is currently undergoing a very close and disruptive encounter with our Galaxy, but this is by no means certain.

Another very interesting object is the variable star R Leporis (RA 04h 59.6m, Dec −14° 48′), near the border with neighbouring Eridanus, to the west of the small triangle formed by Mu, Lambda and Kappa. It is known as Hind's Crimson Star – and the name is appropriate, because it is one of the reddest stars in the sky; observers have described its appearance as 'like a glowing coal; an intense smoky red; a ruby'. The star was first noted in October 1845 by the astronomer John Russell Hind of London, who described it as 'the most intense crimson, resembling a blood-drop on the black background of the sky'. Observing it in the early twentieth century, Agnes Mary Clerke remarked that even the reddish tints of Antares and Betelgeux were 'mere pale shades' when compared with the wine-red hue of R Leporis.

The spectrum of this pulsating giant star shows that it belongs to a rare class of stars referred to as spectral class C – and shows very strong features of molecular carbon. The distinctive red hue may be caused by carbon in the star's outer atmosphere filtering out the blue part of its visible light spectrum. R Leporis has an irregular period of between 418 and 441 days, but recent measurements give a period of 427 days. At maximum it reaches the fringe of naked-eye visibility, and as it never drops below magnitude 11.7 it can be followed even with a small telescope.

Johannes Hevelius (1611–1687). This month is the 400th anniversary of the birth of one of the early lunar observers – Johannes Hewelcke, always known to us by his Latinized name of Hevelius. He was born on 28 January 1611 in Danzig (now Gdańsk), so that he must be regarded as Polish. He set up a private observatory and compiled a catalogue of 1,564 stars, the most comprehensive of its time; he observed planets, comets and (particularly) the Moon. He used the very long-focus refractors of the time, which were incredibly unwieldy (Figure 3). Disaster struck in 1679, when his observatory, instruments and books were destroyed by fire, but he promptly set to work building a new observatory, completing the work in time to observe the great comet of December 1680.

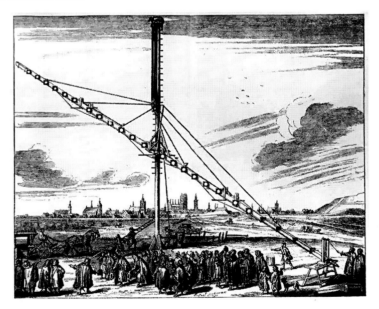

Figure 3. Woodcut illustration of a 45-metre long astronomical refracting telescope built by Johannes Hevelius. (From his book *Machina coelestis* (first part), published in 1673.)

Hevelius compiled an atlas of the Moon (*Selenographia*, published in 1647) containing one of the earliest detailed maps of its surface as well as names for many of its features. A few of his names for lunar mountains (e.g. the Alps) are still in use, and a large lunar crater in the Grimaldi group is named after him. Sadly, his own map of the Moon has been lost; it is said that after his death the copper engraving was melted down and made into a teapot. It would be interesting to know where that teapot is now, though there would be no way of identifying it.

Voyager 2 at Uranus. A quarter of a century ago, on 24 January 1986, NASA's Voyager 2 spacecraft sped past Uranus and sent back thousands of close-range images of that extraordinary world and huge amounts of other scientific data on the planet, its moons, rings, atmosphere, interior and the magnetic environment surrounding Uranus. Because the axial inclination of the planet is more than a right angle, Voyager approached Uranus almost pole-on (Figure 4). The Uranian equator was then in twilight. At its closest, the spacecraft came within 81,500 kilometres (50,600 miles) of Uranus' cloud tops. Voyager 2 found that the temperature of the equatorial regions, which receive less sunlight over a Uranian year, is nevertheless about the same as that at

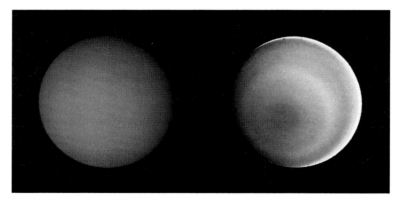

Figure 4. Two images of Uranus acquired by Voyager 2 at a distance of 9.1 million kilometres. The picture on the left is a composite using images from the blue, green and orange filters, processed to approximate Uranus as the human eye would see it. The image on the right was produced using ultraviolet, violet and orange filters to exaggerate the contrast. The dark polar hood is over the south pole of the planet. (Image courtesy of NASA Jet Propulsion Laboratory.)

the poles. The atmosphere is very clear, the planet's blue-green colour coming from the absorption of red light by methane, one of the constituents of the clouds.

Voyager 2's images of the five largest moons around Uranus revealed complex surfaces indicative of varying geological pasts. The cameras also detected ten previously unseen moons. Several instruments studied the ring system, uncovering the fine detail of the previously known rings and two newly detected rings. Voyager 2 data showed that the planet spins in 17 hours 14 minutes. The spacecraft also discovered a strong Uranian magnetic field, unusual in that its axis is tilted 59° from the axis of rotation of the planet. The magnetic field traps high-energy, electrically charged particles in radiation belts around the planet. As the particles move back and forth, they emit radio waves which were detected by Voyager 2.

No comparable images of the Uranian system have been obtained since the Voyager 2 encounter, although the planet has been imaged by the Hubble Space Telescope, and no new Uranus probe is planned, though the New Horizons craft is well on its way to Pluto.

This Month's Solar Eclipse. The partial eclipse of the Sun which occurs at sunrise on the morning of 4 January will be visible right across the British Isles, weather permitting of course. This eclipse will also be observable across much of Europe, North Africa and central Asia.

The eclipse magnitude (the percentage of the solar diameter that will be obscured) from European cities such as Madrid (58 per cent), Paris (73 per cent), London (75 per cent), and Copenhagen (83 per cent) will give early morning risers on 4 January a great chance to photograph a sunrise eclipse with interesting scenery in the foreground. The greatest magnitude will be observed from northern Sweden at 08h 51m UT where the dark disk of the Moon will cut across 86 per cent of the solar diameter at sunrise.

From eastern and south-eastern England the eclipse magnitude will vary between 77 per cent along the north Norfolk coast to 74 per cent at Dungeness. From locations north and west of an imaginary line stretching roughly from the mouth of the Humber estuary down to Bournemouth, maximum eclipse will occur with the Sun still below the horizon, so that at sunrise the amount of the Sun which is obscured will already be decreasing. From locations south and east of this imaginary line, greatest eclipse will be visible with the Sun just above the south-eastern horizon (allowing for atmospheric refraction). In this regard, observers situated in the extreme north-eastern corner of Kent (from Margate and Ramsgate down to Dover) should have the best view. At Greenwich, for example, sunrise is at 8h 05m UT with maximum eclipse occurring just seven minutes later at 8h 12m UT, when 75 per cent of the solar diameter will be obscured.

From places such as Edinburgh, Glasgow, Newcastle, Liverpool, Manchester, Leeds, Sheffield, Birmingham, Bristol and Plymouth, for example, observers will miss greatest eclipse, but will still be able to witness a substantial partial eclipse at sunrise, with a magnitude ranging from 59 per cent in Edinburgh (sunrise 8h 43m UT) to 69 per cent in Liverpool (sunrise 8h 27m UT) and Plymouth (sunrise 8h 16m UT).

Clearly with the Sun very low over the south-eastern horizon, even from locations near London and along the coasts of Norfolk, Suffolk, Essex and Kent, it will be a difficult but interesting event to observe. Of course, one must always take the very greatest care when observing the partially eclipsed sun, even when the sun is low in the sky. One can only hope that the clouds keep away that winter morning!

February

MERCURY, magnitude −0.3, is becoming lost in the glare of the dawn twilight sky for observers in the tropics and the Southern Hemisphere by the end of the first week of February, and observers further north will not see the planet at all this month. The planet is in superior conjunction on 25 February.

VENUS is a brilliant object in the south-eastern sky before dawn, but the far southerly declination of the planet in Sagittarius causes it to appear ever lower in the dawn twilight sky for observers in northern temperate latitudes, although it is now much better placed for observers in the tropics and Southern Hemisphere. Venus fades slightly from magnitude −4.3 to −4.1 during February. The planet appears gibbous, the phase increasing from 61 per cent to 71 per cent during the month.

MARS is in conjunction with the Sun on 4 February and will not be visible this month.

JUPITER remains a lovely sight in the south-western evening twilight sky, but by the end of the month the planet will be setting only two-and-a-half hours after the Sun from northern temperate latitudes; rather less from locations further south. The planet fades slightly from magnitude −2.2 to −2.1 during the month.

SATURN may be seen rising in the eastern sky in the late evening. The planet is moving retrograde in Virgo. It brightens slightly from magnitude +0.6 to +0.5 during the month.

Venera 1. The first of all planetary missions was launched half a century ago, on 12 February 1961. It was Venera 1, a Soviet probe. In those days the USSR generally took the lead, and it was so on this occasion.

It may seem strange now that Venus was selected rather than Mars, but in 1961 nobody had any real idea what Venus was like. According to some astronomers the surface was no more than pleasantly warm, while F. L. Whipple and D. Menzel championed the idea that there could be extensive oceans. The possibility of life was certainly not ruled out. Venus was definitely attractive.

Venera 1 was not an intended lander; that, the Kremlin said, would follow sooner or later – sooner more probably than later. The Americans were still having problems, and at that stage, of course, there was no collaboration between East and West. Each team had one outstanding leader, Wernher von Braun in the USA and Sergei Korolev in the USSR; they never met. (I remember von Braun telling me (P.M.) how much he regretted that he had had no chance to talk with the USSR's 'Chief Designer'.)

Venera 1 was launched successfully in two stages. First it was lofted into a 229 × 282 kilometre parking orbit around the Earth with a Molniya launcher. Then, Venera 1 was launched towards Venus by a further rocket stage. This was the first demonstration of the highly efficient manoeuvre of launching from Earth orbit. Venera 1 had a

Figure 5. The Russian spacecraft Venera 1 which passed Venus in May 1961. (Image courtesy of NASA NSSDC.)

cylindrical body just over a metre in diameter and just over 2 metres high; there were two solar panels, and two antennae (Figure 5). During its flight it was spin-stabilized, and course corrections could be made by fixing on the Sun and Canopus. In all these respects it sounds remarkably 'modern'.

Data began to flood in with respect to cosmic rays and the solar wind, exactly as planned. After discovering the solar wind with Luna 2, Venera 1 provided the first confirmation that it was uniformly present in deep space. But then, when Venera 1 was 7,500,000 kilometres from Earth, contact was lost, and was never regained. Every effort was made, both by the Soviets and by Sir Bernard Lovell and his team at Jodrell Bank; some weak signals picked up by the giant radio telescope in June 1961 may have come from Venera, but it was impossible to be sure. After that – silence. In all probability, Venera passed Venus in May 1961 at a distance of around 100,000 kilometres and continued in solar orbit, in which case it is still circling the Sun unseen, unheard and untrackable. The Soviets believed that the trouble was due to the over-heating of a vital solar-direction sensor.

Though it did not achieve what had been hoped of it, Venera 1 cannot be classed as a complete failure. It was a pioneer, and the true ancestor of the many Venus missions that have followed.

Bright Variable Stars in Gemini. Gemini is a bright, large and rich constellation with Pollux and Castor as its leaders (Figure 6). There are two famous naked-eye variable stars, Zeta (Mekbuda) and Eta (Propus).

At fourth magnitude, Mekbuda lies just south-west of the brighter Wasat (Delta Geminorum). It is a G-type supergiant star, about 1,100 light years from the Sun. Mekbuda is one of the few easily visible classical Cepheid variable stars, a type of pulsating variable with an extremely regular period. Cepheids are dying supergiants that have become unstable, and that brighten and fade due to the rhythmic expansion and contraction of their surface layers. The second of these pulsating variable stars to be discovered was Delta Cephei (the first was Eta Aquilae – see notes for August), after which the class of stars was named. Mekbuda varies from magnitude 3.6 to 4.2 and back again every 10.2 days.

Cepheid variables are usually classed as F- and G-type yellow supergiant stars, although they are not as massive as true supergiants. They vary by between one and a couple of magnitudes over periods of from

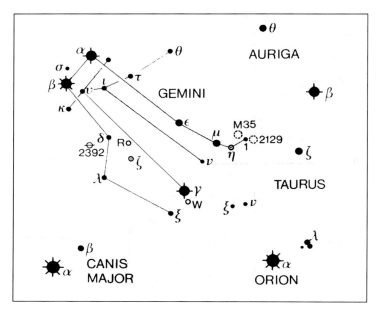

Figure 6. The principal stars of Gemini, the Twins, showing the location of the bright Cepheid variable star ζ (Zeta) Geminorum (left of centre) and the semi-regular variable η (Eta) Geminorum (right of centre).

one to 100 days. Cepheids are extremely useful stars because there is a clear relationship between a Cepheid's pulsation period and its luminosity as defined by its absolute magnitude (the magnitude the star would appear to have if observed from a standard distance of 32.6 light years): the longer the period, the more luminous the star. Once we know the form of this so-called period–luminosity relationship, we can determine the distances of Cepheids. For any particular Cepheid, the pulsation period gives the absolute magnitude, and comparison of this with the apparent magnitude gives the distance. Cepheids are of major importance in measuring the distances to other galaxies.

Propus is a different type of variable; it is classed as a semi-regular, with a range of magnitude from 3.1 to 3.9 and a period of 234 days. The distance from Earth is 350 light years. To be more precise it is a spectroscopic binary, and it is the primary – a red giant of spectral type M3 – that is variable, while the companion (probably spectral type B) orbits with a period of 8.2 years. A third star, a class G dwarf, orbits the main pair with a period of at least several hundred years.

I (P.M.) have followed the variations of Eta Geminorum for years, and have never seen a minimum as faint as 3.9, but I do not claim that my magnitude estimates are precise. If you want to follow the star's fluctuations, useful comparison stars are Mu (2.9), Epsilon (3.0), Xi (3.4), Nu (4.1) and 1 (4.2).

March

New Moon: 4 March   *Full Moon:* 19 March

Equinox: 20 March

Summer Time in the UK commences on 27 March.

MERCURY moves rapidly east of the Sun and reaches greatest eastern elongation (19°) on 23 March. It is visible in the western sky in the evenings, for about two weeks in the middle of the month, for observers in tropical and northern latitudes. For Northern Hemisphere observers this is the most favourable evening apparition of the year. Figure 7 shows, for observers in latitude 52°N, the changes in azimuth (true bearing from the north through east, south and west) and altitude of Mercury on successive evenings when the Sun is 6° below the

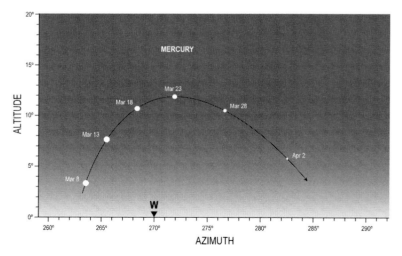

Figure 7. Evening apparition of Mercury, from latitude 52°N. The planet reaches greatest eastern elongation on 23 March. It will be at its brightest in early March, before elongation.

horizon. This is at the end of evening civil twilight, which in this latitude and at this time of year occurs about 35 minutes after sunset.

During its period of visibility before and after greatest eastern elongation, Mercury fades from magnitude −1.3 to +1.2. The changes in the brightness of the planet are indicated in Figure 7 by the relative sizes of the white circles marking Mercury's position at five-day intervals: Mercury is at its brightest before it reaches elongation. The diagram gives positions for a time at the end of evening civil twilight on the Greenwich meridian on the stated date. Observers in different longitudes should note that the actual positions of Mercury in azimuth and altitude will differ slightly from those given in the diagram due to the motion of the planet.

From 12 to 18 March, the planet Jupiter will be in the same part of the sky as Mercury, and will be a useful guide to locating the slightly fainter planet. On 14–15 March, for locations in Europe and North America, at the end of evening civil twilight, Jupiter and Mercury will be at about the same altitude above the horizon, with Jupiter slightly further towards the south-west and about two-and-a-half times brighter than Mercury.

Towards the end of March, Mercury's elongation from the Sun rapidly decreases as the planets draws in towards inferior conjunction.

VENUS, magnitude −4.0, moves from Sagittarius into Capricornus early in the month and its southerly declination means that it is increasingly difficult to observe from northern temperate latitudes. On 1 March the waning crescent Moon and Venus will be close together in the early morning sky and will make for a pleasing spectacle, but observers in the tropics and the Southern Hemisphere will have the best view. Indeed, for observers in these latitudes, the planet is a lovely sight in the dawn twilight, still rising more than two hours before the Sun on 31 March when, once again, the waning crescent Moon and Venus will make a nice pairing in the eastern sky.

MARS was in conjunction with the Sun in early February and is consequently not visible this month.

JUPITER, magnitude −2.0, is in conjunction with the Sun in early April and will be lost in the evening twilight by the third week of

March. In the middle of the month, Jupiter will be visible low in the western sky not far from the planet Mercury as twilight falls.

SATURN may be seen rising in the eastern sky in the early evening. The planet is moving retrograde in Virgo. The planet is at opposition at the beginning of April and it brightens slightly from magnitude +0.5 to +0.4 during March. Figure 1, given with the notes for January, shows the path of Saturn against the background stars during the year.

John Herschel's Descriptions of Mercury and Venus. The leading astronomer of the nineteenth century was Sir John Herschel, son of the great Sir William. His book *Outlines of Astronomy* was regarded as the standard work. This is what he had to say about Mercury and Venus in the tenth edition of the book, published in 1869:

> Of Mercury we can see little more than that it is round, and exhibits phases. It is too small, and too much lost in the constant neighbourhood of the Sun, to allow us to make out more of its nature . . . Nor does Venus offer any remarkable peculiarities; although its real diameter is 7,800 miles, and although it occasionally attains the considerable apparent diameter of 61″, which is larger than that of any other planet, it is yet the most difficult of them all to define with telescopes. The intense lustre of the illuminated part dazzles the sight, and exaggerates every imperfection of the telescope; yet we see clearly that its surface is not mottled over with permanent spots like the Moon. We notice in it neither mountains nor shadows, but a uniform brightness, in which we may indeed fancy, or perhaps more than fancy, brighter or obscurer portions, but can seldom or never rest fully satisfied of the fact. It is from some observations of this kind that both Venus and Mercury have been concluded to revolve on their axes in about the same time as the Earth, though in the case of Venus, Bianchini and other more recent observers have contended for a period of 24 times that length. The most natural conclusion, from the very rare appearance and want of permanence in the spots, is that we do not see, as in the Moon, the real surface of these planets, but only their atmospheres, much loaded with clouds, and which may serve to mitigate the otherwise intense glare of their sunshine.

This description is hardly true of either planet. Mercury spins on its axis in 58.65 days, while Venus spins backwards in 243 days, although the atmosphere of Venus is in a state of vigorous circulation and super-rotation, circling the planet in just four Earth days (Figure 8). Venus has a very thick mainly carbon dioxide atmosphere which traps the Sun's heat and makes the planet's surface intolerably hot at around 470°C, with a surface pressure more than 90 times greater than that found on the Earth at sea level. By contrast, Mercury has an extremely tenuous and highly variable atmosphere (or surface-bound exosphere) containing hydrogen, helium, oxygen, sodium, calcium, magnesium, potassium and water vapour, with a combined pressure of only about 10^{-14} bar (one hundred trillionth of Earth's atmospheric pressure at sea level) – corresponding to what we would call a good laboratory vacuum.

Figure 8. An enhanced Venus cloud mosaic created from multiple orange and ultraviolet filter images taken by the spacecraft Mariner 10 in 1974. (Image courtesy of NASA/JPL/ Mosaic by Mattias Malmer.)

But John Herschel had no way of learning more about either of these planets, and he was using the best information available to him.

Urbain Le Verrier. The French astronomer Urbain Jean Joseph Le Verrier was born 200 years ago this month, on 11 March 1811. Of his brilliance there is no doubt at all; his correct prediction of the position of Neptune, leading to its discovery in September 1846 by Johann Galle and Heinrich D'Arrest at the Berlin Observatory, was only one of his many achievements. Yet he has gone down in history as one of the rudest men who has ever lived, and one of his contemporaries wrote that 'although he might not be the most detestable man in France, he was certainly the most detested'.

Was this true? Certainly there were many people who disliked him, and he was dismissed as director of the Paris Observatory on account of his 'irritability', though he was reinstated when his successor, Charles-Eugène Delaunay, was drowned in a boating accident. Yet there is one possible hint that history may have been rather unkind to him.

The story of the discovery of Neptune has been told many times, and we do not propose to repeat it here. Suffice to say that following Herschel's discovery of Uranus, in 1781, irregularities in its motion indicated that it was being perturbed by a more distant planet, and a position for this planet was worked out independently by John Couch Adams in England and Le Verrier in France. Adams actually finished first, but the planet (Neptune) was identified by Galle and D'Arrest solely from Le Verrier's calculations; they knew nothing about Adams. Naturally, Le Verrier received great credit. When the French learned about Adams's independent work they were furious, and accused him of trying to steal the glory of the discovery. It nearly led to a serious international incident!

Subsequently the two astronomers met. One might have expected friction – but this did not happen. Though Adams spoke no French and Le Verrier was equally unversed in English, they struck up an immediate friendship and remained on the best of terms for the rest of their lives. This does not seem to fit in with the usual picture of Le Verrier, who died in 1877.

One other point is worth making. Neptune was not discovered by either Adams or Le Verrier. The actual discoverers were Galle and D'Arrest.

April

MERCURY is in inferior conjunction on 9 April and thereafter moves rapidly west of the Sun, becoming visible in the morning for observers in the tropics and the Southern Hemisphere towards the end of the month. Figure 10 given with the notes for May shows the changes in azimuth and altitude of Mercury at the beginning of morning civil twilight, about 30 minutes before sunrise, for observers in latitude 35°S. The changes in the brightness of the planet are indicated on the diagram by the relative sizes of the white circles marking Mercury's position at five-day intervals. Mercury brightens from magnitude +1.6 to +1.0 during the last week of April. The planet will not be observable from the latitudes of northern Europe and North America.

VENUS is still a beautiful object (magnitude −4.0) in the east-north-eastern sky in the mornings before sunrise, but only for observers in the tropics and the Southern Hemisphere. On 30 April, from these latitudes, there will be a nice grouping of the thin crescent Moon and planets in the pre-dawn twilight sky. The Moon and Venus will be highest above the horizon, with Mercury below Venus, then Mars and Jupiter side-by-side much lower down.

MARS, magnitude +1.2, is slowly emerging in the morning sky before dawn, and by the end of the month it may be glimpsed very close to the much brighter Jupiter, but only by those in the tropics and the Southern Hemisphere. The two planets will be less than half a degree apart on 30 April, with Mars lying to the north of Jupiter. Mars will not be visible from more northerly latitudes this month. There is no opposition of Mars in 2011.

JUPITER is in conjunction with the Sun on 6 April. By the end of the month, the planet may be seen low in the east-north-eastern twilight sky before dawn by equatorial observers and those in the Southern

Hemisphere. Its magnitude is −2.0. The planet will not be visible from northern temperate latitudes this month.

SATURN rises in the early evening and is visible throughout the hours of darkness as it reaches opposition on 3 April, magnitude +0.3. The tilt of the rings, as viewed from the Earth, has decreased slightly since January to about 8°. The planet is moving retrograde in Virgo, and at opposition its distance is 1,289 million kilometres (800 million miles) from the Earth.

The Solitary One. At a reasonable altitude in the south during April evenings (assuming that you live in the Northern Hemisphere) you will find the reddish star Alphard (Alpha Hydræ). It is the only bright star in Hydra, the Watersnake, which is the largest constellation in the sky now that the old Argo Navis has been ruthlessly chopped up into a keel (Carina), a poop (Puppis) and sails (Vela).

There is a very easy way to locate Alphard. Find the two brightest stars in the Twins, Pollux and Castor, which most people know; they point straight down to Alphard, which is so much on its own that the Arabs called it 'the Solitary One'. The great Danish astronomer Tycho Brahe called it 'Cor Hydræ', the Heart of the Snake. Lying about 180 light years distant, and with an estimated age approaching 450 million years, Alphard has started to evolve away from the main sequence to become an orange giant star with a spectral classification of K3. Alphard is about three times as massive as the Sun, and 400 times as luminous, with a diameter of perhaps 70 million kilometres – fifty times that of the Sun.

When Sir John Herschel was sailing home after his sojourn at the Cape, in the 1830s, he noted that Alphard was definitely variable. In view of its spectral type this would not be at all surprising, but variability has never been confirmed, and the official magnitude is 1.98. Naked-eye estimates are difficult to make, owing to the lack of suitable stars at comparable altitude. However, the Solitary One is worth watching.

The First Man in Space. Half a century ago the era of manned space exploration began. On 12 April 1961, Yuri Gagarin, of the USSR, soared aloft in Vostok 1 and completed a full orbit of the Earth before making a safe landing.

The Russian success was not really a surprise; at that stage the

Americans were still having severe problems. But one must not underestimate the value of Gagarin's flight. Nobody really knew about the effects of zero gravity upon the human body; what would be the danger from meteoroids and cosmic radiation, and would an astronaut be hopelessly space-sick? Gagarin was venturing into the unknown. Those who followed had at least a reasonable idea of what to expect.

Much of our knowledge of that momentous day comes from Gagarin's own report, which he delivered to the State Commission the day after his landing, but was not published for decades. On the morning of 12 April, Gagarin and the back-up cosmonaut Gherman Titov were woken at 5.30 a.m. They had breakfast, followed by routine medical check-ups, which they both passed easily. To reduce Gagarin's time inside the hot spacesuit, he was dressed after Titov. On suiting up, Gagarin spent a few minutes in the test seat, as technicians carried out various checks. Then, accompanied by his colleagues, he left by bus for

Figure 9. A pensive Yuri Gagarin in the bus on the way to the launch pad on the morning of 12 April 1961. Behind him, seated, is his back-up, Gherman Titov. Standing behind are cosmonauts Grigoriy Nelyubov and Andrian Nikolayev. (Image courtesy of NASA.)

the pad (Figure 9), where he was taken, by elevator, to the top of the launch vehicle and to the hatch of his Vostok 1 spacecraft. On closure of the hatch, one of its sensors would not turn on, so the hatch had to be re-opened, the sensor adjusted and the hatch closed again.

Blast-off took place more or less as scheduled at 09:06:59.7 Moscow Time and, as far as Gagarin was aware, orbital insertion went smoothly. However, unknown to Gagarin, the core, second stage of the rocket burned longer than scheduled, leaving the spacecraft in a higher 327-kilometre apogee orbit, instead of the planned 230 kilometres. Upon reaching orbit, Gagarin confirmed activation of the landing sequence mechanism. He also attempted to communicate with the ground with mixed success, and jotted some notes in his flight journal. However, when he used the journal to experiment with weightlessness, it floated back to him without the pencil which had been attached to it by string – so that was then end of his note-writing! He then turned to the voice recorder, but it quickly ran out of tape because the ultra-sensitive voice activation system reacted to noise in the cabin even when he was not speaking. He partially rewound the tape and restarted the recording, but apparently erased previous data.

Gagarin had some food out of tubes and watched the Earth passing below. Everything looked perfect until a scheduled 40-second burn of the braking engine, which was supposed to send the spacecraft back into the Earth's atmosphere. In his post-flight report, Gagarin wrote:

> As soon as TDU [the braking engine] shut down, there was a sharp jolt. The spacecraft started spinning about its axis with a very high speed. The Earth was passing in the Vzor [observation visor] from top to bottom and from right to left. The speed of rotation was around 30 degrees per second, no less. Everything was spinning. One moment I see Africa – it happened over Africa – another the horizon, another the sky. I barely had time to shade myself from the Sun, so the light did not blind my eyes. I put my legs toward the (bottom) window, but did not close the blinds. I wanted to find out myself, what was going on.

Gagarin expected separation of his re-entry capsule from the instrument module to take place 10–12 seconds after the de-orbit burn, but it did not happen. In the meantime, the spacecraft continued tumbling wildly as it approached denser layers of the atmosphere. The separation did finally take place at 10.35, not 10.25, as he had expected. It turned out that a single valve within the braking engine had failed to close completely at the beginning of the engine burn. This had led to propellant escaping through the main nozzle and steering thrusters, causing the spacecraft to spin wildly. Although the engine was later cut off by a timer, the fault also caused the flight control system to scrub the sequence for separation of the re-entry capsule and the instrument module. Fortunately, a back-up system did perform the separation, some ten minutes later than planned, as sensors detected the rising heat of re-entry.

As the craft plunged into the atmosphere, Gagarin saw a bright crimson glow appearing behind his windows, accompanied by the noise of thermal protection layers burning in the fiery heat of re-entry. Gagarin estimated that as the craft slowed he experienced a peak deceleration force of about 10G. He recalled: 'There was a moment, about 2–3 seconds, when data on the control gauges started to look blurry. It was starting to turn grey in my eyes. I braced and composed myself. It helped, everything kind of returned to its place.'

As G-forces subsided and the capsule descended safely, Gagarin prepared to eject from his craft. At an altitude of seven kilometres, the main hatch was jettisoned and seconds later Gagarin ejected. The main parachute deployed successfully, but the back-up chute deployed as well after some delay; consequently Gagarin approached the Earth's surface under two parachutes, landing gently on a soft surface of freshly ploughed soil in an open field in the Saratov region of the USSR.

Launched into space under a veil of secrecy, Yuri Gagarin returned to Earth 108 minutes later an international hero. The flight of Vostok 1 had dealt another major blow to American pride, increasing their determination to invest heavily in the manned spaceflight programme, and making it politically easier for the US government to commit huge funds to the risky and ambitious goal of landing a man on the Moon within ten years.

Sadly, the flight of Vostok 1 was Gagarin's only space flight; he was killed in an accident in what should have been a routine aircraft flight.

On 12 April 1981, twenty years after Gagarin's mission, came the first launch of the US Space Shuttle *Columbia*. By the time this *Yearbook* appears in print, the Shuttle is likely to have made its penultimate flight, and in view of US President Obama's recently outlined plans it may will be that the next lunar visitor will be Chinese, but we must wait and see. Meanwhile, let us not forget Yuri Gagarin.

May

New Moon: 3 May   ***Full Moon:* 17 May**

MERCURY reaches greatest western elongation (27°) on 7 May, and the planet is visible in the morning for observers in tropical and southern latitudes. Unfortunately for observers in the latitudes of the British Isles the planet remains unsuitably placed for observation throughout the month. For Southern Hemisphere observers this is the most favourable morning apparition of the year. Figure 10 shows, for observers in latitude 35°S, the changes in azimuth (true bearing from the north through east, south and west) and altitude of Mercury on successive mornings when the Sun is 6° below the horizon. This is at

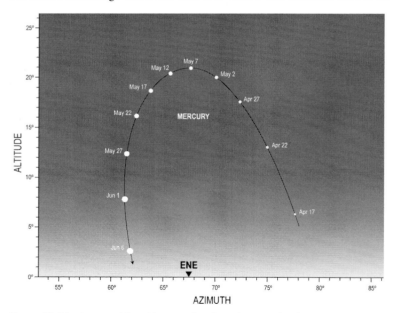

Figure 10. Morning apparition of Mercury, from latitude 35°S. The planet reaches greatest western elongation on 7 May. It will be at its brightest in early June, after elongation.

the beginning of morning civil twilight, which in this latitude and at this time of year occurs about 30 minutes before sunrise.

During its long period of visibility, which runs from late April until the beginning of June, Mercury brightens from magnitude +1.6 to −1.0. The changes in the brightness of the planet are indicated in Figure 10 by the relative sizes of the white circles marking Mercury's position at five-day intervals. It should be noted that Mercury is at its brightest at the beginning of June, some three weeks after it reaches greatest western elongation. The diagram gives positions for a time at the beginning of morning civil twilight on the Greenwich meridian on the stated date. Observers in different longitudes should note that the actual positions of Mercury in azimuth and altitude will differ slightly from those given in the diagram, due to the motion of the planet.

Mercury will be located quite close to the much brighter Venus from 6 to 19 May, the two planets remaining more or less side-by-side – with Venus to the north (left) of Mercury – for a fortnight. Jupiter passes the pair on 11–12 May.

VENUS, magnitude −3.9, remains a prominent object in the east-north-east before dawn for observers in the tropics and the Southern Hemisphere, although the planet now rises less than two hours before the Sun. On 1 May, there will be a nice grouping of Venus and Mercury, with the thin crescent Moon, Mars and Jupiter below, in the early morning sky. Indeed, throughout the first two weeks of May, from these southern latitudes, Venus, Jupiter and Mercury will form a nice, changing grouping in the pre-dawn twilight sky with Mars located slightly below the other three, brighter planets. Figure 11 overleaf shows this interesting grouping for 11 May when Jupiter appears close to Venus and Mercury.

MARS, magnitude +1.2, continues to emerge in the morning sky before dawn, but is visible only by those in the tropics and the Southern Hemisphere. On 1 May, Mars will appear close to Jupiter in the dawn twilight sky, the two planets being about half a degree apart, with Mars lying to the north of Jupiter. Mars is still not visible from more northerly latitudes this month.

JUPITER, magnitude −2.1, becomes visible low down in the eastern sky before dawn for observers in Europe and North America by the end

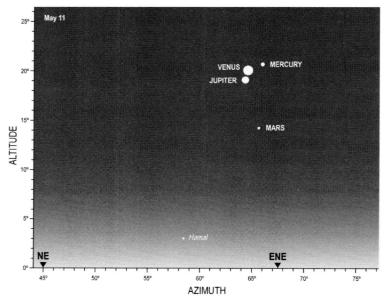

Figure 11. An interesting grouping of Jupiter, Venus and Mercury, with Mars below, in the morning sky on 11 May 2011, from latitude 35°S. The angular diameters of the planets are not to scale.

of the month. For those living in equatorial and southern latitudes, the planet rises several hours before the Sun and is a prominent object in the east-north-east in the early morning sky. The planet is in Pisces during May, and forms a pleasing grouping with Venus and Mercury in early May, as described above.

SATURN becomes visible as soon as darkness falls and is observable for most of the night, moving retrograde in Virgo. It fades very slightly from magnitude +0.5 to +0.7 during the month, and the ring angle decreases to 7.3° by the end of the month.

The Faintest Star in the Plough. To Northern Hemisphere observers Ursa Major, the Great Bear, is almost overhead during May evenings. It is one of the most famous constellations in the sky, rivalled only by Orion and the Southern Cross.

The seven main stars make up the pattern known as the Plough or, occasionally, King Charles's Wain (Americans refer to it as the Big Dipper). They are Alpha (Dubhe), Beta (Merak), Gamma (Phad), Delta (Megrez), Epsilon (Alioth), Zeta (Mizar) and Eta (Alkaid); Gamma can also be called Phekda or Phecda, while Eta has the alternative name of Benetnasch. Six of the seven are around the second magnitude, but Delta is below the third. This is obvious at a glance, but as Delta (δ) is the fourth letter in the Greek alphabet Megrez should be the fourth brightest star in the constellation. What is wrong?

There have been suggestions that Megrez has faded in historic times, but the evidence is extremely slender. The only catalogues to make the seven Plough stars reasonably equal were due to Tycho Brahe in 1590 and Johann Bayer, who allotted the Greek letters when he compiled his catalogue in 1603. Moreover, Megrez is not the kind of star which would be expected to show variations, secular or otherwise. It is an A3-type dwarf, 81 light years away and about 17 times as luminous as the Sun; no fluctuations have been reported since photometers came into use. It is much more likely that the solution is positional, with the Plough stars lettered in order of increasing right ascension from Alpha (11h 03m) through to Eta (13h 47m). There are other cases of this, and there are also constellations where the Greek lettering is totally chaotic; thus in Sagittarius the brightest stars are Epsilon and Sigma, while the brightest star in Octans is Nu.

From Maid to Famous Astronomer. Wilhelmina Fleming who died of pneumonia one hundred years ago – on 21 May 1911 – has an honoured place in the history of astronomy. She was Scottish, born in Dundee on 15 May 1857; she married James Orr Fleming, and the couple emigrated to Boston, Massachusetts, when Wilhelmina was 21. While she was pregnant with their son, Edward, her husband deserted her, and to earn money to support herself and her baby she had to find work, so she became a maid in the home of Professor Edward Charles Pickering, Director of the Harvard College Observatory.

Pickering was engaged in the spectral classification of stars, and was dissatisfied with his male assistants. 'My maid could do a better job,' he snapped, and gave Wilhelmina her chance – which she took with a vengeance. From 1881 she became a full-time astronomer at the observatory and proved to be exceptionally capable. While there, she devised and helped to implement a system of assigning stars a letter according to how much hydrogen could be observed in their spectra. Stars classified as A had the most hydrogen, B the next most, and so on. (Annie Jump Cannon later improved upon this work to develop a simpler classification system based on temperature.) Wilhelmina was a major contributor to the famous Henry Draper Catalogue; in nine years she catalogued over 10,000 stars. She discovered 310 variable stars, and ten novae as well as 59 gaseous nebulae. She also published a list of 222 variable stars she had discovered.

She was awarded many honours, including Honorary Membership of the Royal Astronomical Society of London, the first American woman to be so honoured. Unquestionably Wilhelmina Fleming ranks as one of the greatest of all women astronomers.

June

New Moon: 1 June   *Full Moon:* 15 June

Solstice: 21 June

MERCURY may be glimpsed just before dawn, low in the east-north-east, by observers in the tropics and Southern Hemisphere in the first few days of June. The planet then passes through superior conjunction on 12 June and reappears in the evening sky, low in the west-north-west after sunset, for the last few days of June. From more northerly latitudes the planet will not be visible this month.

VENUS, magnitude −3.9, continues to be visible low in the east-north-east before dawn for observers in equatorial and more southerly latitudes, but by the end of the month it will be inconveniently low even from such locations.

MARS, magnitude +1.3, may be seen low in the morning sky before dawn. For most of June it is visible only from the tropics and the Southern Hemisphere, but by the end of the month it may be glimpsed from more northerly latitudes. Figure 12 shows the path of Mars against the background stars from May to September this year.

JUPITER continues to be visible as a conspicuous object in the early morning sky, moving direct among the stars of Pisces and into neighbouring Aries during the month. Its brightness increases very slightly from −2.1 to −2.2 during June.

SATURN is visible as an evening object in Virgo throughout June, setting in the early morning hours. Its brightness decreases from magnitude +0.7 to +0.9 during the month and the angle at which the rings are displayed, as viewed from Earth, reaches its minimum for the year, at 7.2°. On 14 June, Saturn reaches its second stationary point, resuming its direct motion.

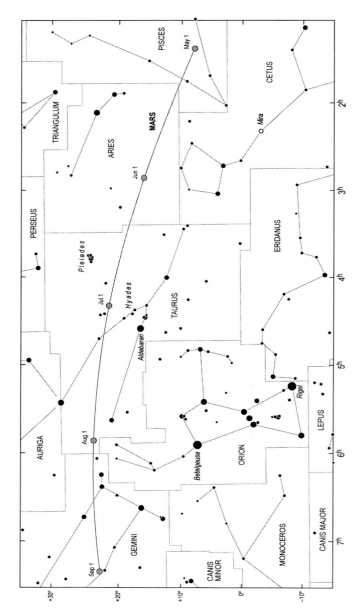

Figure 12. The path of Mars as it moves through the Zodiacal constellations from Pisces to Gemini between May and September 2011.

PLUTO reaches opposition on 28 June, in the constellation of Sagittarius, at a distance of 4,643 million kilometres (2,885 million miles). It is visible only with a moderate-sized telescope, since its magnitude is +14.

Sunspots. The earliest written records of naked-eye sunspots (made when the Sun was close to the horizon or when it was covered by a thin veil of cloud or mist) were made by Chinese astronomers around 800 BC. Court astrologers in ancient China and Korea, who believed sunspots foretold important events, kept intermittent records of them for hundreds of years. It is possible that the Greek philosopher Anaxagoras observed a spot in 467 BC, but in the cosmology of the highly influential Aristotle, the heavens were considered to be perfect and unchanging. A spot that came and went on the Sun would mean that there *were* changes in the heavens. Consequently, given this dominant viewpoint, the difficulty of observing the Sun and the cyclical nature of sunspots, it is little wonder that records of sunspots are rare in Europe before the seventeenth century, although an English monk called John of Worcester made the first drawing of sunspots in December 1128. Johannes Kepler unwittingly observed one in 1607, but mistook it for a transit of Mercury.

The scientific study of sunspots began after the invention of the telescope in 1609. Although there is still some argument about exactly when sunspots were first observed through a telescope, and by whom, there is little doubt that both Galileo in Italy and Thomas Harriot in England recorded them towards the end of 1610. What is more certain is that the Dutch observer David Fabricius and his son, Johannes, observed them in March 1611, and that they were the first to publish their observations. The pair observed the solar disk using a camera obscura. They noted that the spots appeared to move from day to day. Spots would appear on the eastern edge of the solar disk, steadily move to the western edge, disappear, and then sometimes reappear at the eastern edge again after a period of time which was the same as that taken for them to cross the visible hemisphere. This suggested that the Sun rotated on its axis, an idea that had been put forward earlier but not substantiated with hard evidence.

David and Johannes Fabricius described their sunspot observations in a book with the engaging title of *De Maculis in Sole Observatis, et Apparente earum cum Sole Conversione Narratio* ('Narration on Spots

Observed on the Sun and their Apparent Rotation with the Sun'). It was published 400 years ago this month, in June 1611. It was printed in Wittenberg, ready for the Frankfurt Book Fair that autumn, but it remained unknown to other observers for some time and was subsequently overshadowed by the independent discoveries and publications about sunspots by Christoph Scheiner and Galileo.

Scheiner began his serious study of sunspots in October 1611 and his first treatise on the subject, *Tres Epistolae de Maculis Solaribus Scriptae ad Marcum Welserum* ('Three Letters on Solar Spots written to Marc Welser'), appeared in January 1612. Galileo had shown sunspots to people in Rome in the spring of 1611, but he did not undertake a detailed study until March 1612.

Various theories were proposed to explain the spots. Scheiner believed the spots to be dark bodies orbiting close to the solar surface; Galileo was much nearer the truth. His careful observations of the dark

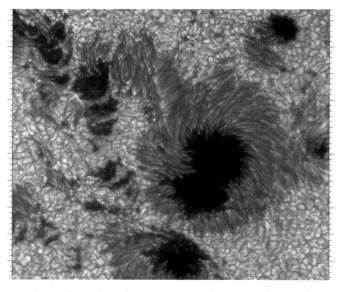

Figure 13. A view of the solar surface with sunspots, showing granulation in those parts of the surface where there are no spots. Each spot consists of a dark central part (umbra) surrounded by a not-so-dark part (penumbra). The largest umbra in the picture is about the size of Earth. (Image courtesy of the Swedish Solar Telescope, La Palma, Canary Islands and the Institute for Solar Physics, Royal Swedish Academy of Sciences.)

spots led him to believe that they were actually located on the surface of the rotating Sun. (Today we know that sunspots are areas which are about 1,000 K cooler than the typical 5,800 K temperature of the Sun's visible surface (the photosphere) and so appear dark by contrast (Figure 13). They are not permanent features of the solar surface, but are effects of the Sun's ever-changing magnetic field.)

Much later than Galileo, no less a person than Sir William Herschel believed the Sun to be a cool globe which might well be inhabited! His theory, admittedly somewhat modified, persisted for an amazingly long time. Here is a quote from William's son, John Herschel, from the 10th edition of his *Outlines of Astronomy*, published in 1869:

> But what are the spots? Many fanciful notions have been broached upon this subject, but only one seems to have any degree of physical probability, *viz* that they are the dark, or at least comparatively dark, solid body of the Sun itself, laid bare to our view by those immense fluctuations in the luminous regions of its atmosphere, to which it appears to be subject.

Such were the views of our leading astronomers a mere century and a half ago. How much will we learn about the Sun during the next century and a half? Time will tell.

Luis Alvarez and the Disappearance of the Dinosaurs. Luis Walter Alvarez, an American scientist of Spanish extraction, was born one hundred years ago, on 13 June 1911. He became a brilliant experimental physicist, and in 1968 received the Nobel Prize for Physics, but he is probably best remembered for his theory that the dinosaurs became extinct due to the impact of a 10–15 kilometre diameter asteroid which caused global devastation. His classic paper, written together was his son Walter, a geologist, was published in 1980.

The evidence for this 'impact hypothesis' came to light quite unexpectedly when Luis and Walter were working together on a geology expedition in Italy (Figure 14). They had been studying the walls of a gorge which contained layers of rock both above and below the so-called K–T boundary, separating the Cretaceous and Tertiary periods, corresponding to a time about 65 million years ago. At the boundary there is a clay layer about a centimetre thick. Analysing the composition of this clay layer, Luis Alvarez and nuclear chemists at the

Lawrence Berkeley Laboratory were astounded to discover that exactly at the clay boundary there were unusually high levels of a rare element, iridium, but not in the limestone on either side. Within a few years of the publication of their paper, more than a hundred iridium-containing clay sites had been found. Knowing of no terrestrial source which could produce and deliver so much iridium, the team concluded that the source had to be extraterrestrial. In subsequent years the clay layer was also found to contain soot, glassy spherules, shocked quartz crystals, microscopic diamonds and other rare minerals formed only under conditions of high temperature and pressure.

Figure 14. Luis Alvarez (left), with his son Walter, standing next to the layers at the K–T boundary in Gubbio, Italy, in 1981. (Image courtesy of Lawrence Berkeley National Laboratory.)

After considering a number of possible sources for the high levels of iridium, the team concluded that an asteroid impact was the only hypothesis which could satisfy all of the conditions. The impact hypothesis for the death of the dinosaurs was born. Ten years after the initial proposal, evidence of a huge impact crater called Chicxulub off the coast of Mexico strongly confirmed their theory. Unfortunately for Luis Alvarez, the finding of the crater came after his death.

There is no doubt that the dinosaurs, which had ruled the world for so long, vanished comparatively suddenly at the end of the Cretaceous period, approximately 65 million years ago. So did many other species, and an asteroid of sufficient size could certainly have been responsible. The Alvarez hypothesis has been widely – if not universally – accepted. If this is correct, we must admit that a comparable impact could happen at any time in the future. We must hope that if it happens, we will cope with the situation better than the dinosaurs did.

July

New Moon: 1 and 30 July   *Full Moon:* 15 July

EARTH is at aphelion (furthest from the Sun) on 4 July at a distance of 152 million kilometres (94.5 million miles).

MERCURY reaches greatest eastern elongation (27°) on 20 July and the planet is visible in the morning, throughout the month, for observers in equatorial and southern latitudes. Unfortunately for observers in the latitudes of the British Isles the planet is not suitably placed for observation during the month, but for Southern Hemi-

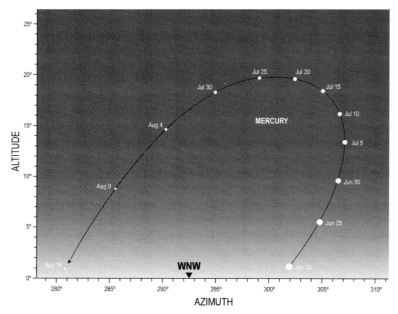

Figure 15. Evening apparition of Mercury, from latitude 35°S. The planet reaches greatest eastern elongation on 20 July. It will be at its brightest in late June, before elongation.

sphere observers this is the most favourable evening apparition of the year. Figure 15 shows the changes in azimuth and altitude of Mercury at the end of evening civil twilight, about 30 minutes after sunset, for observers in latitude 35°S. The changes in the brightness of the planet are indicated by the relative sizes of the white circles marking Mercury's position at five-day intervals: Mercury is at its brightest before it reaches greatest eastern elongation. The diagram gives positions for a time at the end of evening civil twilight on the Greenwich meridian on the stated date. Observers in different longitudes should note that the actual positions of Mercury in azimuth and altitude will differ slightly from those given in the diagram due to the motion of the planet. Mercury's brightness decreases from magnitude −0.4 to +1.3 during the month of July.

VENUS, magnitude −3.9, will be in superior conjunction next month and as its elongation from the Sun decreases it is increasingly difficult to see in the dawn twilight sky. The planet is inconveniently low from northern temperate latitudes throughout the month, but observers in equatorial and southern latitudes may glimpse it low in the east-north-east for the first few days of the month, but thereafter even they will lose it in the brightening sky.

MARS, magnitude +1.4, is an early morning object, but still rather low in the east-north-eastern sky. The planet moves fairly rapidly against the background stars of Taurus during the month; at the beginning of July it is roughly midway between the Pleiades and Aldebaran, but by the end of the month it is approaching the border with neighbouring Gemini.

JUPITER is a conspicuous object in the early morning sky, moving direct among the stars of Aries and rising before midnight by the end of the month. Its brightness increases very slightly from −2.2 to −2.4 during July.

SATURN, magnitude +0.9, continues to be visible as an evening object moving direct in Virgo, although it now sets before midnight. The angle at which the rings are displayed begins to increase slightly again, reaching 8° by the end of the month.

The Celestial Poles. The poles of the sky are marked by the direction of the Earth's axis; go to the North Pole, and the north celestial pole will be directly above you. Not very many people have done that, but there is already an active observatory at the South Pole, where the seeing conditions are extremely good. So far as the astronomers are concerned, the main problem is the intense cold.

Almost everyone knows how to locate the North Pole star. It is closely marked by the second-magnitude star Polaris, in Ursa Minor (the Little Bear), and all you have to do is to use the two Pointers, Merak and Dubhe, in the Plough pattern of Ursa Major. At present, Polaris is 44 arcminutes (about 0.7°) away from the true north celestial pole so, as the Earth spins on its axis, Polaris revolves around the pole in a small circle about 1.5° in diameter. Only twice during every sidereal day does Polaris accurately define the azimuth of true north – when it is either directly above or below the north celestial pole. Similarly, only twice every sidereal day does the angle between Polaris and the northern horizon accurately define the latitude of the observer – when it is either directly east or west of the north celestial pole. For the rest of the time its position is only a close approximation, and must be corrected using tables. The closest approach of Polaris to the celestial pole will be on 24 March 2100. Its declination will then be +89° 32′ 51″, placing it less than half a degree from the pole.

The direction of the Earth's axis of rotation in space changes very slowly due to precession, so Polaris will not always be the North Pole star. Over time, perturbations to Earth's axis, caused by the gravitational forces of the Moon and Sun acting on Earth's equatorial bulge, will cause it to point to other regions of the sky, tracing out a huge circle against the background stars over 25,800 years. Other stars along this circle will serve as the pole star in the future; in 7,500 years it will be the turn of Alderamin (Alpha Cephei), and in 12,000 years from now the North Pole will be a few degrees from the brilliant Vega (Alpha Lyrae), but meantime we are very happy with Polaris.

Things are not so good in the Southern Hemisphere, because the south celestial pole lies in a particularly barren part of the sky – in the constellation of Octans, the Octant, added to the sky by Lacaille in the eighteenth century. Octans has no distinctive shape; its brightest stars are Nu (magnitude 3.8), Beta (4.2) and Delta (4.3).

The actual South Pole star, Sigma Octantis – sometimes called Polaris Australis – is of magnitude 5.5, which means that it is not too easy to see with the naked eye even against a clear sky; the slightest haze or mist will obscure it, and it is of very little use to navigators. In 1900, Sigma lay only about 45 arcminutes from the south celestial pole, but that distance has now increased to about 1° 03′.

Remarkably, Sigma Octantis is the dimmest star to be represented on a national flag. It appears on the flag of Brazil, representing the capital city, Brasilia (Brazilian name Distrito Federal). Other unlikely stars are also shown on the flag, such as Gamma Canis Majoris (representing the Brazilian state Rondônia), Kappa Scorpii (Paraiba), Gamma Hydrae (Acre) and Beta Trianguli Australis (Santa Catarina). Sirius (Mato Grosso) and Canopus (Goiás) also appear, but it cannot be claimed that the star patterns shown on the flag are very accurate!

Mistaking Mars. During this month Mars is an early morning object in Taurus. It is well below the first magnitude, and with the naked eye it does look exactly like a reddish star. This is a good time to compare it with the star Aldebaran (Alpha Tauri), which has a K-type spectrum and is obviously orange; Aldebaran is almost half a magnitude the brighter of the two.

Another star which can be mistaken for Mars is the reddish supergiant Antares (Alpha Scorpii), which is well placed on July evenings. The name Antares derives from the Greek words for 'Rival of Ares (Mars)', due to the similarity of its reddish hue to the appearance of the Red Planet.

Unwary observers have often misidentified Mars, and have even reported it as a nova. Even professional astronomers, who work mainly with computers, have fallen into this trap. Yet when at its best Mars can outshine every object in the night sky apart from the Sun, the Moon and Venus.

August

New Moon: 29 August   *Full Moon:* 13 August

MERCURY may be glimpsed in the west-north-west, about 30 minutes after sunset, by observers in equatorial and southern latitudes early in the month, but it rapidly draws back in towards the Sun, passing through inferior conjunction on 17 August. After conjunction, the planet moves out to the west of the Sun, reaching greatest western elongation at the beginning of September. The planet is consequently visible from northern and tropical latitudes as a morning object from the last week of August until mid-September. For observers in the northern temperate latitudes this is the best morning apparition of the year. Figure 18 given with the notes for September shows, for observers in latitude 52°N, the changes in azimuth and altitude of Mercury on successive mornings when the Sun is 6° below the horizon. This condition is known as the beginning of morning civil twilight, which in this latitude and at this time of year occurs about 35 minutes before sunrise. The changes in the brightness of the planet are indicated by the relative sizes of the circles marking Mercury's position at five-day intervals: Mercury is at its brightest after it reaches greatest western elongation. During its period of visibility its magnitude brightens from +1.6 to −1.2. Figure 18 gives positions for a time at the beginning of morning civil twilight on the Greenwich meridian, on the stated date. Observers in different longitudes should note that the actual positions of Mercury in azimuth and altitude will differ slightly from those shown in the diagram.

VENUS is in superior conjunction on 16 August and is too close to the Sun to be visible this month.

MARS, magnitude +1.4, continues to be visible as an early morning object, rising not long after midnight from northern temperate latitudes, but much later for those living further south. The planet moves from Taurus into neighbouring Gemini during the month.

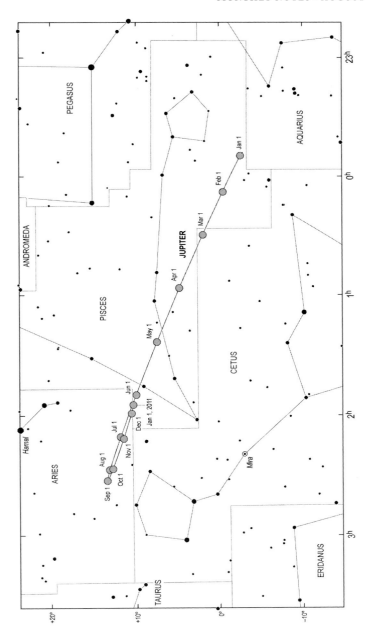

Figure 16. The path of Jupiter as it moves against the background stars of Pisces, Cetus (briefly in late February/early March) and Aries during 2011.

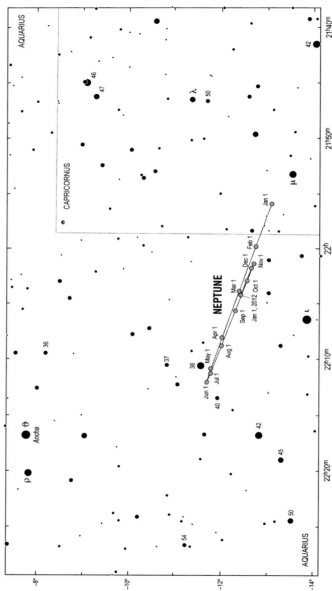

Figure 17. The path of Neptune against the stars of Capricornus and Aquarius during 2011. The stars Mu Capricorni and the brighter Iota Aquarii are lower right and in the bottom centre of the chart, respectively. The stars 38 and 42 Aquarii are below centre and towards the left of the chart. Phi and Theta Aquarii are upper left.

JUPITER reaches its first stationary point in Aries on 30 August, when it begins its retrograde motion. The planet is a brilliant object, brightening from magnitude −2.4 to −2.6 during August, and rising in the mid-evening by the end of the month. Figure 16 shows the path of Jupiter against the background stars during the year.

SATURN, magnitude +0.9, is visible low in the west-south-west as darkness falls at the beginning of August, but Northern Hemisphere observers will lose the planet in the twilight before month end, although it continues to be visible from the tropics and Southern Hemisphere.

NEPTUNE is at opposition on 22 August, in the constellation of Aquarius. It is not visible with the naked eye since its magnitude is +7.8. At opposition Neptune is 4,338 million kilometres (2,695 million miles) from the Earth. Figure 17 shows the path of Neptune against the background stars during the year.

Eta Aquilae. The Summer Triangle (Vega, Deneb and Altair) is still dominant in the evening sky, which means that Aquila, the Eagle, is high above the horizon. The leading star is of course the first-magnitude Altair, flanked to either side by Beta (Alshain) and the orange-red Gamma (Tarazed), both of which are actually much more luminous than Altair itself.

South of Altair lies a line of three stars, Theta (magnitude 3.2), Eta (variable) and Delta (3.3). The middle star, Eta, is of special interest, as it is a Cepheid variable. (The name 'Cepheid' derives from the first of this class of variable star to be discovered – Delta Cephei.) Eta Aquilae does have a name; the Hebrews called it Bezek, but this name is hardly ever used. Yet Eta is of special note, because it ranks with Delta Cephei, Zeta Geminorum (see notes for February) and the Southern Hemisphere's Beta Doradûs as the brightest of its class; had it been studied first, these vitally important variables might well have been called Aquilids!

The magnitude range of Eta Aquilae is from 3.5 to 4.4, and the period is 7.18 days, so that the fluctuations may be followed with the naked eye and are quite obvious, from one night to the next. Suitable comparison stars, all in Aquila, are Theta (magnitude 3.2), Delta (3.4), Beta (3.9), Iota (4.4) and Nu (4.6). Delta Cephei, which is very high during summer evenings and is circumpolar from Britain, also has a range of magnitude from 3.5 to 4.4 and a period of 5.37 days. According to the period–luminosity relationship, it follows that since the period of Eta Aquilae is greater than that of Delta Cephei, Eta Aquilae must be more luminous than Delta Cephei; and as the two appear equally bright (or virtually so), Eta must be the more distant of the two.

Not many Cepheids are conspicuous objects with the naked eye. The brightest Cepheid in the sky is the Pole Star, Polaris, although with a range of just one tenth of a magnitude in a period of about four days, its variations are too small to be detected by the naked eye. The other brightest members of the class are given in the following table:

Star	Max.	Min.	Period (days)
Zeta Geminorum	3.6	4.2	10.15
Eta Aquilae	3.5	4.4	7.18
Delta Cephei	3.5	4.4	5.37
Kappa Pavonis	3.9	4.8	9.09
Beta Doradûs	3.5	4.1	9.94

Kappa Pavonis and Beta Doradûs are, of course, too far south to be seen from anywhere in Britain.

Aquila has several other interesting features. The Milky Way runs through it, so that it is very rich. In 1918, a brilliant nova (V603 Aquilae) flared up in the constellation, reaching magnitude −1.4 and rivalling Sirius; it was the brightest nova of modern times.

There is one interesting note. The star Rho Aquilae is now in the constellation of Delphinus, because its proper motion has carried it over the boundary between the two neighbouring constellations. It is of the 5th magnitude, and therefore visible with the naked eye.

William Fowler. William Alfred Fowler was born 100 years ago this month, on 9 August 1911, in Pittsburgh, Pennsylvania, although he was raised in Lima, Ohio. He was an American physicist, whose career in nuclear physics and nuclear astrophysics spanned more that 60 years. Fowler was primarily concerned with studies of nuclear fusion reactions – how the nuclei of lighter chemical elements fuse to create the heavier ones in a process known as nucleosynthesis. Fowler wrote a classic paper on this topic entitled 'Synthesis of the Elements in Stars', produced jointly with Fred Hoyle, E. Margaret Burbidge and Geoffrey Burbidge, in which it was demonstrated that all of the naturally occurring chemical elements from carbon to uranium could be produced by nuclear processes in stars starting with the hydrogen and helium produced in the Big Bang. The paper was published in 1957 (*Reviews of Modern Physics*, vol. 29, Issue 4, pp. 547–650), and it is widely regarded as one of the most important ever to have appeared. For his work on nucleosynthesis, Fowler was awarded the Nobel Prize for Physics in 1983. His co-workers, however, did not receive the Nobel Prize, and some people regarded this as rather unfair. Fowler continued his work until shortly before his death in Pasadena, California, on 14 March 1995.

September

New Moon: 27 September   *Full Moon:* 12 September

Equinox: 23 September

MERCURY reaches greatest western elongation (18°) on 3 September. The planet is consequently visible from northern and tropical latitudes as a morning object from late August until mid-September. For Northern Hemisphere observers this is the most favourable morning apparition of the year. Figure 18 shows the changes in azimuth and altitude of Mercury at the beginning of morning civil twilight, about 35 minutes before sunrise, for observers in latitude 52°N. The changes in the brightness of the planet are indicated on the diagram by the relative sizes of the white circles marking Mercury's position at five-day

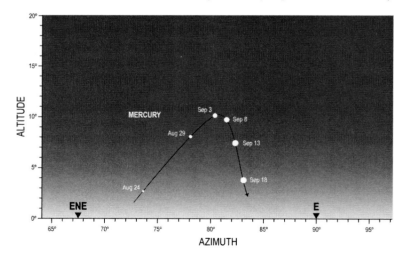

Figure 18. Morning apparition of Mercury, from latitude 52°N. The planet reaches greatest western elongation on 3 September. It will be at its brightest later in the month, after elongation.

intervals: Mercury is at its brightest in mid-September, when it attains magnitude −1.2. After the middle of the month, Mercury draws in towards the Sun and the planet passes through superior conjunction on 28 September.

VENUS, magnitude −3.9, was in superior conjunction last month and by the end of the September it is emerging very low in the western sky after sunset, but the planet may only be glimpsed by observers in equatorial and more southerly latitudes.

MARS, magnitude +1.4, continues to be visible as an early morning object, rising not long after midnight from northern temperate latitudes, but rather later for those living further south. The planet's fairly rapid apparent motion takes it through Gemini and into Cancer during the month.

JUPITER brightens from magnitude −2.6 to −2.8 during September; it is at opposition next month. The planet is moving retrograde in Aries. It rises soon after sunset and is then visible throughout the hours of darkness.

SATURN, magnitude +0.9, is in Virgo. It is no longer visible to observers in northern temperate latitudes, but in early September it may be glimpsed rather low down in the western sky after sunset by those living in the tropics and the Southern Hemisphere.

URANUS is at opposition on 26 September, in the constellation of Pisces. Uranus is barely visible to the naked eye as its magnitude is +5.7, but it is easily located using binoculars. Figure 19 shows the path of Uranus against the background stars during the year. At opposition Uranus is 2,854 million kilometres (1,773 million miles) from the Earth.

Uranus and its Moons. Sir William Herschel discovered the planet Uranus on 13 March 1781, using a 6.2-inch (15.7-centimetre) reflecting telescope of seven-foot focal length that he had made himself. Herschel realized that the object – then in Gemini – was not a star, but he thought at first that he had discovered a comet and indeed his communication to the Royal Society was headed An Account of a Comet.

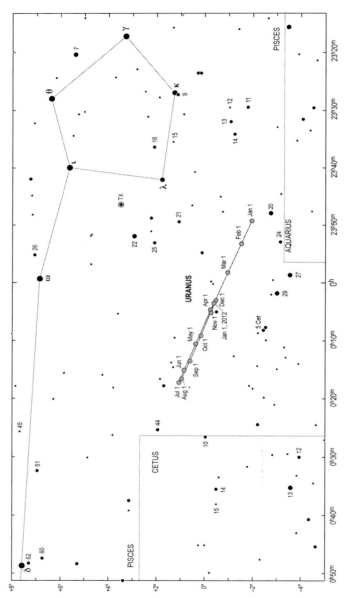

Figure 19. The path of Uranus against the background stars of Pisces during 2011. The stars of the distinctive 'Circlet', which marks the head of the western fish in Pisces, and may be found south of the Square of Pegasus, are shown towards the top right of the chart.

The new object was first recognized as a planet independently, but at about the same time, by the French amateur astronomer de Saron and by the Finnish mathematician Anders Lexell. Lexell calculated the orbit, finding that the planet was about 19 AU from the Sun, with an orbital period of between 82 and 83 years; the modern values are 19.181 AU and 84.01 years, respectively.

Following the discovery, Herschel became world famous, and was appointed King's Astronomer (not Astronomer Royal by the way; that post was held by the Reverend Dr Nevil Maskelyne). Uranus can just be seen with the naked eye, but a powerful telescope is needed to show anything on its greenish, bland, disk. Here is what is said about it by William Herschel's son, Sir John Herschel, in 1869:

> Of Uranus we see nothing but a small round uniformly illuminated disk, without rings, belts, or discernable spots. Its apparent diameter is about 4 second of arc, from which it never varies much, owing to the smallness of our orbit in comparison to its own. Its real diameter is about 35,000 miles and its volume is about 82 times that of the Earth. It is attended by four satellites, whose existence may be considered as conclusively established (and more have been suspected).

Today we know that the equatorial diameter of Uranus is 51,118 kilometres (31,764 miles) – rather less than Herschel's figure – and that it has 64 times the volume and 14.6 times the mass of the Earth. Although only four satellites were known in 1860, the satellite system is extensive and the current tally stands at 27, although only five were discovered prior to the Space Age. The first two moons to be discovered were Oberon and Titania, by William Herschel himself, in 1787. Titania is, in fact, the largest moon of the Uranian system, but its diameter is only 1,578 kilometres (less than half the diameter of our own Moon); Oberon is the second largest, with a diameter of 1,523 kilometres. Two further moons, Ariel and Umbriel (measuring 1,158 and 1,169 kilometres, respectively) were discovered by the English amateur astronomer William Lassell in October 1851. These were the four moons known in Herschel's time (Figure 20). It was not until February 1948 that a fifth, smaller moon, Miranda, was detected photographically by Gerard Kuiper, using the 82-inch reflector at the McDonald Observatory in Texas. What Herschel did not know, of course, is that

Uranus has a remarkable axial tilt – 98°, more than a right angle – unlike that of any other planet, and the satellites move in the plane of the Uranium equator.

Figure 20. A montage of Uranus' large moons and one smaller moon: from left to right Puck, Miranda, Ariel, Umbriel, Titania and Oberon. Other moons are not yet photographed in detail. The proportions of the moons are correct. (Original images taken by the Voyager 2 spacecraft and are reproduced courtesy of NASA Jet Propulsion Laboratory.)

The Names of the Uranian Satellites. Up to the time of the discovery of Uranus, all planetary satellites had been given mythological names; thus the two moons of Mars were called Phobos and Deimos, after the attendants of the God of War. The same principle applied to the satellites of Jupiter and Saturn. Names had to be found for the satellites of Uranus and these were suggested by John Herschel – who may well have thought he was entitled to take this action, because Uranus itself had been discovered by his father. But for some reason John Herschel departed from tradition and gave the four known satellites names either from William Shakespeare's plays or from Alexander Pope's poem *The Rape of the Lock*.

The four moons known in Herschel's time were called Ariel,

Umbriel, Titania and Oberon – two (Titania and Oberon) from Shakespeare's *A Midsummer Night's Dream*, one (Ariel) from both Shakespeare's (*The Tempest*) and Pope's poem, and Umbriel also from *Rape of the Lock*. Just why John Herschel made this decision is unknown, and many people regard it as a highly undesirable departure from tradition. Yet, when new moons of Uranus were discovered many years later, Herschel's system was followed. The name Miranda (the daughter of Prospero in Shakespeare's *The Tempest*) was proposed by its discoverer, Gerard Kuiper. Now we have Cordelia, Ophelia, Bianca, Cressida, Desdemona, Juliet, Portia and many others, all from Shakespearean plays, and Belinda, from *Rape of the Lock*.

The present situation is therefore that all satellite names are mythological apart from those of Uranus. The decisions must rest with the appropriate commission of the International Astronomical Union. But the Shakespearean names have been used for so long that they will certainly not be changed now, and we have to accept them whether we like them or not.

October

New Moon: 26 October   *Full Moon:* 12 October

Summer Time in the UK ends on 30 October

MERCURY passed through superior conjunction at the end of September and remains unobservable until the middle of October when it becomes visible in the western sky after sunset. For observers in the latitudes of the British Isles, the planet is not suitably placed for observation during the month, but for observers in equatorial and southern latitudes the planet will be visible to the south of due west in the evening twilight sky from mid-October onwards.

What makes this evening apparition of Mercury all the more interesting is the planet's proximity to Venus towards the end of October and during early November, the brilliant Venus acting as a useful guide to locating the much fainter and more elusive planet. Figure 25, given with the notes for November, shows the changes in azimuth and altitude of both Mercury and Venus at the end of evening civil twilight, about 30 minutes after sunset, for observers in latitude 35°S. The changes in the brightness of Mercury are indicated on the diagram by the relative sizes of the white circles marking its position at five-day intervals. Mercury's brightness decreases from magnitude -0.6 to -0.3 during the last two weeks of October. It will be noted that Venus and Mercury are at about the same altitude above the horizon, with Venus slightly to the west of Mercury, during the last few days of the month.

VENUS, magnitude -3.9, emerges into the western sky after sunset for observers in equatorial and more southerly latitudes. The planet will not be visible from the latitudes of the British Isles this month. The proximity of the brilliant Venus to the much fainter Mercury during the last few days of October has already been described above.

MARS continues to be visible as an early morning object, and by the end of the month it is rising at around midnight from northern

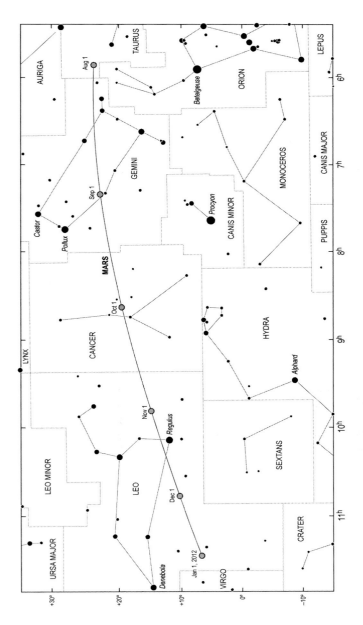

Figure 21. The path of Mars as it moves through the Zodiacal constellations from Taurus to Leo during the last five months of 2011.

temperate latitudes, although somewhat later for those living further south. The planet's rapid apparent motion takes it from Cancer and into Leo this month. Figure 21 shows the path of Mars against the background stars until the end of the year. Mars brightens slightly from magnitude +1.3 to +1.1 during October.

JUPITER, magnitude −2.9, is at its brightest this month since it is at opposition on 29 October and therefore available for observation throughout the night wherever you are located. The planet is in the constellation of Aries. Figure 16, given with the notes for August, shows the path of the planet against the background stars during the year. When closest to the Earth its distance is 594 million kilometres (369 million miles).

SATURN passes through superior conjunction on the far side of the Sun on 13 October. Consequently it is unobservable this month.

Unusual Events on Jupiter. Jupiter, in Aries, is at opposition this month, and therefore well placed for observation from the British Isles, since it is north of the celestial equator. Unusual events have been taking place on Jupiter during the past couple of years. One occurred on 19 July 2009, when amateur astronomer Anthony Wesley in Murrumbateman, Australia, using the telescope in his observatory, discovered that a black spot had suddenly appeared in Jupiter's south polar region. At first, he thought that he was seeing one of Jupiter's moons or a shadow transit on the planet, but the location, size and speed of the spot ruled out those possibilities. After checking images taken two nights earlier and not seeing the spot, he realized that he had discovered something new.

Wesley began e-mailing others, and the spot was quickly confirmed by scientists using NASA's Infrared Telescope Facility on the summit of Mauna Kea, Hawaii. The infrared images showed the visibly dark 'scar' with bright upwelling particles in the upper atmosphere detected in near-infrared wavelengths, and a warming of the upper troposphere with possible extra emission from ammonia gas detected at mid-infrared wavelengths.

While other telescopes, including the Keck II telescope and the Gemini Observatory, both in Hawaii, were trained on the spot (Figure 22), it was decided that the Hubble Space Telescope should take a look

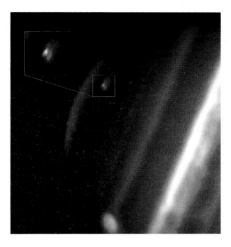

Figure 22. Infrared observations taken at the Keck II telescope in Hawaii reveal a bright spot where the 19 July 2009 impact occurred. The spot looks black at visible wavelengths. (Image courtesy of Paul Kalas/Michael Fitzgerald/Franck Marchis/LLNL/UCLA/UC Berkeley/ SETI Institute.)

because its images are the sharpest at visible wavelengths. Hubble can also observe at ultraviolet wavelengths, which can reveal impact débris that has been lofted high into Jupiter's atmosphere. As it happened, Hubble was in the middle of the testing and calibration of its new instruments, installed by astronauts during the servicing mission in May. However, Hubble managers decided that the impact event was rare enough and important enough to pause testing to get a look with the new Wide Field Camera 3, which, although not fully calibrated, was able to image the region around the dark spot (Figure 23).

The evidence gathered all suggested that the spot was due to an impacting body, presumably either a comet or wandering asteroid. Impacts have been seen before – remember the line of dark spots caused by the break-up and subsequent impact of the twenty or so fragments of Comet Shoemaker-Levy 9 in July 1994, fifteen years earlier. The July 2009 impact was probably due to a single fragment of a comet or asteroid a few hundred metres across. The disturbance on Jupiter did not last, but if an impactor of comparable size had hit the Earth it would have caused major devastation.

Equally unexpected were the events of May 2010, when, without

Figure 23. Top: the first full-disk image of Jupiter made with the Hubble Space Telescope's new camera, the Wide Field Camera 3 (WFC3), on 23 July 2009. The dark smudge at bottom right is debris from a comet or asteroid that plunged into Jupiter's atmosphere and disintegrated. (Image courtesy of NASA, ESA, Michael Wong (Space Telescope Science Institute, Baltimore, MD), H. B. Hammel (Space Science Institute, Boulder, Colorado) and the Jupiter Impact Team.) **Bottom**: the sharpest visible-light picture taken of the impact feature, made using Hubble's WFC3 on 23 July 2009. The expanding spot is twice the size of the USA. (Image courtesy of NASA, ESA and H. B. Hammel (Space Science Institute, Boulder, Colorado), and the Jupiter Impact Team.)

warning, Jupiter's South Equatorial Belt (SEB) completely disappeared. The North Equatorial Belt (NEB) and the SEB are regarded as virtually permanent features of the planet's cloud layers. Generally the NEB is the darker and broader of the two; the SEB is more variable, but at times it can become as prominent as its twin. The reason for its latest vanishing act is unclear. There have been suggestions that it may have been covered with a layer of high-level, cirrus-type cloud, but we must wait and see what happens. Certainly we may be confident that the SEB will return sooner or later – sooner more probably than later.

There have also been small red spots, greatly inferior to the Great Red Spot but decidedly unusual. We are still uncertain about the cause of the red colour; dredged-up phosphorus has been proposed as one possibility. During the absence of the SEB, the Great Red Spot seems to move in splendid isolation.

Then, on 3 June 2010 another surprise! Australian amateur Anthony Wesley was observing Jupiter at 20.31 UT when he fortuitously caught

Figure 24. The bright flash (lower right) observed in the atmosphere of Jupiter by Anthony Wesley of Broken Hill, Australia, at 20:31:06 UT on 3 June 2010. The flash was independently confirmed by Christopher Go in the Philippines. Note the almost complete absence of the planet's South Equatorial Belt. (Image courtesy of Anthony Wesley.)

the bright flash of some object hitting the planet's cloud tops (Figure 24). The flash was independently confirmed by Christopher Go in the Philippines. A dark 'bruise' was expected to develop around the impact point because that was what happened in the aftermath of previous such impacts. But this time, despite careful scrutiny by observers round the world, a prominent dark débris spot did not emerge.

So what happened to the débris this time? One possibility is that the flash was not an impact at all, but a giant Jovian lightning bolt. However, this is thought highly unlikely; Jovian lightning has been seen by spacecraft many times, but only on the nightside of the planet. This dayside event would have to be unimaginably more powerful than any previous bolt seen. Even Jupiter does not produce lightning that big. Nor could it be a lightning flash in Earth's atmosphere happening, by chance, in front of Jupiter. The observations of the same flash from widely spaced locations in Australia and the Philippines rule that out. For the same reason, it could not be a meteor or any other phenomenon in Earth's atmosphere. No, the flash really happened at Jupiter. Curiously, the impactor (if indeed this was an impact event) struck right in the middle of where Jupiter's SEB should have been – if it had not disappeared earlier in 2010.

Maybe this latest impactor was too small to produce much débris, packing just enough punch to make a flash, but without leaving a visible dark mark. One thing is certain: Jupiter is getting hit more than we expected. Back in 1994, at the time of the Shoemaker-Levy 9 impacts, it was calculated that we should see an impact on Jupiter once every hundred years or so. Now Anthony Wesley has observed two impacts within one year. Clearly, scientists still have a lot to learn, not only about how often Jupiter gets hit, but also what happens when such impacts occur.

The Draconid Meteors. On two occasions during the twentieth century, on 9 October 1933 and, thirteen years later, on 10 October 1946, spectacular showers of meteors were observed emanating from the head of Draco, the Dragon; visual rates were greater than one meteor every second, but the total duration of each display was only about an hour. Lesser Draconid displays were also observed in 1926, 1952, 1985, 1998 and 2005, but none in other years. All the observed showers occurred when the parent comet of the swarm, 21P/Giacobini-Zinner, passed close to the orbit of the Earth.

Now calculations have indicated that there is the possibility of another fine Draconid display on 8 October 2011 between about 18h and 21h UT – not at the level of the great storms of the past, but still expected to produce an outstanding shower. Increased Draconid activity may begin at around 16h UT, as it is getting dark that evening, and continue until about 23h. The peak ZHR is highly uncertain, but could be as high as 800 meteors per hour according to some forecasts. Draconid meteors are exceptionally slow-moving.

November

New Moon: 25 November   *Full Moon:* 10 November

MERCURY reaches greatest eastern elongation (23°) on 14 November and, for observers in tropical and southern latitudes, it is visible as an evening object until the last week of the month. The planet is unobservable for observers in the latitudes of the British Isles. For observers in the Southern Hemisphere this will be a most interesting evening apparition of Mercury on account of its proximity to Venus during the first two weeks of November. The brilliant Venus will be a useful guide to locating the much fainter Mercury. Figure 25 shows, for observers in latitude 35°S, the changes in azimuth and altitude of Mercury and Venus on successive evenings when the Sun is 6° below the horizon. This condition is known as the end of evening civil twilight, which in this latitude and at this time of year occurs about 30 minutes after sunset. The changes in the brightness of Mercury are indicated by the relative sizes of the circles marking its position at five-day intervals: Mercury is at its brightest before it reaches greatest eastern elongation and during the first three weeks of November its brightness decreases from magnitude −0.3 to +0.5. The diagram gives positions for a time at the end of evening civil twilight on the Greenwich meridian, on the stated date. Observers in different longitudes should note that the observed positions of Mercury in azimuth and altitude will differ slightly from those shown in the diagram.

VENUS, magnitude −3.9, is visible in the western sky after sunset for observers in the tropics and the Southern Hemisphere. The proximity of the brilliant Venus to the much fainter Mercury during the first two weeks of November has already been noted above. Venus will not be visible from the latitudes of the British Isles until the very end of November when it may be glimpsed low in the south-western twilight sky.

MARS brightens from magnitude +1.1 to +0.7 during the month. The planet is in Leo and by the end of month it is rising before midnight

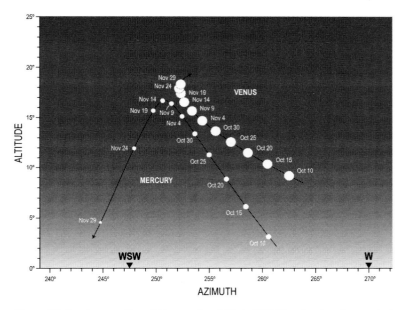

Figure 25. Evening apparition of Mercury, from latitude 35°S. The planet reaches greatest eastern elongation on 14 November. It will be at its brightest in mid-October, before elongation. The chart also shows the positions of the brilliant Venus, in relation to Mercury, between 10 October and 19 November. Venus is a useful guide to locating the much fainter Mercury between 30 October and 14 November. The angular diameters of Mercury and Venus are not drawn to scale.

from the Northern Hemisphere and only slightly after midnight for observers in the Southern Hemisphere.

JUPITER, magnitude −2.9, is only just past opposition and is visible all night long. The planet is in Aries, but its retrograde motion carries it back towards the border with Pisces during November. The four Galilean satellites, which Galileo first saw in January 1610, are readily observable with a small telescope or even a good pair of binoculars provided that they are held rigidly.

SATURN passed through superior conjunction in mid-October and is now becoming visible low in the eastern sky just before dawn. The planet is in Virgo, magnitude +0.9.

Fomalhaut. During November, the Square of Pegasus is prominent in the evening sky. Well below it, to Northern Hemisphere observers, it will be possible to see Fomalhaut, leader of the little constellation of Piscis Australis (or Piscis Austrinus), the Southern Fish. Fomalhaut is the southernmost of the first-magnitude stars to be visible from Britain, but from the north of Scotland it is never easy to see at all. Go south, look at it when it is high up, and you will be able to appreciate how bright it really is. The apparent magnitude is 1.16. The name means 'mouth of the whale', from the Arabic *fum-al-hawt*.

At its distance of 25 light years Fomalhaut is one of our nearer stellar neighbours. Its spectral type is A3, so that it is practically pure white; it is 18 times as luminous as the Sun, and more than two times as massive, with a diameter nearly twice that of the Sun. By stellar standards Fomalhaut is a young star, with an age of only about 200 million years.

All this sounds ordinary enough – yet to us, Fomalhaut may lay claim to being one of the most interesting stars in the sky. Some time ago it was found to be surrounded by a débris disk of dust, toroidal in shape with a sharp inner edge at a distance of just over 130 astronomical units (AU) from the star. The dusty disk was about 25 AU wide, and inclined at approximately 25° from edgewise-on. From observations of its influence on the Fomalhaut dust belt, astronomers inferred the existence of a planet, just inside the débris ring, in 2005; the belt is not centred on the star, and it has a sharper inner boundary than would normally be expected. However, the planet was only located in May 2008 after Paul Kalas and James Graham located it on Hubble Space Telescope photographs taken in 2004 and 2006 (Figure 26). NASA released the composite discovery photograph, obtained by the Hubble Space Telescope's Advanced Camera for Surveys, three years ago, on 13 November 2008.

The planet orbits Fomalhaut at a distance of approximately 115 AU (17,200 million kilometres), about 18 AU closer to the star than the inner edge of the débris disk. The orbital period is 872 years. Extrasolar planets had been tracked down before, but this was the first to be observed directly in visible light, the first imaged planet since Neptune to have been predicted prior to discovery, and the first planet to have been correctly predicted based on its interaction with a débris disk. Astronomers were elated. The planet was officially catalogued as Fomalhaut b (Figure 27).

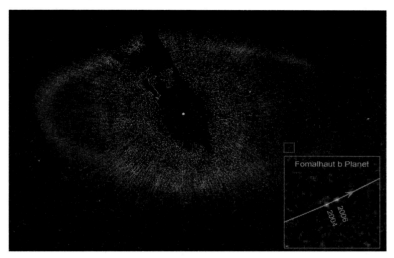

Figure 26. The dusty disk around the young star Fomalhaut. This Hubble Space Telescope image of Fomalhaut shows the surrounding disk of dust, about 130 AU from the star. In 2008, the analysis of additional Hubble Space Telescope images taken in 2004 and 2006 revealed the presence of a giant planet within this disk (see inset). (Image courtesy of NASA, ESA, P. Kalas and J. Graham (University of California, Berkeley), and M. Clampin (NASA/GFSC).)

Fomalhaut b is suspected, on the basis of its brightness in visible light and dimness in infrared, to be surrounded by a circumplanetary disk with a radius approximately 20–40 times the radius of Jupiter. This size is similar to the orbital radii of Jupiter's Galilean satellites and therefore may represent a stage in the formation of a system of moons around the planet.

Life? Most likely not. The planet is estimated to be approximately the same size as Jupiter, with a maximum mass of three Jupiters and a most probable mass of between half and twice that of Jupiter, which means that it must be a giant with a gaseous surface. But if one planet exists, there may well be others in the Fomalhaut system – possibly planets similar to the Earth and where life of some kind could one day appear. Remember that Fomalhaut is still a young star, so even if the conditions for life exist, it may well be hundreds of millions of years before life gets going. And, even if we do locate a planet where life *could* appear, there is no guarantee that it *will*.

Figure 27. Artist's impression of the star Fomalhaut and the Jupiter-type planet that the Hubble Space Telescope observed. A ring of débris appears to surround Fomalhaut as well. The planet, called Fomalhaut b, orbits the 200-million-year-old star every 872 years. (Image courtesy of ESA, NASA and L. Calcada (ESO for STScI).)

Aries. The brilliant planet Jupiter, just past opposition, is in Aries, although moving slowly retrograde towards the border with neighbouring Pisces. Figure 28 shows the location of Aries in relation to the principal stars of Pegasus and Andromeda. Aries, the celestial Ram, is regarded as the first constellation of the Zodiac, even though the vernal equinox (also called the first point of Aries) has now shifted into Pisces. In mythology Aries represents a ram with a golden fleece, sent by the god Hermes to rescue the two children of the King of Thebes from an assassination plan by their stepmother. The ram could fly, and the rescue was duly carried out. After the ram's death the fleece lay in a sacred grove until it was forcibly removed by Jason and the Argonauts.

The brightest stars are Alpha (Hamal) magnitude 2.0; Beta (Sheratan) 2.6; c or 41 (Nair al Butain or Bharani) 3.6 and Gamma (Mesartim) 3.9. Mesartim is a splendid double; the components are virtually equal (each of magnitude 4.8) and the separation is 7.5 seconds of arc, so that the pair can be split with a very small telescope.

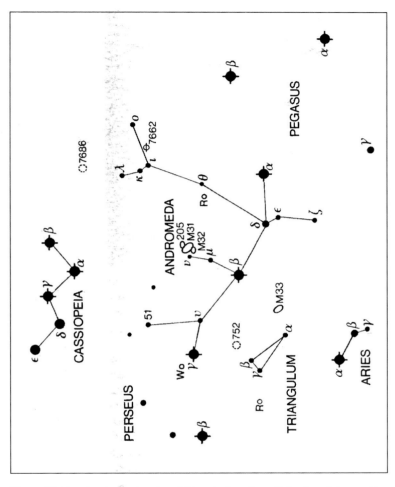

Figure 28. Map showing the location of Aries, the Ram, beneath the line of stars marking Andromeda, which extends to the east from the upper left corner of the Square of Pegasus. The small pattern of Triangulum lies between Andromeda and Aries.

December

New Moon: 24 December   *Full Moon:* 10 December

Solstice: 22 December

MERCURY passes through inferior conjunction on 4 December, and rapidly moves out to the west of the Sun, reaching greatest western elongation (22°) on 23 December. The planet is consequently visible as an early morning object from mid-December until the end of the year. From northern temperate latitudes, it will be seen low in the south-eastern sky about the time of the beginning of morning civil twilight; from more southerly latitudes it will be in the east-south-east. Mercury is at its brightest after it reaches greatest western elongation and during the last two weeks of December the planet brightens from magnitude +0.2 to −0.4.

VENUS, magnitude −4.0, is a lovely object in the early evening sky after sunset, setting about two-and-half hours after the Sun by the end of December. On 27 December the waxing crescent Moon will make a nice pairing with Venus in the evening twilight sky.

MARS is in Leo, rising in the late evening by the end of the month and well placed during the early morning hours. The planet brightens from magnitude +0.7 to +0.2 during December.

JUPITER is a splendid object visible in the southern sky as soon as darkness falls and does not set until the early morning hours. It begins the month in Aries but its retrograde motion carries it across the border into neighbouring Pisces. However, the planet reaches its second stationary point on 26 December and thereafter resumes its direct motion. It fades from magnitude −2.8 to −2.6 during the month as its distance from the Earth increases. The waxing gibbous Moon will lie just north of Jupiter on 6 December and the two objects will be a nice sight in the evening sky.

SATURN, magnitude +0.7, is moving eastwards in Virgo and it continues to be visible in the eastern sky before dawn. The apparent tilt of the rings, as viewed from Earth, has increased to over 14° by year end.

Two Anniversaries. This month we mark the births of two very different and rather unusual astronomers: Jean-Louis Pons and Grote Reber.

Pons was French, born at Peyres (in the Hautes Alpes) on 24 December 1761 – 250 years ago. He came of a poor family, and had little in the way of formal education, but he became interested in astronomy at a very early age, and in 1789 he joined the staff of the Marseilles Observatory – not as an observer, but as a doorkeeper and caretaker! Gradually he began assisting astronomers with their work, and was eventually able to start making observations himself. On 11 July 1801 he made his first discovery: a comet – and from that time onward comets were his main interest

With greater opportunities he was able to spend most clear nights observing, and all in all he discovered 37 comets between 1801 and 1827. Pons received the French Academy of Science's Lalande Prize in 1818 for his discovery of three comets in that year. A rather pleasing story is attached to one of them. On 26 November 1818 he found a comet which proved to have a period of only 3.3 years, still the shortest known. The orbit was calculated by the German astronomer Johann Encke, and we know it today as comet 2P/Encke (or Encke's comet); with modern instruments it can be kept in view even when it is at aphelion. Encke himself always maintained that as he was the calculator, not the discoverer, the credit should not be his, and generously he always called it 'Pons' Comet'.

Apart from the one now known as Encke's comet, Pons discovered three other periodic comets, and two of them, 7P/Pons-Winnecke and 12P/Pons-Brooks, carry his name. The third – the comet formerly called 'Pons-Coggia-Winnecke-Forbe' – is today known as 27P/Crommelin after Andrew Crommelin, who calculated its orbit.

In 1819, Pons became director of the new observatory at Marlia, near Lucca, which he left in 1825 for the observatory of the museum in Florence where he taught astronomy (Figure 29). By 1827, Pons's eyesight had begun to fail him, and he retired from observing altogether shortly before his death. He died, greatly honoured, on 14 October 1831.

Grote Reber was born on 22 December 1911 at Wheaton in Illinois,

Figure 29. Portrait of Jean-Louis Pons by Ernesto Bonaiuti, *c*. 1830, pastel on paper. On the reverse of the portrait is displayed a drawing of the observatory at the museum in Florence with the upper part of the tower still under construction, and the epitaph for Pons, entombed in the church of San Marco. (Image courtesy Florence Museum of the History of Science.)

a suburb of Chicago. He graduated in radio engineering, and heard about Karl Jansky's experiments in picking up signals from the Milky Way. Reber decided to go further, and built a radio telescope in his backyard – the first intentional radio telescope in history. It consisted of a parabolic sheet metal reflector 9.6 metres in diameter, focusing to a radio receiver 6 metres above the reflector (Figure 30). The receiver amplified the faint cosmic signals making them strong enough to be recorded on a chart. The telescope was completed in 1937, and at that time Reber was the only radio astronomer in the world. How times have changed!

Reber built a parabolic dish reflector because this shape brings radio waves to the same focus for all wavelengths, and so is usable over a broad wavelength range. This principle had been used for a long time by astronomers in the design of optical telescopes, and Reber knew that

Figure 30. The radio telescope, with 9.6-metre diameter parabolic dish reflector (made of sheet metal), that was constructed by Grote Reber in 1937 in the backyard of his home in Wheaton, Illinois. He built the telescope at his own expense while working full time for a radio company in Chicago. The cylinder above the dish contains the radio receiver which amplified the faint cosmic signals. The wooden tower at the left was used for access to the receiver. (Image courtesy of the National Radio Astronomy Observatory.)

it would be important to observe a wide range of radio wavelengths from the sky to understand how the radiation was being produced.

From Wheaton, Reber continued his radio experiments, and in 1954 he moved to Tasmania to continue his work. By then, of course, radio astronomy had become a vitally important branch of research, but Reber was still able to make contributions. In the 1950s, Reber had turned his attention to cosmic radio waves at very low frequencies (1–2 MHz, or wavelength of 150–300 metres). Waves of these frequencies cannot penetrate the Earth's ionosphere except in certain places on the Earth at times of low solar activity. One such place is Tasmania, where Reber lived until his death, in Hobart, on 20 December 2002.

Rho Cassiopeae. During December evenings Cassiopeia is almost overhead as seen from northern Europe and North America, and most people can recognize the famous W-shaped pattern. The central star,

Gamma Cassiopeae, is an unpredictable variable with an extreme range of magnitude 1.6 to 3.2; generally it hovers around 2.2. Close to it, the reddish Alpha (Shedir) has been suspected of slight variability, but this has never been confirmed.

Then do not forget Rho Cassiopeae, the middle star in a line of three rather inconspicuous stars close to Beta; the stars Tau Cassiopeiae (magnitude 4.9) and Sigma (5.0), on either side, and two fainter stars (magnitudes 5.5 and 6.2) quite near Rho, act as useful comparison stars for the binocular observer. Usually Rho is about magnitude 4.8 but sometimes, as in 1946 and 2000, it descends briefly to magnitude 6. At present it is of spectral type F, but during minima this may change temporarily to type M.

Rho is a hypergiant star – far more powerful than the normal supergiant – and one of only a handful known in our Galaxy. Its distance is at least 8,000 light years and may be as much as 10,000 light years. Its luminosity is at least 250,000 times that of the Sun. It is unstable and there is no doubt that it will explode as a supernova; the only question is when? It may not be for centuries but it may be tomorrow. When it does, it will temporarily alter the whole aspect of that part of the sky, just as Tycho Brahe's supernova did when it flared up in Cassiopeia in 1572.

Eclipses in 2011

MARTIN MOBBERLEY

During 2011 there will be six eclipses, four partial eclipses of the Sun and two total eclipses of the Moon.

1. *A partial eclipse of the Sun* on 4 January will be visible across Europe, Africa and central Asia, peaking at 08h 52m UT when the lunar disk will cut across 86 per cent of the solar diameter as observed at sunrise from northern Scandinavia. From the south-eastern UK 75 per cent of the Sun will be eclipsed at sunrise, which could make for an interesting view provided suitable safe solar filters are used.

Figure 1. The penumbral shadow of the Moon at the maximum of the 4 January solar eclipse. (Diagram generated using *Wineclipse* by Heinz Scsibrany.)

Figure 2. The Moon covering most of the Sun just after sunrise above the south-eastern London horizon on 4 January at 08h 07m UT. (Diagram generated using *Guide 8.0* by Bill Gray.)

2. *A partial eclipse of the Sun* on 1 June will be visible across eastern Asia, northern North America and Iceland, peaking at 21h 17m UT when the lunar disk will cut across 60 per cent of the solar diameter as observed from northern Russia's Arctic coast, close to local midnight, in the land of the midnight summer Sun. From northern Canada only 20 per cent of the Sun, at most, will be covered. The event occurs just after sunset from the UK.

3. *A total lunar eclipse* on 15 June will be visible from South America, Europe, Africa, Asia and Australia. The umbral magnitude will be 1.7 and the total phase will last 1 hour 40 minutes peaking at 20h 14m UT. Observers from southern Africa to India will be best placed with all phases of the eclipse visible. From the UK the Moon starts to leave the umbra shortly after moonrise. The lunar disk passes slightly north of the centre of the Earth's shadow at mid-eclipse.

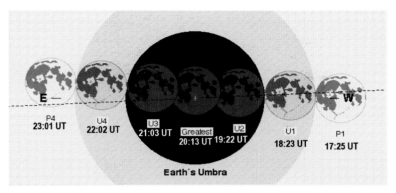

Figure 3. The path of the Moon through the Earth's umbra and penumbra on 15 June. (Diagram by NASA/Fred Espenak.)

4. *A partial eclipse of the Sun* on 1 July occurs only one lunar month after the 1 June eclipse meaning that two partial solar eclipses (and a total lunar eclipse) have just squeezed into the one node, a relatively rare event. As often occurs during these circumstances, an eclipse visible from the far north of the Earth is followed by one visible in the far south a month later. Thus the 1 July partial eclipse is only visible in Antarctic waters peaking at 08h 38m UT. Less than 10 per cent of the solar disk is cut into by the lunar limb at the point of greatest eclipse.

5. *A partial eclipse of the Sun* on 25 November is visible from South Africa, Antarctica, Tasmania and New Zealand, although, as in July, only Antarctica sees a significant eclipse, varying from 35 per cent on the South Africa/Tasmania hemisphere to 90 per cent with the Sun on the horizon, near the South American side of the Antarctic continent. The eclipse peaks at 06h 21m UT.

6. *A total lunar eclipse* on 10 December is visible from Eastern Europe, East Africa, Asia, Australia and the Pacific. Eastern Asia, Indonesia, Australia and Japan are best placed for viewing this eclipse near midnight and at a good altitude. From the UK the Moon has already started leaving the umbra before moonrise. The umbral magnitude of this eclipse is 1.1 and the Moon is never far from the southern edge of the Earth's shadow. The greatest eclipse occurs at 14h 32m UT.

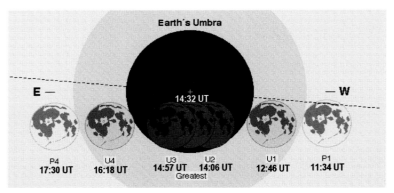

Figure 4. The path of the Moon through the Earth's umbra and penumbra on 10 December. (Diagram by NASA/Fred Espenak.)

Occultations in 2011

NICK JAMES

The Moon makes one circuit around the Earth in just over 27 days and as it moves across the sky it can temporarily hide, or occult, objects that are further away, such as planets or stars. The Moon's orbit is inclined to the ecliptic by around 5.1° and its path with respect to the background stars is defined by the longitude at which it crosses the ecliptic passing from south to north. This is known as the longitude of the ascending node. After passing the node the Moon moves eastward relative to the stars reaching 5.1° north of the ecliptic after a week. Two weeks after crossing the ascending node it crosses the ecliptic moving south and then it reaches 5.1° south of the ecliptic after three weeks. Finally it arrives back at the ascending node a week later and the cycle begins again.

The apparent diameter of the Moon depends on its distance from the Earth but at its closest it appears almost 0.6° across. In addition the apparent position of the Moon on the sky at any given time shifts depending on where you are on the surface of the Earth. This effect, called parallax, can move the apparent position of the Moon by just over 1°. The combined effect of parallax and the apparent diameter of the Moon means that if an object passes within 1.3° of the apparent centre of the Moon as seen from the centre of the Earth it will be occulted from somewhere on the surface of our planet. For the occultation to be visible the Moon would have to be some distance from the Sun in the sky and, depending on the object being occulted, it would have to be twilight or dark.

For various reasons, mainly the Earth's equatorial bulge, the nodes of the Moon's orbit move westwards at a rate of around 19° per year taking 18.6 years to do a full circuit. This means that, while the Moon follows approximately the same path from month to month, this path gradually shifts with time. Over the full 18.6-year period all of the stars that lie within 6.4° of the ecliptic will be occulted.

Only four first-magnitude stars lie within 6.4° of the ecliptic. These are Aldebaran (5.4°), Regulus (0.5°), Spica (2.1°) and Antares (4.6°). As the nodes precess through the 18.6-year cycle there will be a monthly series of occultations of each star followed by a period when the star is not occulted. In 2011 there will be no occultations of first-magnitude stars.

In 2011 there will be three occultations of bright planets, one each of Venus, Mars and Mercury. Only one of these events takes place at a solar elongation of greater than 20° and this is not visible from the British Isles.

The following table shows events potentially visible from somewhere on the Earth when the solar elongation exceeds 20°. More detailed predictions for your location can often be found in magazines or the *Handbook of the British Astronomical Association*.

Object	Time of Minimum Distance (UT)	Minimum Distance °	Elong- ation °	Visibility
Mars	27 July 2011 16h 46m	0.5	−39	Pacific

Comets in 2011

MARTIN MOBBERLEY

Several dozen short-period comets will reach perihelion in 2011. All these returning comets orbit the Sun with periods of between three and thirty years and many are too faint for amateur visual observation, even with a large telescope. Bright or spectacular comets have much longer orbital periods and, apart from a few notable exceptions like 1P/Halley, 109P/Swift-Tuttle and 153P/Ikeya-Zhang, the best performers usually have orbital periods of many thousands of years and are often discovered less than a year before they come within amateur range. For this reason it is important to regularly check the best comet websites for news of bright comets that may be discovered well after this *Yearbook* is published. Some recommended sites are:

British Astronomical Association Comet Section: www.ast.cam.ac.uk/~jds/
Seiichi Yoshida's bright comet page: www.ast.cam.ac.uk/~jds/
CBAT/MPC comets site: www.minorplanetcenter.org/iau/Ephemerides/Comets/index.html
Yahoo Comet Images group: http://tech.groups.yahoo.com/group/Comet-Images/
Yahoo Comet Mailing list: http://tech.groups.yahoo.com/group/comets-ml/

The CBAT/MPC web page above also gives accurate ephemerides of the comets' positions in right ascension and declination.

Nine periodic comets are expected to reach magnitude 13 or brighter during 2011 and so should be observable with a visual telescope, or with CCD imaging equipment, in a reasonably dark sky. In addition the long-period comet C/2006 S3 (LONEOS) will reach perihelion early in 2012 and so be observable late in 2011. The infamous comet 29P/Schwassmann-Wachmann 1 will usually be too faint for visual observation even in large amateur telescopes, but is renowned for going into outburst several times per year when it can reach magnitude 11. As discussed below, whether chunks of comet 73P/Schwassmann-Wachmann 3 do actually reach magnitude 13 remains to be seen!

The comets in question are listed below in the order they reach perihelion.

Comet	Period (years)	Perihelion	Peak Brightness
29P/Schwassmann-Wachmann 1	14.7	2004 July 3	11 when in outburst
103P/Hartley 2	6.5	2010 Oct 28	5 in Oct 2010
9P/Tempel 1	5.5	2011 Jan 12	12 in Jan 2011
213P/2009 B3 (Van Ness)	6.3	2011 June 16	13 in June 2011
27P/Crommelin	27.9	2011 Aug 4	10 in Aug 2011
45P/Honda-Mrkos-Pajdusakova	5.3	2011 Sept 28	7 in Sept 2011
73P/Schwassmann-Wachmann 3	5.4	2011 Oct 13	Unknown/Oct 2011
P/2006 T1 (Levy)	5.3	2012 Jan 12	8 in Jan 2012
78P/Gehrels 2	7.2	2012 Jan 13	11 in Jan 2012
21P/Giacobini- Zinner	6.6	2012 Feb 13	10 in Feb 2012
C/2006 S3 (LONEOS)	long	2012 Apr 16	13 in Apr 2012

As 2011 starts, comet 103P/Hartley 2, which will have peaked a couple of months earlier at fifth magnitude, should still be a tenth- or even ninth-magnitude object. However, 103P is only bright because it can approach the Earth quite closely. All being well the comet will have passed only 0.12 AU from the Earth on 20 October 2010 but is now moving away from Earth and Sun and fading rapidly not far from the brightest star in the sky, Sirius in Canis Major.

Comet 9P/Tempel 1 reaches perihelion on 12 January. Many astronomers will remember this comet well from 2005 when the NASA Deep Impact probe fired a projectile into the nucleus causing the comet to brighten by several magnitudes and leaving a crater some 200 metres in diameter and 40 metres deep. The Stardust spacecraft will be revisiting Tempel 1 this year, making the object unique among the smaller solar system bodies by being visited twice by spacecraft. Astronomers are keen to re-examine the impact site six years on from its formation. Unfortunately the comet is unlikely to become any brighter than magnitude 12 and, lying in southern Ophiuchus, it will be virtually impossible for far Northern Hemisphere observers at perihelion.

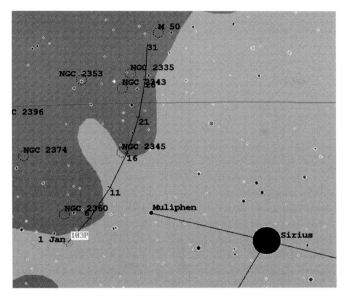

Figure 1. The path of 103P/Hartley 2, near Sirius, in January.

Comet 213P/Van Ness, also formerly known as 2009 B3 and 2005 R2, is a recently discovered periodic comet which reaches perihelion in June while crossing Aquarius. This will be primarily a magnitude 13 CCD target for amateurs and is very poorly placed for astronomers in the far Northern Hemisphere.

Comet 27P/Crommelin last reached perihelion some 28 years ago but, sadly, due to its position in Cancer at perihelion, on 4 August, it too will be a very tricky object to observe.

Comet 45P/Honda-Mrkos-Pajdusakova is a comet that returns to perihelion every five years and often makes a surprisingly close fly-by of the Earth. This year is no exception as on 15 August it passes just nine million kilometres from us, although, at a declination of −70°, you will need to be in the far Southern Hemisphere to observe it in the dawn sky. Comet 45P does move rapidly north after its close approach though, and Northern Hemisphere observers should be able to pick it up low in the dawn sky in September and October in Leo, but it will steadily fade from seventh to eleventh magnitude.

Trying to predict what, if anything, of Comet 73P/Schwassmann-Wachmann 3 will become visible this year is virtually impossible. First discovered in 1930, the comet started to break up into five pieces at its 1995 return. Amateur astronomers worldwide imaged its further break-up into fragments B, C, G, H, J, L, M and N in 2006 with the Hubble Space Telescope recording 66 cometary fragments, mainly from the complete disintegration of the objects labelled B and G. It is thought that the biggest fragment, C, may be observable at this year's return. However, it is quite possible that nothing will be observed and the comet will be reclassified as number 73D, the D standing for defunct. In addition the comet will be very poorly placed with an elongation of 30° from the Sun and a southerly declination at the critical time.

Comet P/2006 T1 (Levy) is, perhaps, the best cometary prospect for 2011 although as bright comets can, even now, still remain undiscovered until only six months before they peak, new discoveries are always likely to steal the show. P/2006 T1 was David Levy's twenty-second

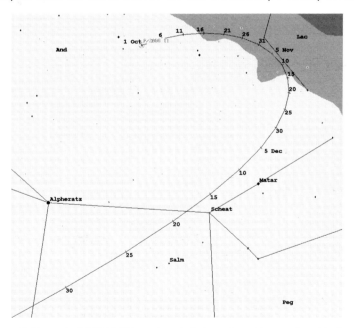

Figure 2. The track of P/2006 T1 Levy through Andromeda and Pegasus from October to December.

comet discovery and his ninth visual discovery. The comet will actually reach perihelion next year, on 12 January, but will be well placed in Andromeda, Lacerta and Pegasus from October, brightening from twelfth to seventh magnitude.

Comet 78P/Gehrels 2 is another comet that reaches perihelion next year but is a good target for CCD imagers, at least in the dying months of 2011. While not a bright visual target it is very well placed from October to December, as a magnitude 13 or 14 object in Pisces.

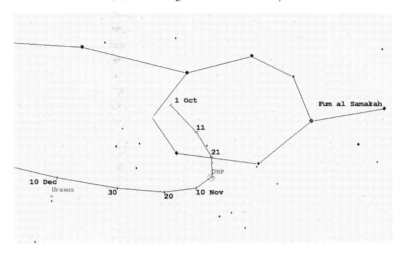

Figure 3. The track of the faint comet 78P/Gehrels 2, in Pisces, from October to December.

Finally, in late December, those UK observers with an excellent south-west horizon may be able to pick up the brightening 21P/Giacobinni-Zinner as a twelfth-magnitude object. It should brighten to magnitude 10 two months later.

The tables below list the right ascension and declination of the five most promising comets as well as the distances, in AU, from the Earth and Sun. The elongation, in degrees from the Sun, is also tabulated along with the estimated visual magnitude, which can only ever be a rough guess as comets are a law unto themselves!

103P/Hartley

Date		RA (2000)			Dec.			Distance from Earth (AU)	Distance from Sun (AU)	Elongation from Sun °	Mag.
		h	m	s	°	′	″				
Jan	9	07	11	55.7	−15	14	33	0.524	1.435	142.5	10.2
Jan	19	07	06	30.6	−12	31	34	0.609	1.520	144.3	11.1
Jan	29	07	04	13.6	−09	32	48	0.707	1.607	143.0	11.9
Feb	08	07	05	11.1	−06	36	13	0.822	1.696	139.2	12.7
Feb	18	07	09	09.2	−03	54	06	0.952	1.785	133.8	13.4

45P/Honda-Mrkos-Pajdusakova

Date		RA (2000)			Dec.			Distance from Earth (AU)	Distance from Sun (AU)	Elongation from Sun °	Mag.
		h	m	s	°	′	″				
July	28	21	57	37.4	−25	53	11	0.273	1.273	158.1	12.8
Aug	7	22	22	51.0	−39	16	20	0.133	1.133	151.8	10.2
Aug	17	07	58	27.3	−50	05	52	0.065	0.990	67.8	7.5
Aug	27	09	20	09.8	−04	10	49	0.179	0.846	20.9	8.3
Sept	9	09	34	32.6	+04	48	33	0.330	0.709	20.6	8.1
Sept	16	09	48	58.8	+08	06	46	0.508	0.595	26.4	7.5
Sept	26	10	11	44.2	+08	50	48	0.717	0.533	30.8	7.3
Oct	6	10	43	04.9	+07	41	08	0.938	0.552	32.9	8.2
Oct	16	11	17	03.0	+05	26	16	1.140	0.642	34.1	9.9
Oct	26	11	48	42.5	+02	54	12	1.309	0.769	35.8	11.8

73P/Schwassmann-Wachmann (may be defunct)

Date		RA (2000)			Dec.			Distance from Earth (AU)	Distance from Sun °	Elongation from Sun	Mag.
		h	m	s	°	′	″				
Sept	26	13	58	23.2	−10	58	56	1.740	0.991	29.0	13.1
Oct	6	14	38	28.0	−15	54	57	1.681	0.956	30.0	12.8
Oct	16	15	22	58.5	−20	37	01	1.634	0.943	31.6	12.7
Oct	26	16	12	02.3	−24	42	49	1.604	0.953	33.7	12.7

| Nov | 5 | 17 | 05 | 00.5 | −27 | 48 | 13 | 1.594 | 0.984 | 36.1 | 12.9 |
| Nov | 15 | 18 | 00 | 08.9 | −29 | 34 | 07 | 1.608 | 1.035 | 38.4 | 13.3 |

P/2006 T1 (Levy)

Date		RA (2000)			Dec.			Distance from Earth (AU)	Distance from Sun (AU)	Elong- ation from Sun °	Mag.
		h	m	s	°	′	″				
Oct	1	23	32	51.0	+43	38	01	0.782	1.664	137.5	12.2
Oct	11	23	12	50.4	+44	31	02	0.701	1.575	135.2	11.7
Oct	21	22	52	59.4	+44	18	15	0.634	1.488	130.6	11.2
Oct	31	22	36	50.8	+43	02	30	0.576	1.402	124.4	10.8
Nov	10	22	27	20.5	+40	59	27	0.525	1.319	117.7	10.3
Nov	20	22	25	57.8	+38	26	29	0.477	1.241	110.9	9.8
Nov	30	22	33	28.2	+35	33	43	0.427	1.169	104.6	9.3
Dec	10	22	50	28.9	+32	18	39	0.375	1.108	99.1	8.8
Dec	20	23	18	08.6	+28	15	12	0.320	1.058	94.5	8.3
Dec	30	23	59	04.2	+22	24	54	0.266	1.024	91.3	7.7

21P/Giacobini-Zinner

Date		RA (2000)			Dec.			Distance from Earth (AU)	Distance from Sun (AU)	Elong- ation from Sun °	Mag.
		h	m	s	°	′	″				
Nov	25	18	07	19.3	−02	25	50	2.163	1.481	35.9	13.2
Dec	5	18	37	01.6	−03	18	46	2.106	1.394	33.4	12.8
Dec	15	19	09	25.0	−04	00	02	2.048	1.311	31.3	12.3
Dec	25	19	44	30.5	−04	28	13	1.993	1.234	29.3	11.9

Minor Planets in 2011

MARTIN MOBBERLEY

Some 500,000 minor planets (also known as asteroids) are known. They range in size from hundreds of kilometres in diameter to tens of metres across. More than 200,000 of these now have such good orbits that they have a numbered designation and 15,000 have been named after mythological gods, famous people, scientists, astronomers and institutions. Most of these objects live between Mars and Jupiter, but some 6,000 have been discovered between the Sun and Mars and more than 1,000 of these are classed as potentially hazardous asteroids (PHAs) due to their ability to pass within eight million kilometres of the Earth while also having a diameter greater than 200 metres. The first four asteroids to be discovered were Ceres (1), now regarded as a dwarf planet, Pallas (2), Juno (3) and Vesta (4) which are all easy binocular objects when at their peak due to them all having diameters of hundreds of kilometres.

In 2011 Ceres, Pallas, Juno, Vesta, Iris (7), Metis (9) and Hygiea (10) are all conveniently placed and brighter than magnitude 10 at their best. Iris is the first to reach opposition, transiting at midnight in January at magnitude 7.9 while in Cancer. Next is Juno which peaks at magnitude 8.9 in March near the Leo/Virgo border. Hygiea reaches magnitude 9.1 in May, far south of the celestial equator in Libra while, two months later, in July, Pallas reaches magnitude 9.5 near the Sagitta/Aquila border. In July and August asteroid Metis should make magnitude 9.6 but will be well below the celestial equator near the Capricornus/Sagittarius border region. The best performance of any asteroid will be that of Vesta. In August it becomes, technically, at least, a magnitude 5.7 object while in Capricornus. Finally, Ceres, formerly classified as an asteroid but now, as mentioned earlier, reclassified as a dwarf planet, reaches magnitude 7.6 in September while in Cetus.

Ephemerides for the best placed/brightest minor planets at opposition in 2011

Dwarf planet 1 Ceres

Date		RA (2000)			Dec.			Distance from Earth (AU)	Distance from Sun (AU)	Elong- ation from Sun °	Mag.
		h	m	s	°	′	″				
Aug	19	00	20	20.6	−14	16	08	2.098	2.975	143.8	8.1
Aug	29	00	15	15.1	−15	20	26	2.036	2.973	153.2	7.9
Sept	8	00	08	22.2	−16	23	50	1.999	2.970	161.1	7.7
Sept	18	00	00	20.1	−17	19	29	1.988	2.968	164.0	7.6
Sept	28	23	51	57.0	−18	01	14	2.005	2.965	159.4	7.7
Oct	8	23	44	07.0	−18	24	28	2.049	2.961	150.7	7.9
Oct	18	23	37	37.9	−18	27	23	2.117	2.958	140.9	8.1

2 Pallas

Date		RA (2000)			Dec.			Distance from Earth (AU)	Distance from Sun (AU)	Elong- ation from Sun °	Mag.
		h	m	s	°	′	″				
June	10	20	28	58.4	+18	34	42	2.825	3.398	116.2	9.9
June	20	20	25	04.0	+19	08	44	2.734	3.401	123.4	9.8
June	30	20	19	27.1	+19	22	27	2.659	3.405	130.2	9.7
July	10	20	12	28.5	+19	12	16	2.600	3.407	136.2	9.6
July	20	20	04	40.8	+18	36	14	2.563	3.409	140.5	9.6
July	30	19	56	41.5	+17	34	26	2.548	3.411	142.5	9.5
Aug	9	19	49	12.4	+16	09	17	2.558	3.412	141.6	9.5
Aug	19	19	42	51.0	+14	25	41	2.592	3.412	138.0	9.6
Aug	29	19	38	05.3	+12	29	40	2.648	3.412	132.4	9.7
Sep	8	19	35	14.5	+10	27	45	2.726	3.411	125.5	9.8

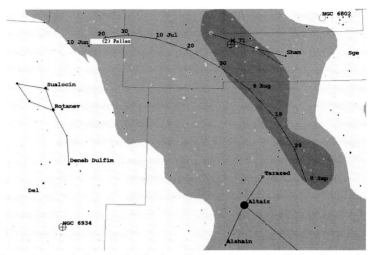

Figure 1. The path of asteroid 2 Pallas from 10 June to 8 September 2011 as it moves from Delphinus, through Sagitta, and into Aquila.

3 Juno

Date		RA (2000)			Dec.			Distance from Earth	Distance from Sun	Elong-ation from Sun	Mag.
		h	m	s	°	′	″	(AU)	(AU)	°	
Jan	11	11	52	11.1	−02	38	31	2.099	2.617	111.0	9.8
Jan	21	11	53	55.1	−02	19	18	2.001	2.644	120.9	9.7
Jan	31	11	53	08.1	−01	39	23	1.915	2.671	131.5	9.6
Feb	10	11	49	50.7	−00	38	43	1.845	2.698	142.8	9.4
Feb	20	11	44	20.6	+00	40	13	1.798	2.724	154.7	9.3
Mar	2	11	37	11.2	+02	12	27	1.776	2.750	167.0	9.1
Mar	12	11	29	11.2	+03	50	29	1.783	2.776	179.3	8.9
Mar	22	11	21	19.1	+05	25	36	1.819	2.801	168.1	9.2
Apr	1	11	14	27.7	+06	50	13	1.884	2.826	156.0	9.4
Apr	11	11	09	18.6	+07	58	49	1.975	2.851	144.6	9.7
Apr	21	11	06	16.3	+08	48	43	2.087	2.875	133.8	9.9

4 Vesta

Date		RA (2000)			Dec.			Distance from Earth	Distance from Sun	Elong-ation from Sun	Mag.
		h	m	s	°	′	″	(AU)	(AU)	°	
June	20	21	31	18.4	−17	36	54	1.422	2.204	128.7	6.5
June	30	21	31	13.5	−18	26	20	1.346	2.212	138.4	6.3
July	10	21	27	58.9	−19	32	24	1.286	2.219	148.9	6.1
July	20	21	21	51.9	−20	50	16	1.246	2.227	159.8	5.9
July	30	21	13	32.2	−22	12	21	1.228	2.235	170.3	5.7
Aug	9	21	04	08.3	−23	29	15	1.235	2.244	172.2	5.7
Aug	19	20	55	05.2	−24	32	36	1.267	2.252	162.4	5.9
Aug	29	20	47	40.8	−25	17	26	1.322	2.261	151.5	6.2
Sept	8	20	42	55.0	−25	42	08	1.398	2.271	140.9	6.4

7 Iris

Date		RA (2000)			Dec.			Distance from Earth	Distance from Sun	Elong-ation from Sun	Mag.
		h	m	s	°	′	″	(AU)	(AU)	°	
Jan	1	08	41	39.9	+12	15	01	1.195	2.105	150.0	8.3
Jan	11	08	32	20.0	+12	11	34	1.174	2.130	161.8	8.1
Jan	21	08	21	27.3	+12	20	47	1.177	2.156	171.9	7.9
Jan	31	08	10	36.5	+12	38	43	1.207	2.182	168.8	8.0
Jan	10	08	01	20.7	+13	00	52	1.263	2.208	157.8	8.4
Jan	20	07	54	49.4	+13	22	58	1.342	2.234	146.6	8.7

9 Metis

Date		RA (2000)			Dec.			Distance from Earth	Distance from Sun	Elong-ation from Sun	Mag.
		h	m	s	°	′	″	(AU)	(AU)	°	
June	30	20	56	59.1	−24	02	08	1.668	2.583	147.3	10.2
July	10	20	50	18.5	−24	57	51	1.602	2.573	158.0	9.9
July	20	20	41	25.9	−25	55	02	1.560	2.563	168.3	9.7
July	30	20	31	14.1	−26	47	14	1.544	2.553	171.8	9.6

| Aug | 9 | 20 | 20 | 55.6 | −27 | 28 | 27 | 1.554 | 2.542 | 163.3 | 9.7 |
| Aug | 19 | 20 | 11 | 47.5 | −27 | 55 | 06 | 1.590 | 2.531 | 152.5 | 10.0 |

10 Hygiea

Date		RA (2000)			Dec.			Distance from Earth	Distance from Sun	Elong-ation from Sun	Mag.
		h	m	s	°	′	″	(AU)	(AU)	°	
Apr	11	15	35	18.9	−24	11	40	1.913	2.779	143.0	9.8
Apr	21	15	30	21.7	−23	58	50	1.840	2.777	153.8	9.6
May	1	15	23	31.4	−23	34	41	1.791	2.776	164.8	9.4
May	11	15	15	35.3	−23	00	32	1.768	2.775	174.5	9.1
May	21	15	07	33.4	−22	19	36	1.771	2.774	170.1	9.2
May	31	15	00	22.9	−21	36	18	1.802	2.773	159.3	9.5
June	10	14	54	52.3	−20	55	34	1.857	2.774	148.5	9.7
June	20	14	51	33.5	−20	21	38	1.933	2.774	138.2	9.9

As well as observing bright binocular asteroids some advanced amateur astronomers with large telescopes and CCDs are often interested in imaging the PHAs, typically hundreds or thousands of metres in diameter, that sail close to the Earth and those bigger objects that, while they are not a conceivable hazard, are coming unusually close. In 2011 one PHA, 2000 AZ93, makes an approach to the Earth within 0.05 AU. This object closes to a distance of 0.04769 AU, or 7.13 million kilometres on January 11.73 but it will only be visible from the southern sky, as the encounter takes place in the constellation of Puppis. It will be a definite CCD target at magnitude 15.9 and will be moving at 14 arcseconds per minute. The most significant 'named' asteroid to pass reasonably close to the Earth in 2011 is 3103 Eger, which will pass within 0.1528 AU (23 million kilometres) on August 5.0 while in the constellation of Cetus. It should be magnitude 13.8 at this time and moving at almost nine arcseconds per minute. However, it will be quite low in the south-eastern pre-dawn sky as seen from the UK.

Accurate ephemerides can be computed for your location on Earth using the MPC ephemeris service at:

www.minorplanetcenter.org/iau/MPEph/MPEph.html

Meteors in 2011

JOHN MASON

Meteors (popularly known as 'shooting stars') may be seen on any clear moonless night, but on certain nights of the year their number increases noticeably. This occurs when the Earth chances to intersect a concentration of meteoric dust moving in an orbit around the Sun. If the dust is well spread out in space, the resulting shower of meteors may last for several days. The word 'shower' must not be misinterpreted – only on very rare occasions have the meteors been so numerous as to resemble snowflakes falling.

If the meteor tracks are marked on a star map and traced backwards, a number of them will be found to intersect in a point (or within a small area of the sky) which marks the radiant of the shower. This gives the direction from which the meteors have come.

Bright moonlight has an adverse effect on visual meteor observing, and within about five days to either side of Full Moon, lunar glare swamps all but the brighter meteors, reducing, quite considerably, the total number of meteors seen. In 2011, useful observation of several of the major annual meteor showers will be hampered by moonlight: the most active parts of the Lyrids, Perseids, Taurids, Leonids and Geminids are all affected. However, it is sometimes possible for visual observers to minimize the effects of moonlight by positioning themselves so that the Moon is behind them and hidden behind a wall or other suitable obstruction.

There are, however, still some good observational opportunities in 2011, with the Quadrantids particularly well placed. Although one of the most active showers, the Quadrantids have been poorly observed in recent years because of the narrow period of high activity, poor January weather and moonlight interference in at least one year out of three! Timing of the Quadrantid peak in January 2011 is quite favourable from the perspective of observers in the British Isles: the shower maximum is expected around January 04d 00h UT, and observations in the early morning hours of 4 January, as the radiant climbs, should be quite productive. Dark evening skies also prevail during late July, when several showers with radiants below the Square of Pegasus are at their most active. The combined activity of the Delta Aquarids, Iota Aquarids and Alpha Capricornids, together with good background sporadic rates and early Perseids will make watches at this time very worthwhile. The post-maximum activity of the Orionids should also not be too badly affected by the waning crescent Moon.

The year's surprise package could be the October Draconids which are associated with comet 21P/Giacobini-Zinner. This shower produced brief, but spectacular, meteor storms in 1933 and 1946 with subsequent periodic outbursts of lesser activity, mainly in years when the parent comet has returned to perihelion. There is a strong possibility of a significant shower on 8 October 2011 between about 18h and 21h UT. Increased Draconid activity may begin at around 16h UT and continue until about 23h. The peak ZHR is highly uncertain, but could be as high as 800 meteors per hour according to some forecasts. Draconid meteors are exceptionally slow-moving.

The following table gives some of the more easily observed showers with their radiants; interference by moonlight is shown by the letter M:

			Radiant		
Limiting Dates	Shower	Maximum	RA	Dec.	
			h m	°	
1–6 Jan	Quadrantids	4 Jan, 00h	15 28	+50	
19–25 Apr	Lyrids	22–23 Apr	18 08	+32	M
24 Apr–20 May	Eta Aquarids	5–6 May	22 20	−01	
17–26 June	Ophiuchids	19 June	17 20	−20	M
July–Aug	Capricornids	8, 15, 26 July	20 44	−15	
			21 00	−15	
15 July–20 Aug	Delta Aquarids	29 July, 6 Aug	22 36	−17	
			23 04	+02	
15 July–20 Aug	Piscis Australids	31 July	22 40	−30	
15 July–20 Aug	Alpha Capricornids	2–3 Aug	20 36	−10	
July–Aug	Iota Aquarids	6–7 Aug	22 10	−15	
			22 04	−06	
23 July–20 Aug	Perseids	13 Aug, 04h	3 04	+58	M
6–10 Oct	Draconids	8 Oct, 19h	17 28	+54	
16–31 Oct	Orionids	20–22 Oct	6 24	+15	

20 Oct–30 Nov	Taurids	2–7 Nov	3	44	+22	M
			3	44	+14	
15–20 Nov	Leonids	18 Nov, 08h	10	08	+22	M
Nov–Jan	Puppid-Velids	early Dec	9	00	−48	
7–16 Dec	Geminids	14 Dec, 14h	7	32	+33	M
17–25 Dec	Ursids	22 Dec	14	28	+78	

Some Events in 2012

There will be four eclipses, two of the Sun and two of the Moon.

20 May: Annular eclipse of the Sun – Hong Kong, Guangzhou, northern Taiwan, south-eastern Japan, northern Pacific Ocean to the south of the Aleutian Islands (USA), Oregon (USA), California, Nevada, Utah, Arizona, Colorado, New Mexico and Texas

4 June: Partial eclipse of the Moon – Pacific Ocean, including Hawaii, New Zealand, central and eastern Australia, western United States and western Canada

13 November: Total eclipse of the Sun – northern tip of Northern Territory (Australia), northern Queensland (Cape York Peninsula), central southern and eastern Pacific Ocean

28 November: Penumbral eclipse of the Moon – Alaska (USA), Pacific Ocean, including Hawaii, New Zealand and Australia, and much of Asia

THE PLANETS

Mercury may be seen more easily from northern latitudes in the evenings about the time of greatest eastern elongation (5 March) and in the mornings about the time of greatest western elongation (16 August and 4 December). In the southern hemisphere the corresponding most favourable dates are 1 July and 26 October (evenings) and 18 April (mornings).

Venus is at greatest eastern elongation (46°) on 27 March. It is visible in the evenings from the beginning of the year until the middle of May. After passing through inferior conjunction on 5–6 June, it will then be visible in the mornings until the end of the year. It reaches greatest western elongation (46°) on 15 August.

At inferior conjunction on 5–6 June, Venus will transit across the face of the Sun. This is the second in the current pair of transits; the first was on 8 June 2004. After the 2012 transit of Venus, there will not be another until December 2117 – a gap of 105.5 years!

Mars is at opposition on 3 March in Leo.

Jupiter is at opposition on 3 December in Taurus.

Saturn is at opposition on 15 April in Virgo.

Uranus is at opposition on 29 September in Pisces.

Neptune is at opposition on 24 August in Aquarius.

Pluto is at opposition on 29 June in Sagittarius.

Part II

Article Section

Water Ice on the Moon

DAVID M. HARLAND

After many years of speculation about whether there might be water ice on the Moon, this has recently been established to be the case.

THE NATURE OF THE LUNAR SURFACE

As William Herschel was passing sunlight through a prism in 1800, he found that heat was refracted just beyond the red end of the visible spectrum, so he named this infrared radiation. The Estonian physicist Thomas Johann Seebeck discovered in 1821 that if two wires of different metal are formed into a loop by soldering their ends together, then an electric current will flow if the joins are at different temperatures. In 1856 Charles Piazzi Smyth used such a thermocouple to detect solar infrared reflecting off the Moon. Laurence Parsons inherited the 72-inch reflecting telescope built by his father at Birr Castle in Ireland. At that time, it was the largest telescope in the world. The common view was that since the airless lunar surface was exposed to the intense cold of space, it simply must be covered by ice. In 1870 Parsons equipped his telescope with a thermocouple and found that at lunar noon the temperature of the equatorial zone – where the Sun would pass close to the zenith – exceeded that of the boiling point of water, which indicated that the surface could not be ice. If ice were indeed present, it would have to be subterranean.

In 1930 Edison Pettit and Seth B. Nicholson put a thermocouple on the 100-inch reflector on Mount Wilson, by now the largest telescope in the world, and discovered that the surface temperature in the equatorial zone varied by several hundred degrees during the monthly cycle. At the start of a lunar eclipse in 1939 they measured the temperature plunge by 120°C in an hour as the Moon entered the Earth's shadow. This implied that the material on the surface was poor at retaining heat. More sophisticated measurements showed that at the equator the temperature was +101°C at noon, fell to −39°C at sunset and −160°C at midnight. In 1948 A. J. Wesselink in Holland inferred from these cooling rates that the Moon could not be exposed solid rock but must be covered by a blanket of loose material. Meanwhile, the Moon was being investigated at radio wavelengths. In 1946 R. H. Dicke and Robert Beringer in America detected thermal emission at the microwave wavelength of 1.25 cm. Using the same wavelength, in 1949 J. H. Piddington and H. C. Minnett in Australia measured the temperature of the whole disk at a variety of phases over three lunations. The variation proved to be less extreme than it was at infrared wavelengths. The fact that the radio temperature lagged behind the optical phase of the Moon by 3.5 days suggested the presence of a thin insulating layer with low thermal conductivity. In 1950 J. C. Jaeger in Australia matched materials to the microwave observations made by Piddington and Minnett; agreeing with Wesselink's inference of loose material, he argued for a layer of 'dust' on top of a granular material. Observations of lunar eclipses on 29 January 1953 and 18 January 1954 at microwave wavelengths by the US Naval Research Laboratory implied that only the uppermost part of the surface underwent a large variation in temperature. This was consistent with a thin layer of dust over a loose granular material. In 1962 J. F. Denisse in France announced that for wavelengths exceeding 30 cm there was *no variation* in temperature over the monthly cycle.

Overall, these investigations indicated that whereas an optical telescope fitted with a thermocouple measured the temperature of the surface itself, the radio temperatures were *averages* for granular material to depths corresponding to several times the wavelength. The constancy at wavelengths greater than 30 cm implied that the material in the uppermost metre or so was such a poor conductor of heat that even when the Sun was at the zenith its heat did not penetrate that far. And at night, although the surface rapidly radiated away the heat it had gained during the day, the poor conductivity of the deeper material served to insulate it. The temperature at a depth of about a metre was estimated to be a constant −40°C. In 1961 A. Deutsch in Leningrad suggested there might be life in the granular material where the temperature was constant, and that it lived off gases leaking out from the interior. Expanding upon this, Carl Sagan in America speculated that if the granular material were tens of metres deep, then it might contain a considerable amount of ice and organic material.

APOLLO

Between July 1969 and December 1972, six Apollo crews landed on the Moon to collect samples and set up geophysical instruments (Figure 1). The samples showed that the material that forms the surface of the Moon is a 'regolith' of rocks that are being reduced to ever finer fragments by the incessant rain of micrometeoroids. Because a side-effect is to 'turn over' the material to a depth depending on the size of an impact, this process was named 'gardening'. One of the most stunning findings was that the samples seemed devoid of hydrated minerals. Although the astronauts obtained core samples to a depth of 2.5 metres, well into the thermally stable zone, there was no evidence of ice. Unfortunately, operational factors had made it impracticable to land at sites in the polar regions.

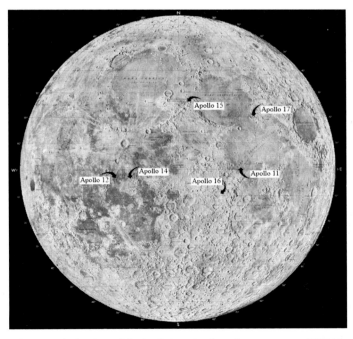

Figure 1. The locations of the Apollo lunar landings. (Image courtesy of NASA.)

CLEMENTINE

The Clementine spacecraft (Figure 2) rose from Vandenberg Air Force Base, California, on 25 January 1994 on a refurbished Titan II missile and was inserted into 'parking orbit' around Earth. On 3 February it set off for the Moon, and on 19 February entered into an orbit that was inclined at an angle of 90° relative to the lunar equator and varied in altitude between 430 and 2,950 km, with the lowest point at about 30°S. While near perilune the spacecraft undertook laser altimetry and obtained pictures across the spectrum from the near-infrared to ultraviolet to undertake a multispectral investigation of the composition of the surface, and then at the apolune of its 5-hour orbit this data was downlinked to Earth. Over the period of a month, as the Moon rotated on its axis beneath the plane of the vehicle's orbit, Clementine was able to inspect the entire range of longitudes. In late March the perilune was moved to the northern hemisphere to complete the coverage. One welcome result from this mission was a vertical perspective of each of the polar regions.

Whereas the Earth's rotational axis is tilted at 23.5° to the plane in

Figure 2. An artist's depiction of the Clementine spacecraft developed by the US Department of Defense. (Image courtesy of Naval Research Laboratory.)

which the planet orbits the Sun, this plane being called the ecliptic, the axis of the Moon is inclined 1.6° to the ecliptic. Consequently, there might be craters in the lunar polar regions whose floors are never illuminated. However, because the plane in which the Moon orbits Earth is inclined at 5.15° to the ecliptic, when the Moon is south of the ecliptic we can see several degrees beyond its north pole at a time when that is illuminated, and when the Moon is north of the ecliptic we can see beyond its south pole when that is lit. In 1961 Kenneth Watson, Bruce Murray and Harrison Brown at the California Institute of Technology in Pasadena suggested that the floors of permanently shadowed craters might form 'cold traps' in which the temperature would hover at about 100 K, and in which water ice delivered over the aeons by comets would tend to accumulate.[1]

Clementine's near-polar orbit offered an opportunity to test this idea. Water ice has a unique 'signature' when probed by radio energy. It also reflects more efficiently when the angle of incidence of the 'illumination' is near-zero (this is a phenomenon known as coherent backscatter) and, unlike rock, ice preserves the polarization of the wave. At a time when the geometry was suitable in March and April 1994, a bistatic experiment was undertaken in which the spacecraft 'beamed' its radio signal into the shadowed craters at each pole and the large antennas of NASA's Deep Space Network monitored the reflection. The results in March were inconclusive, but those in April were intriguing: two passes over the north pole were unremarkable, as was a pass near the south pole, but on orbit 234, when the 'beam' tracked across the shadowed areas right at the pole the terrestrial antennas noted both an increase in the strength of the reflection and a greater percentage of the signal preserving the original polarization. In 1996 the team led by Paul Spudis announced the possible detection of water ice making up part of the surface layer near the south pole.[2]

LUNAR PROSPECTOR

Lunar Prospector (Figure 3) lifted off from Cape Canaveral on an Athena 2 launch vehicle on 6 January 1998. It entered a highly elliptical lunar polar orbit on 11 January. After circularizing at an altitude of 100 km, it initiated science activities on 16 January. Its task was to undertake remote-sensing of the Moon on a global basis by using a

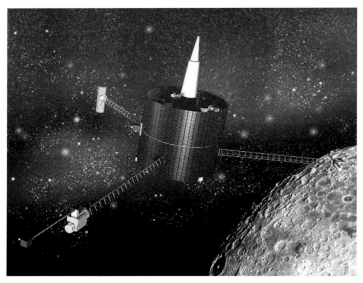

Figure 3. An artist's depiction of the Lunar Prospector spacecraft, developed as a low-cost Discovery class mission, approaching the Moon. (Image courtesy of NASA Ames Research Center.)

magnetometer and an electron reflectometer to chart the patchy lunar magnetic field, a gamma-ray spectrometer to determine the composition of the regolith, an alpha-particle spectrometer to detect any outgassing and a neutron spectrometer to sense ice in the polar regions.

The first rumour of a discovery was leaked a month later, and on 5 March it was announced that the neutron spectrometer's data suggested the presence of significant water ice at both poles. The preliminary analysis was published in September.[3] The instrument did not detect water ice directly; this was inferred from the presence of hydrogen, which was itself inferred by remotely sensing neutrons. When a high-energy cosmic-ray particle strikes the nucleus of an atom in the regolith, neutrons are spat out. Most of these neutrons are 'hot', meaning that they fly off at high speed, but if one subsequently encounters a lightweight nucleus it will yield some of its energy and slow down. Each molecule of water contains two hydrogen atoms, the lightest of atoms. The presence of hydrogen was inferred from the energy spectrum of the neutrons. The instrument sensed neutrons in three energy categories: thermal, epithermal and fast. It reported an epithermal flux 4.6 and 3.0 per cent below the low-latitude average at the north and south poles respectively. Although the 100-km spatial resolution was unable to precisely identify the sites of this hydrogen enrichment, there was a correlation with the suspected cold traps. Data to the end of the mission in 1999 supported the initial findings. It was concluded that the data were consistent with hydrogen enrichment in the form of water ice covered by as much as 40 cm of desiccated regolith.[4,5] However, since the ice was inferred from the presence of hydrogen, and the solar wind irradiates the lunar surface, others argued the hydrogen was more likely to be present in this form.[6,7]

TERRESTRIAL RADAR STUDIES

When conditions are suitable, the beam from a terrestrial radio telescope acting as a radar can provide shallow-angle 'illumination' of some of the permanently shadowed craters at the lunar poles. It can penetrate a loosely packed material such as the lunar regolith to a depth several times that of its wavelength. So, in principle, a radar is able to 'probe' for the presence of ice deposits. The 1,000-foot-diameter dish of the Arecibo Observatory on the island of Puerto Rico is operated by Cornell University for the US National Astronomy and Ionosphere Center (Figure 4). After the announcement of the Clementine results, Arecibo studied the polar regions at a wavelength of 12.6 cm. The results, reported in 1997, were ambiguous: whereas the strongest reflections were from sites at the south pole that might well be in permanent shadow, strong reflections were also received from areas nearby that were not. This prompted the team to explain their results in terms of the roughness of the terrain.[8]

After Lunar Prospector charted the distribution of hydrogen in the Moon's polar regions, it was decided to employ the Goldstone Solar System Radar in California to locate the cold traps (Figure 5). The 70-metre-diameter antenna illuminated the target zones at a wavelength of 3.5 cm, and the echoes were received by a pair of 34-metre-diameter antennas set 20 km apart. By processing the signals using an interferometry technique, surface elevations could be measured to a vertical accuracy of 50 m at horizontal intervals of 150 m, to produce the first three-dimensional digital elevation model of these regions. In

Figure 4. The 1,000-foot-diameter dish of the Arecibo radio telescope on the island of Puerto Rico is the world's most powerful 'planetary radar'. (Image courtesy of Arecibo Observatory: National Astronomy and Ionosphere Center, a national facility operated by Cornell University for the National Science Foundation.)

1999 it was announced that after a computer had calculated how the Sun would illuminate these landscapes, it was evident that the floors of five large craters in the south polar region were in eternal shadow. The south pole itself is located just inside the rim of Shackleton, which is some 20 km in diameter, and one of the five craters identified by the study. There was a 30-km crater to the west, and a line of three 50-km craters, the middle one of which was Shoemaker. Of course, the radar had not been able to survey their entire interiors because their near rims were blocking the line of sight of the beam, but much of their floors had been 'visible'.[9] These craters constituted the largest potential deposits of water ice at the south pole – and Lunar Prospector had detected a high hydrogen abundance in the crater Shoemaker.

However, a wavelength of 3.5 cm provided high resolution for mapping but could not penetrate very far into the regolith to search for evidence of ice. The Arecibo telescope was used for a follow-up study which probed the interesting areas at a wavelength of 70 cm. When the results were published in 2003, they were not encouraging.[10] It was not

Figure 5. The 70-metre-diameter antenna of the Goldstone Solar System Radar in California. (Image courtesy of NASA/JPL-Caltech.)

possible to say that there was no ice, but the results imposed strict constraints. In order to explain both the hydrogen detected by Lunar Prospector in the upper half-metre of regolith and the absence of any radar backscatter from a depth of several metres, there could not be solid ice at or near the surface; such ice as might be present at shallow depth must either be in the form of thin layers (i.e. less than the radar wavelength) interbedded with regolith, or as individual grains mixed in with the lithic fragments. Observations were then made at 12.6 cm at the high spatial resolution of 20 m in order to localize specific samples. The results reported in 2006 suggested that thin layers at shallow depth were unlikely.[11] This left individual grains of ice mixed in with the fragmental material as the only possibility.

Meanwhile, D. H. Crider and R. R. Vondrak had modelled the evolution of a cold trap as a function of depth in terms of the 'space weathering' process by which the plasma that was delivered to the lunar surface by the solar wind was 'gardened' into the regolith by micrometeoroids. The results reported in 2001–2003 concluded that the regolith would achieve a steady state of around 4,000 parts per million of water.

Of course, the water was not present in the plasma; it was created by hydrogen in the solar wind combining with oxygen drawn from iron oxides in the regolith.[12–14] Although the solar wind irradiates the entire surface of the Moon, Crider and Vondrak argued that water would be stable only in the cold traps of the permanently shadowed areas. The early idea was that the water arrived in comets that vaporized on impact, with some of the molecules of water straying into the cold traps, but, surprisingly, Crider and Vondrak found the amount of cometary water was insignificant compared to that from the solar wind. Importantly, this analysis was consistent with the radar data. The model suggested that the thickness of the layer in which the ice was present increased with time, and reached 1.6 m after a billion years – although that was not to say that it formed a slab of ice. The topographical survey by radar had estimated there to be 5,000 km^2 in permanent shadow at the south pole, and half as much again in the north, so there could be a considerable amount of water ice overall.

THE LATEST MISSIONS

In 2005 NASA directed the Goddard Space Flight Center to initiate a Robotic Lunar Exploration Program, and the first mission was Lunar Reconnaissance Orbiter (LRO).[15–17] This was a three-axis stabilized platform with a side-mounted solar panel and a boom-mounted high-gain antenna (Figure 6). To maintain its 50-km circular polar orbit, it performed frequent manoeuvres to counter the mascon gravity anomalies. It was to create a global geodetic grid so as to define precisely the locations of objects in terms of three-dimensional topography; map mineralogical resources; survey the permanently shadowed areas near the poles; and seek to confirm the presence of water ice therein. It was also to identify continuously illuminated areas near the poles and map their detailed topography to assist in the selection of safe landing sites for future missions.

As a finale to its mission, on 31 July 1999 Lunar Prospector was steered to impact in a permanently shadowed crater with terrestrial telescopes monitoring. It had been calculated that there was a 10 per cent chance of vaporizing sufficient water to produce a detectable plume but nothing was observed, possibly because it hit at too shallow an angle to excavate material from a sufficient depth.[18,19]

Figure 6. An artist's depiction of Lunar Reconnaissance Orbiter (LRO) in orbit around the Moon. (Image courtesy of NASA.)

When NASA decided to switch LRO from a Delta II to an Atlas V booster in order to relieve mass constraints, it became possible to install a secondary payload. NASA selected the Lunar Crater Observation and Sensing Satellite (LCROSS) devised by the Ames Research Center.[20] The plan was that after the Centaur stage of the launch vehicle had achieved translunar trajectory and released LRO, LCROSS would steer the spent stage to a lunar flyby that would put it in a steeply inclined elliptical orbit of Earth which would return to the vicinity of the Moon several months later, at which time the still-attached LCROSS would refine the trajectory to make the spent stage crash into one of the hydrogen-enriched craters (Figure 7). With the trajectory set, LCROSS would separate, and adjust its speed to trail six minutes behind. It was calculated that the near-vertical impact of the 2,250-kg stage ought to make a crater 30 m across and 5 m deep, in so doing excavating as much as 1,000 tonnes of material. Most of the ejecta was expected to travel on shallow trajectories and remain in shadow, but some would rise in a plume which would emerge into sunlight – hopefully making it visible to terrestrial telescopes. As it

Figure 7. An artist's depiction of the LCROSS spacecraft following its Centaur stage on a plunging dive towards the Moon. (Image courtesy of NASA.)

observed the impact and passed through the plume, LCROSS was to employ its instruments to analyse the ejecta for water ice before it too crashed. On its next overflight, LRO would make follow-up observations.

The LRO/LCROSS mission was launched on 18 June 2009, and LRO entered lunar orbit on 23 June. That same day, the Centaur/LCROSS combination made its lunar flyby and used the gravitational slingshot to enter an Earth orbit which was inclined at about 80° to the ecliptic and had a period of 37 days. The phasing was such that after three orbits the vehicle would smash into the south pole of the Moon.

Soon after initiating its scientific observations, LRO provided evidence of the presence of water. The Lunar Exploration Neutron Detector employed a set of collimated detectors for epithermal and fast neutrons to map the distribution of hydrogen enrichment in the uppermost metre of regolith in the polar areas at a spatial resolution of about 10 km. It measured a decrease in the neutron flux, and by implication an enrichment of hydrogen, on many parts of the surface – and not just in the permanently shadowed craters. The Lyman Alpha

Mapper used starlight and ultraviolet sky-glow as a source of illumination to perform optical imaging of areas not illuminated by sunlight. It detected absorption at 1,600 Å in the vicinity of the south pole at a spatial resolution of about 500 m per pixel which was interpreted as *direct* evidence of the presence of a water frost on the surface. The Diviner Lunar Radiometer Experiment, which measured surface temperatures, discovered that some of the polar craters were 35 K, even colder than the surface of Pluto, proof that the Moon does indeed possess permanently shadowed areas.

Meanwhile, the Indian lunar orbiter Chandrayaan-1 (Figure 8), which had been placed into lunar orbit on 8 November 2008, suffered a communications failure on 29 August 2009 that curtailed its mission. One of the instruments was the Moon Mineralogy Mapper, provided

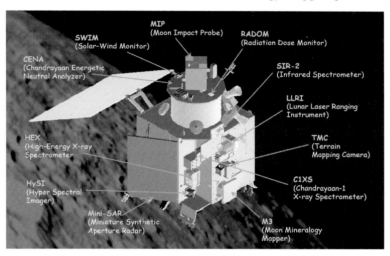

Figure 8. The Chandrayaan-1 spacecraft. (Image courtesy of ISRO.)

by the USA. By the time the spacecraft was written off, the imaging spectrometer had observed more than 95 per cent of the surface. In addition to measuring the infrared reflectance, it detected absorption features indicative of water molecules – *in the equatorial zone*. The water was present in the uppermost few millimetres (by the nature of the observation, the instrument could not 'see' any deeper than that) as a thin film of molecules on the grains in the regolith.

Carle Pieters of Brown University was the instrument's principal investigator. When she discussed the data with a colleague working on the Cassini mission, it was realized that when that spacecraft made its lunar flyby in August 1999 the Visual and Infrared Mapping-Spectrometer detected evidence of water *at all latitudes*. (It had not been possible to interpret this signature properly until the instruments were calibrated following the 2004 arrival of the spacecraft in the Saturnian system.) At this point, scientists on the Deep Impact mission were asked to make observations when their spacecraft flew by the Moon in June 2009 on its way to intercept comet 103P/Hartley-2. It was decided to conduct observations over the period of a week, and the results were conclusive: there was indeed water at all latitudes. The strength of the signature was correlated with the surface temperature. Furthermore, there was a temporal pattern. The signature was strong at sunrise, diminished towards noon, and returned to its initial level by sunset. It was evident that there was a 'diurnal cycle' at work, operating on the lunar timescale. The fact that the strength of the signature did not increase during the fortnight-long lunar night indicated that the process was related to the solar wind. The conclusion was that (as Crider and Vondrak had proposed) protons in the solar wind react with oxides in the regolith to produce water molecules. Although these are vaporized in the midday heat, the process resumes in the afternoon. The midday temperature is hottest at the equator and decreases with latitude. In the polar regions the variation in the strength of the water absorption diminishes, and in the permanently shadowed areas there is a progressive accumulation of water over time. The discovery was announced on 24 September 2009.[21,22]

The final targeting of the LCROSS mission was not performed until the last few days of the approach. It was decided to aim for the 100-km-diameter crater Cabaeus (Figure 9), because LRO showed it to be enriched with hydrogen and because, by virtue of being 5° from the pole on the Earth-facing side, it would offer terrestrial observers a fair chance to observe any plume rising from the 3.5-km deep cavity. The Centaur impacted at 11h 31m UTC on 9 October with the energy equivalent of detonating a tonne of TNT. Terrestrial observers detected no plume, possibly because a mountain peak blocked their view of the permanently shadowed area where the impact occurred, but LCROSS, making a near-vertical dive, had a clear line of sight. If the Centaur struck solid rock, then most of the energy would be converted into a bright flash which, whilst looking spectacular, would actually be bad news for the mission. It was hoped that the Centaur would strike a deep blanket of regolith. The flash would be much fainter, because the energy would be expended in ejecting loosely consolidated material, hopefully with some ice mixed in. LCROSS provided data on the Centaur's impact site for six minutes before itself crashing nearby. Its instruments detected the faint flash of the impact and also the presence of a plume rising into sunlight.

On 13 November 2009, NASA announced multiple lines of evidence which showed that water was present in both the high-angle plume of

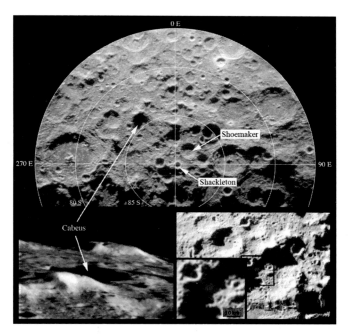

Figure 9. LCROSS dived into the shadowed crater Cabaeus. Top: an image of the south polar region of the Moon by the Arecibo Observatory operating as a radar at a wavelength of 70 cm. (Image courtesy of Arecibo Observatory and Bruce Campbell of the Center for Earth and Planetary Studies at the Smithsonian Institution.) Lower left: a near-infrared image taken using adaptive optics at the time of the impact. (Image courtesy of Palomar Observatory/Caltech.) Lower right: a visible-light image taken by the LCROSS spacecraft twenty seconds after the impact of the Centaur stage, showing the rising plume catching sunlight. (Image courtesy of NASA.)

vapour and the lateral ejecta created by the Centaur impact. A spectrum from the near-infrared spectrometer averaged over a period from about 20 to about 60 seconds after the impact showed a number of strong absorption features (Figure 10). A spectrum modelled by assuming a given abundance of water in the plume fitted the observed spectrum well in bands where water vapour and water ice absorb at wavelengths of about 1.4 and 1.9 microns. The amount of water required to produce the fit amounted to 100 kg within the spectrometer's field of view, which encompassed most but not all of the plume. Independently, the ultraviolet spectrometer also obtained a spectrum of the plume, showing an emission peak at a wavelength of 306 to 310 nanometres from hydroxyl ions produced by the dissociation of water molecules as they rose into sunlight. The mission's principal investigator, Tony Colaprete, said that seeing this emission line was 'the eureka moment' that confirmed the presence of water.[23] The LRO/LCROSS results were expanded upon by multiple presentations at the American Geophysical Union meeting in December 2009.

If the impact of the Centaur excavated the expected 30-m crater, then the estimated 100 kg of water that was released represents a

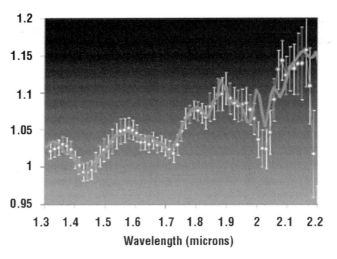

Figure 10. The near-infrared spectrometer on LCROSS observed the plume from the impact of the Centaur stage. The data are well modelled by various compounds, including water. (Image courtesy of LCROSS/NASA Ames Research Center and A. Colaprete.)

regolith fraction of ten parts per million, which is more a sprinkling of ice crystals in the regolith than a slab. However, as announced at the Lunar and Planetary Science Conference in March 2010, the Miniature Radio-Frequency (Mini-RF) synthetic-aperture radar on LRO, which irradiated the lunar surface with pulses of radio energy that had a left-handed polarization and measured the left/right polarization of the reflection as the circular polarization ratio, and had a surface resolution of 30 m, found that the ratio for the site where LCROSS impacted was comparable to the lunar average, implying that, despite its being shadowed, it was not a likely location to find a thick deposit of ice.[24]

Chandrayaan-1 also had a synthetic-aperture radar, called Mini-SAR. It was supplied by the same team as created Mini-RF for LRO and operated at the same wavelength, but had a resolution of 150 m. Many craters ranging in size up to 15-km diameter near the north pole showed a high circular polarization ratio in their interiors and a low ratio exterior to their rims. Almost all these craters are in permanent shadow, and correlate with sites of ice suggested by the Lunar Prospector neutron data. This has been interpreted to mean there are deposits of relatively pure water ice several feet thick inside these craters.[25] Analysis of the data for the south polar region is still under-way. As Paul Spudis, the principal investigator for the Mini-SAR, put it, 'The emerging picture from the multiple measurements and resulting data of the instruments on lunar missions indicates that water creation, migration, deposition and retention are occurring on the Moon.'

THE APOLLO SAMPLE PARADOX

All this begs the question of the analysis of the samples collected by the Apollo astronauts. Although the sample return containers used by those missions were meant to retain the vacuum of the lunar environment, their seals proved less than perfect and air leaked in once they reached Earth. Most of the containers were opened in a nitrogen environment which proved to contain 20 parts per million of water. As no samples contained water above this contamination level, it was decided that they were arid. This conclusion was reinforced by the discovery that the samples did not contain hydrated minerals. The paucity of water and other volatiles such sodium and chlorine was consistent with the theory developed for the origin of the Moon, by which a body the

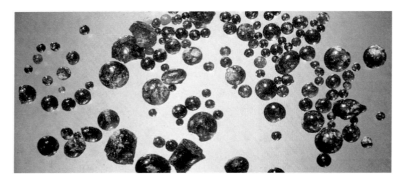

Figure 11. Tiny beads of volcanic glass found in lunar samples returned by the Apollo astronauts. (Image courtesy of NASA.)

size of Mars struck the Earth shortly after it had formed, ejecting a lot of material that did not have sufficient energy to escape and coalesced in orbit as the Moon.

However, in 2008 Alberto Saal of Brown University, Rhode Island, studied small beads of volcanic glass collected on the Moon and found water at 50 parts per million, and the fact that this water was *inside* the beads effectively ruled out contamination.[26] The glass beads were issued by fire fountains, with the magma rising up through the crust so rapidly that it did not have time to interact chemically, making it representative of the source melt. The presence of water in the beads implies that there was water in the melt, perhaps delivered by comets early in the Moon's history, when it was a 'magma ocean' to a considerable depth.

In addition, studies of lunar basalts by teams led by Francis McCubbin of the Carnegie Institution for Science in Washington DC and by Jeremy Boyce at the California Institute of Technology using techniques that were not available in the Apollo years, found sufficient hydroxyl chemically bound in the mineral apatite to confirm indigenous water in the lunar mantle.[27,28] On the other hand, a study led by Zachary D. Sharp of the University of New Mexico, Albuquerque found chlorine so scarce as to imply the lunar interior to be essentially anhydrous.[29] Given that determining the amount of water present in the lunar interior is an area of research that is only just beginning, it is entirely understandable that the various teams, investigating only a few samples each, and not the same samples in each case, are obtaining different results.

The important point in relation to this article is that the amount of water which is chemically bound in the minerals in the interior of the Moon, or the rocks that were either volcanically erupted or mechanically ejected onto the surface, has no relevance to the 'hydrological cycle' that flyby and orbital spacecraft have found to be currently active across the entire surface, nor to the presence of water ice in the shadowed craters at the poles. These ongoing processes are a manifestation of the external factors, namely the solar wind, meteorites and comets.

IN-SITU EXPLOITATION OF LUNAR RESOURCES

In recent years a number of missions have been proposed which would land a probe in one of the permanently shadowed craters of the Moon and drill into the regolith in search of water ice. As yet, none of these proposals has been funded. Such a mission will enable us to determine whether there is a significant amount of water of cometary origin, such as ammonia and methane, which on the Moon would be a valuable resource.

It is not clear when we will resume exploring the Moon in person, but when we do so we are likely to establish a base at one or other of the lunar poles. At a press conference to announce the Clementine results in December 1996, team leader Paul Spudis noted that there was an elevated feature near the south pole that appeared to be in continuous sunlight. Dubbing this the Mountain of Eternal Light, he described it as "the most valuable piece of extraterrestrial real estate" because a base there would both have continuous solar illumination for electrical power and, with the Sun circling low around the horizon, would not be subjected to the thermal extremes of the equatorial zone, where the ±140°C temperature range between noon and midnight would impose severe operational problems. The regolith is predominantly oxides of iron, titanium and aluminium. Heating it in a furnace could liberate oxygen and yield raw construction materials. But the key would be water. Whilst it would be difficult to 'harvest' ice crystals sparsely distributed in the regolith in a cold trap, it will be easier to do so from a slab of pure ice. In addition to serving a vital life-support role, the molecules could then by dissociated to hydrogen and oxygen to serve as rocket propellants. The long-term prospects for mankind as a space-faring species are therefore encouraging.

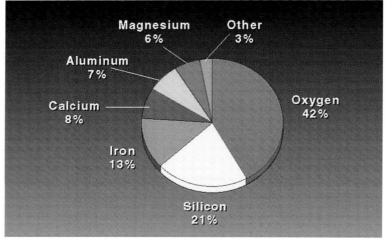

Figure 12. The proportions of the main elements in the lunar regolith as derived from the Apollo samples. (Image courtesy of University of Wisconsin-Madison.)

REFERENCES

1. K. Watson, B. C. Murray and H. Brown, 'On the possible presence of ice on the Moon'. *J. Geophys. Res.*, vol. 66, pp. 1598–1600, 1961.
2. S. Nozette, C. L. Lichtenberg, P. D. Spudis, R. Bonner, W. Ort, E. Malaret, M. Robinson and E. M. Shoemaker, 'The Clementine bistatic radar experiment: evidence for ice on the Moon'. *Science*, vol. 274, pp. 1495–8, 1996.
3. W. C. Feldman, S. Maurice, A. B. Binder, B. L. Barraclough, R. C. Elphic and D. J. Lawrence, 'Fluxes of fast and epithermal neutrons from Lunar Prospector: evidence for water-ice at the lunar poles'. *Science*, vol. 281, pp. 1496–1500, 1998.
4. W. C. Feldman, D. J. Lawrence, R. C. Elphic, B. L. Barraclough, S. Maurice, I. Genetay and A. B. Binder, 'Polar hydrogen deposits on the Moon'. *J. Geophys. Res. Planets*, vol. 105, pp. 4175–96, 2000.
5. W. C. Feldman, S. Maurice, D. J. Lawrence, R. C. Little, S. L. Lawson, O. Gasnault, R. C. Wiens, B. L. Barraclough, R. C. Elphic, T. H. Prettyman, J. T. Steinberg and A. B. Binder, 'Evidence for water-ice near the lunar poles'. *J. Geophys. Res.*, vol. 106, pp. 23232–52, 2001.

6. H. H. Schmitt and G. L. Kulcinski, 'Premature lunar assumptions'. *Space News*, vol. 9, pp. 23–4, 1998.

7. H. H. Schmitt, G. L. Kulcinski, J. F. Santarius, J. Ding, M. J. Malecki and M. J. Zalewski, 'Solar-wind hydrogen at the lunar poles'. *Proc. Space 2000 Conf.*, pp. 653–60, Albuquerque, New Mexico, 27 February–2 March 2000.

8. N. J. S. Stacy, D. B. Campbell and P. G. Ford, 'Radar mapping of the lunar poles : a search for ice deposits'. *Science*, vol. 276, pp. 1527–30, 1997.

9. J.-L. Margot, D. B. Campbell, R. F. Jurgens and M. A. Slade, 'Topography of the lunar poles from radar interferometry: a survey of cold trap locations'. *Science*, vol. 284, pp. 1658–60, 1999.

10. B. A. Campbell, D. B. Campbell, J. F. Chandler, A. A. Hine, M. C. Nolan and P. J. Perillat, 'Radar imaging of the lunar poles: long-wavelength measurements reveal a paucity of ice in the Moon's polar craters'. *Nature*, vol. 246, pp. 137–8, 2003.

11. D. B. Campbell, B. A. Campbell, L. M. Carter, J.-L. Margot and N. J. S. Stacy, 'No evidence for thick deposits of ice at the lunar south pole'. *Nature*, vol. 443, pp. 835–7, 2006.

12. D. H. Crider and R. R. Vondrak, 'Space weathering effects on lunar cold traps'. *Proc. Lunar and Planet. Sci. Conf.*, p. 1922, 12–16 March 2001.

13. D. H. Crider and R. R. Vondrak, 'Modelling the stability of volatile deposits in lunar cold traps'. *Workshop on Moon beyond 2002: Next steps in lunar science and exploration*, Taos, New Mexico, p. 3006, 12–14 September 2002.

14. D. H. Crider and R. R. Vondrak, 'Space weathering of ice layers in lunar cold traps'. *Adv. Space Res.* vol. 31, pp. 2293–8, 2003.

15. J. G. Watzin, J. Burt and C. Tooley, 'The Robotic Lunar Exploration Program: an introduction to the goals, approach and architecture'. American Institute of Aeronautics and Astronautics, *First Space Exploration Conf.: Continuing the Voyage of Discovery*, Orlando, Florida, 30 January–1 February 2005.

16. C. Tooley, 'Lunar Reconnaissance Orbiter: spacecraft and objectives'. American Institute of Aeronautics and Astronautics, *Annual Technical Symposium*, Houston, Texas, 19 May 2006.

17. J. Keller, 'Lunar Reconnaissance Orbiter: instrument suite and measurements'. American Institute of Aeronautics and Astronautics, *Annual Technical Symposium*, Houston, Texas, 19 May 2006.

18. 'No water-ice detected from lunar prospector impact', NASA press release 99–119, 13 October 1999.

19. www.ae.utexas.edu/research/cfpl/lunar/pressrelease/discussion. html.

20. www.nasa.gov/mission_pages/LCROSS/overview/index.html.

21. C. M. Pieters et al., 'Character and spatial distribution of OH/H$_2$O on the surface of the Moon seen by M3 on Chandrayaan-1'. *Science*, vol. 326, pp. 568–72, 2009.

22. J. M. Sunshine et al., 'Temporal and spatial variability of lunar hydration as observed by the Deep Impact spacecraft'. *Science*, vol. 326, pp. 565–8, 2009.

23. www.nasa.gov/mission_pages/LCROSS/main/prelim_water_ results.html.

24. C. D. Neish et al., 'Mini-RF observations in support of LCROSS'. *Lunar and Planetary Science Conf.*, p.2075, March 2010.

25. P. D. Spudis et al., 'Initial results for the north pole of the Moon from Mini-SAR, Chandrayaan-1 mission'. *Geophys. Res. Lett.*, vol. 37, L06204, 2010.

26. A. E. Saal et al., 'The volatile content of the lunar volcanic glasses: evidence for the presence of water in the Moon's interior'. *Nature*, vol. 454, pp. 192–5, 2008.

27 'Nominally hydrous magmatism on the Moon', F. M. McCubbin et al. *Proceedings of the National Academy of Sciences*, vol. 107, pp. 11223–11228, 2010.

28 'Lunar apatite with terrestrial volatile abundances', J. W. Boyce et al. *Nature*, vol. 466, pp. 466–469, 2010.

29 'The chlorine isotope composition of the Moon and implications for an anydrous mantle', Z. D. Sharp et al. *Science*, 5 August 2010, DOI, 10.1126/science.1192602.

J. H. Schröter and the Atmosphere of Venus

RICHARD BAUM

On the assumption that whoever proves discovers, William Herschel's (1738–1822) triumph in finding Uranus – 'the comet' – surrenders some of its status to the Finnish astronomer and mathematician Anders Johan Lexell (1740–1784) who having summed up the physical characteristics of the supposed 'comet' concluded that it was in fact another world circling the Sun at the icy rim of the then known local planetary system. To some extent the same division over priority is encountered if we ask who really established that Venus has an atmosphere.

To astronomers of the seventeenth and eighteenth centuries, many of whom believed in a plurality of inhabited worlds, the existence of an atmosphere on Venus had become an article of faith, but as the Hanoverian government official and astronomer Johann Hieronymus Schröter (1745–1816) noted in the *Philosophical Transactions* in 1792, 'so inconclusive are the few observations hitherto made on the atmosphere of Venus, that several of the greatest astronomers have lately thought themselves authorized to doubt its very existence'.

Schröter had no such scruples. Soon after he began his study of the planet in 1779 he realized the gradual fall-off of light from limb to terminator – a phenomenon easily accessed by modest telescopes – was almost certainly due to absorption by the planet's atmosphere.

It was an intuitive leap in the right direction. Even so, it could not be regarded as proof that the planet had an atmosphere. This also applied to the Russian academician Mikhail Vasilevich Lomonosov (1711–1765), of the St Petersburg Academy of Sciences. From luminous effects he witnessed at ingress and egress at the transit of Venus in 1761 (some of which are thought to have been spurious), he concluded: 'the planet Venus is surrounded by a considerable atmosphere equal to, if not greater than, that which envelopes our earthly sphere'. Torbern Bergman

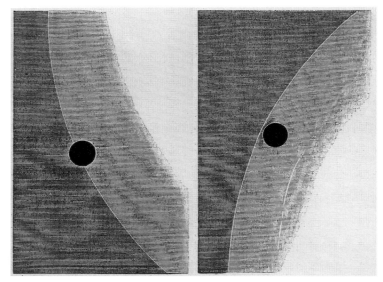

Figure 1. Luminous phenomena observed and drawn by W. J. MacDonnell, Sydney, NSW, Australia, using a 4.25-inch Cooke refracting telescope during the transit of Venus on 8 December 1874. Left: ingress with planet encircled by a ring of light as it encroaches on the solar disk. Right: ingress. The Sun now fully invaded by Venus and joined to its limb by a faint dusky ligament formed of rings concentric to the planet's disk. This is not the celebrated 'black drop' effect. (Images courtesy of *The English Mechanic*, vol. 20 (no. 518), 26 February 1875, p. 604.)

at Uppsala, Samuel Dunn, the Abbé Chappe and others also saw luminous effects at ingress and egress and concurred in this opinion. Similar appearances at the 1769 transit caused a flurry of excitement and again led to speculation about an atmosphere but a consensus could not be reached because of discrepancies between observers. Moreover some observers saw nothing unusual.

The difficulty was complicated by belief in the existence of an atmosphere around Mercury, and that in transit the planet displayed appearances not unlike those seen on Venus. Another factor was the disentanglement of effects due to an atmosphere from those ascribable to instrument defects, indifferent seeing conditions and other elements. Astronomers in general, therefore, tended either to ignore the phenomena, or at least explain them away as visual fallacies. Nor were they inclined to consider alternative methods of tackling the problem such as Christiaan Huygens (1629–1695) interrogatively suggested in his *Celestial Worlds Discovered: Or Conjectures Concerning the Inhabitants, Plants and Productions of the Worlds in the Planets* (1698) by noting:

> What then, must Venus have no Sea, or do the Waters there reflect the Light more than ours do, or their Land less? or rather (which is most probable in my opinion) is not all that light we see reflected from an Atmosphere surrounding Venus, which being thicker and more solid than that in Mars or Jupiter, hinders our seeing anything of the Globe itself, and is at the same time capable of sending back the Rays that it receives from the Sun?

This then was the background to Schröter's statement in the *Philosophical Transactions* and what inspired him to investigate the question of the planet's atmosphere.

In 1782 he had taken up a new appointment and settled in his official residence at Lilienthal, a quiet village about 19 kilometres to the north and east of Bremen where he built and equipped an observatory; today recognized as the first centre primarily devoted to the study of the Moon and planets.

Once established he utilized every opportunity to observe Venus not only daily, 'but, as far as the weather and her position admitted, almost hourly through the whole day and evening'. For many years his labour was fruitless. Venus offered no sure anchorage anywhere on its apparent surface, nothing but a uniform brightness in which he sometimes fancied, or perhaps more than fancied, brighter or darker markings, but could never be certain.

His luck changed around five o'clock in the evening of 28 December 1789, Venus a dazzling half-moon of pale saffron hung motionless in the field of his telescope, a seven-foot Herschelian reflector. His first impression of the planet was of an indented terminator, and a slightly extended north cusp. What he saw at the south cusp, however, was as dramatic as it was unexpected. Where angularity was expected, there was truncation as if the tip of the cusp had been shaved away giving it a blunted look. More astonishing, in the darkness beyond, he distinguished a minute speck of light that glinted uncertainly in the chill air. If he had been looking at the Moon he would have thought nothing of it;

for on that body appearances of this type are routinely visible at the terminator where high peaks touched by the first and last solar rays shine star-like in encircling gloom. But this was Venus and such appearances had not previously been reported. Convinced of its reality he presumed it to be of a mountainous character; ultimately it came to be known as the 'enlightened mountain', a huge massif that features in the history of the mythical 'Himalayas of Venus'. That though, is another story.

Now past dichotomy and in crescent form, daily narrowing as it increased in angular size and brilliance, Venus headed for inferior conjunction on 18 March 1790. Winter relaxed its grip and meteorological conditions improved. Between 9 and 16 March they were particularly favourable, the sky becoming unusually serene and transparent. As Schröter later wrote, the opportunity enabled him to make an observation, which, 'on account of its singularity, and the light it will throw on the physical constitution of this planet will certainly be ever thought important'.

Ever watchful for further disclosures he focused on the horns of the slender crescent as they extended round the limb of the planet to

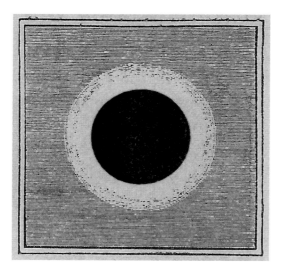

Figure 2. Venus during its transit on 3 June 1769 surrounded by a white ring as seen by various observers, probably an optical deception. (Image courtesy of George F. Chambers. *A Handbook of Descriptive and Practical Astronomy* (1889), vol. 1, p. 349.)

project beyond the angle they would subtend if Venus, like the Moon, had no atmosphere, i.e. 180°. His patience was rewarded. Out from the tip of each cusp crept a barely perceptible thread of light that slowly edged itself along the rim of the dark side, faintly outlining it with a pale bluish-white light.

The phenomenon which was more evident at the north cusp was first noticed after sunset on 9 March 1790. The following evening he recorded, 'each cusp, but chiefly the northern one, had...most evidently a faint tapering prolongation of a bluish-grey cast, which gradually fading, extended along the dark hemisphere, so that the luminous part of the limb was considerably more than a semi-circle'.

Verification of the phenomenon was obtained over the next two evenings and a series of post-inferior conjunction observations. Micrometer measures proved difficult and somewhat imprecise, but gave a value of 8 arcseconds for the extent of the bluish-white streak from the cusps along the dark limb.

Could the phenomenon be due to direct light from the Sun? If so did it signify the existence of immense mountains like the mighty Leibnitz and Doerfel ranges along the southern limb of the Moon? If that were so, surely the thread would not be seen as a continuous streak, but rather in single, detached and distant points as the Sun's rays struck the highest points? In all probability he thought, it is 'a light which partly illuminates the atmosphere of Venus, and partly, being reflected by this atmosphere marks out by a faint glimmer the limb of the dark hemisphere of the planet, in the same manner our morning and evening twilight acts upon ours'.

The truth of the inference was fully borne out by the sharp contrast between the bright horns of the crescent and the weak ashen-blue extensions. For if the latter derived their light directly from the Sun, they would be diminished in the same proportion and have nearly the same degree of brightness as the horns of the crescent themselves, but that was not the case.

Everything thus pointed to the possibility that the phenomenon was sourced in 'light reflected by the atmosphere of Venus into the dark hemisphere of the planet, being in some measure the light of the atmosphere itself, when illuminated by the rays of the Sun: or, in fact, a real twilight'. Should this be so, he mused, 'it will not only prove the existence of an atmosphere, but we shall also . . . be able to draw some inferences concerning its density, and real extent'.

Like many astronomers of the day Schröter assumed the absence of well-defined belts on Venus, such as are characteristic of Jupiter and Saturn, indicated that the planet performed 'its rotation round its axis in a much longer space of time than those planets or the nearly similar ones of our Earth and Mars'. Giovanni Domenico Cassini (1625–1712) perhaps unconsciously influenced by terrestrial analogy, had come to a similar conclusion in 1667. At least this is how his value is usually presented. But a close examination of his text leaves one a little confused, for it is clouded by ambiguity. He also stressed that any result would be compromised by the diffuse character of the markings of Venus.

Schröter too acknowledged his debt to analogy and used his observations of the 'enlightened mountain' to determine the planet's rate of axial spin as 23h 20m 59s.04 (now an obsolete value; the solid body of the planet actually rotates in a retrograde direction in a period of 243.0 days, the upper atmosphere in roughly 4 days). Working on that hypothesis he reasoned that twilight on the planet 'is nearly equal in its extent to that on our globe'. He admitted this was highly conjectural and at best conditional, but 'it supplies us with some farther means of estimating the height and density of the atmosphere of Venus with somewhat greater precision'.

He therefore concluded the atmosphere of the planet 'rises like ours, far above the highest mountains', and although we ascribe to it the greatest possible transparency, it will still remain 'a more opaque covering than, according to my Selenotopographical Observations, that of the moon appears to be'.

Schröter had previously described his observations of cusp extensions in his celebrated *Selenotopographische Fragments* (1791), but when published in the *Philosophical Transactions* a year later, William Herschel was incensed and criticized them with undue severity, engaging Schröter in a spirited debate. These 'extraordinary relations; equally wonderful', he said, induced him to question how he himself had not seen the lofty mountains of which his fellow Hanoverian spoke. He disputed Schröter's working methods and was scornful of his measuring device. Though he agreed with his conclusion that the cusp extensions confirmed that an atmosphere existed, he did not accept the calculations of height and density which 'are so full of inaccuracies, that it would be necessary to go over them again, in order to compare them strictly with my own, for which at present there is no leisure'. According to the American astronomer Henry Norris Russell (1877–1957), writing

Figure 3. Venus with twilight arc. The photograph is one of a series taken with the 61-inch reflector at the Catalina Observatory by Stephen Larson, Lunar and Planetary Laboratory, Tucson, Arizona, USA, in 1972 on June 17.681, at 8 inches of aperture. (Image courtesy of Stephen Larson, Lunar and Planetary Laboratory. Tucson.)

in review of the problem in 1899, 'Schröter, in reducing his observations, used a formula which gives the whole distance between the geometrical terminator and the limb at the apparent cusps, and made no allowance for the Sun's semidiameter'.

Herschel's observations of the planet had begun in April 1777 partly to establish that Venus had an atmosphere 'the existence of which . . . I could not entertain the least doubt'. His study, however, was less extensive than that of Schröter.

Despite the controversy that reverberated in the pages of the *Philosophical Transactions*, Schröter's patient, unremitting efforts had been rewarded. Through close observation he had introduced a new and important element into the equation and provided astronomers with what they had long sought: irrefutable proof that Venus has an atmosphere. This is the reason why in 1885 Agnes Clerke could say, that, 'notwithstanding luminous appearances plainly due to refraction during the transits both of 1761 and 1769, Schröter, in 1792, took the initiative in coming to a definite conclusion on the subject'. In doing so he along with Herschel laid the foundation of modern understanding of the planet.

With the introduction of a totally different type of observation, transit phenomena were supplanted: And yet cusp extension apart, Huygens had already identified what is probably the most obvious proof of an atmosphere in his 1698 statement previously cited. In that relation the contentious note struck by Melchior a Briga (1684–1749), reader in mathematics at the Florentine College, is of great interest. Writing to Francesco Bianchini (1662–1729) at Rome on 7 September 1726, he reasoned: 'How can we reconcile the idea of a dense atmosphere with irregularity in the crescent of Venus such as Philippe de la Hire (1640–1718) described in August 1700? Had not the Academy of Sciences in Paris discussed the matter, and in their wisdom concluded Venus has mountains higher than those of the Moon? Are we then to dispute and oppose the opinion of those savants because Huygens conjectures the planet has a dense atmosphere? He offers only speculation, whereas La Hire gives us proof.' Relying on the authority of the Academy of Sciences and with confidence in the doubtful observations of de la Hire, Briga dismissed Huygens' prescience – but of course he was wrong.

What emerges is that no one astronomer discovered the atmosphere of Venus. The majority relied on transit phenomena but had overlooked the most obvious proof, that postulated by Huygens – the blandness of the apparent surface of the planet; a fact evident to even the most causal of observers and one which John Herschel (1792–1871) later employed in his textbook *Outlines of Astronomy* (1850 edition.). Nevertheless, in various ways Lomonosov, Bergman, the Abbé Chappe, Dunn and all the others had been right. Even so their input did not constitute proof. It was speculation and like a summer breeze quickly dissipated without result.

It was to Schröter at Lilienthal in the fateful days of 1790 that Venus intimated her best kept secret, the twilight arc 'the silver selvedge of the dawn edging the dark limb' as Ellen Clerke described it in her *The Planet Venus* (1893), an appearance of rare and delicate beauty reserved for those daring enough to seek out the planet when it is within 15° of the Sun at inferior conjunction; two luminous threads that creep slowly but inexorably along the dark limb, finally to coalesce and encircle the planet with a fringe or crown of silver-blue light. Yet it must be clearly understood Schröter was fortunate. That another man, William Herschel, had identified the significance of cusp extension showed that recognition was in the air; that others as adventurous and perhaps better equipped would soon take up the hazardous challenge. Schröter seized the opportunity offered by good observing conditions and instead of abandoning the pursuit at the point in its orbit where for safety reasons most observers give up the pursuit, followed Venus directly into the blinding glare of the Sun and in so doing had the good fortune to unlock the secret that provided undisputable proof the planet has an atmosphere.

The Japanese Patrollers: from Honda to Itagaki

MARTIN MOBBERLEY

The Japanese have a formidable reputation in amateur astronomy and yet little is written in the western world about their remarkable achievements, partly because very few English-speaking astronomers can read Japanese and partly because their discoverers also have a reputation for modesty, national pride and teamwork (rather than rivalry). The word 'Tenmon' is that most associated with Japanese astronomy as the word literally means 'Heaven's gate' or 'Heaven's things' and can be associated with both astronomical and meteorological phenomena in the sky. There is much interest in astronomy within Japan and the Japanese publication *Tenmon Guide* is the world's largest circulation astronomy magazine, with monthly sales of over 250,000, which is remarkably large even for a country with a population of 130 million; the vast majority of the copies are sold in Japan. The *Tenmon Guide* is not the only Japanese astronomy magazine either, as both the *Skywatcher* and *Gekkan Tenmon* (monthly heavens) magazines are very popular. Even at school level the teaching of astronomy is encouraged and across Japan there are numerous schools and college buildings with an observatory dome attached.

In 1908 the Tokyo-based Nihon Tenmon Gakkai or Astronomical Society of Japan was formed and encouraged both professional and amateur observations. Twelve years later Issei Yamamoto of Kyoto University formed the Tenmon Doukoukai or Astronomy Association primarily for the purpose of carrying out research but also for fostering friendship among all sky lovers. The new association proved very popular, especially amongst amateurs, and since 1932 it has been known as the Oriental Astronomical Association. The OAA publishes a popular magazine called *The Heavens*. Observers based in the land of the rising sun have not always made regular discoveries though and it was Minoru Honda (1913–1990) who inspired the nation's star gazers to become prolific comet and nova hunters as well as star gazers.

MINORU HONDA

Born in 1913, Honda-san was raised in a small mountain village in the Chugoko district, situated in the west of the country. His life has many notable similarities to that of the British discoverer George Alcock who was born in the previous year. Like Alcock, Honda started his observing career by counting meteors; in fact his first published observation was of the 1932 Lyrid display. But the moment that changed his astronomical life actually occurred two years earlier when he acquired, on 25 December 1930, the book entitled *On Comets*, written by Shigeru Kanda of the Tokyo Observatory. Kanda-san's book included a list of the number of comets discovered by astronomers up to the late 1920s and the countries from which the discoveries were made. Topping the list (due

Figure 1. Minoru Honda (1913–1990) at his 'Ask to stars' observatory, with its collection of Japanese-manufactured telescopes, binoculars and astrographs, captured in December 1987, aged seventy-four. (Photograph by kind permission of Tomohisa Ohno, Kurashiki, Japan. Image relayed to the author via Osamu Ohshima and Seiichiro Kiyota.)

to discoverers like Pons, Messier, Borrelly and Giacobini) was France, from which 149 comets had been found. The USA and Germany came next with 84 and 81 comet discoveries, respectively. Then came Italy with 40 comets and England with 20. The Japanese were only credited with a dismal two comet discoveries, one by Masamitsu Yamasaki in 1928 (deduced to be a recovery of 27P/Cromellin) and the other by the Japanese-American Seiji Nagata in 1931.

To the seventeen-year-old Minoru Honda this was a situation that had to change, but surely even he could not have dreamed that he would go on to discover eleven comets visually between 1940 and 1968? Well, despite only having modest equipment, and initially not even owning a star map, he only went on to discover comets, but novae too. His first comet discovery came in 1940 when, jointly with fellow countryman Shigeki Okabayashi, he discovered Okabayashi-Honda (C/1940 S1) in October of that year. Honda was living at Setomura village, in Hiroshima prefecture, at that time and was involved in the

Figure 2. Minoru Honda in front of his 25-cm aperture Wright-Schmidt camera in October 1989 with his logbook cover indicating his opposition to the Strategic Defense Initiative to put weapons in space. (Photograph by kind permission of Tomohisa Ohno, Kurashiki, Japan. Image relayed to the author via Osamu Ohshima and Seiichiro Kiyota.)

observation of the Zodiacal Light at Dr Issei Yamamoto's Zodiacal Light Observatory. He swept up the comet with a 15-cm reflector. Sadly, Honda's co-discoverer Okabayashi lost his life when his ship was attacked by a US submarine in 1945. Who knows how many discoveries Okabayashi might have made? More comets followed for Honda in 1941, 1947, 1948 (two), 1953, 1955, 1962 and 1968 (three). (Note that Honda is often credited with twelve comet discoveries but only eleven bear his name in the IAU catalogue.) Honda was even observationally active during the war years and in May 1942, while stationed in Singapore, famously made observations of the tenth-magnitude comet Grigg-Skjellerup while using a homemade 80-mm refractor. There is a link here even to the current year. Comet 45P/Honda-Mrkos-Pajdusakova, which was first spotted by Honda in 1948, is on its twelfth return since discovery to the Earth's vicinity this August, when it will pass just nine million kilometres from us in the southern skies. So, although Honda is no longer around, his legacy of discovery most certainly is, and one of his discoveries could be the best comet visible in 2011 skies.

HONDA'S ACOLYTES

Predictably Honda's success and national fame led to others in Japan searching for comets, although the next wave of Japanese comet hunters did not really appear until just before Honda's eighth comet discovery. In October 1961 an amateur astronomer called Tsutomu Seki discovered a bright comet (C/1961 T1 Seki) and co-discovered another (C/1962 C1 Seki-Lines) just four months later; this latter find of February 1962 was made in the same month that Honda would bag his eighth comet. Just one year later, in March 1963, a third (nineteen-year-old) Japanese amateur, named Kaorou Ikeya, would capture a new comet too. The period from 1961 to 1970 would mark a golden era of Japanese comet discoveries, largely fuelled by these two countrymen Seki and Ikeya, who would ultimately discover six comets each with Ikeya finally notching up his sixth discovery thirty-five years after his fifth, when he co-discovered 153P/Ikeya-Zhang in 2002! Such was the intensity of the two men's love for comet hunting in the 1960s that two comets discovered in that decade bore the names of *both* men, being discovered within days of each other on each occasion. The first of these, the brilliant sun-grazing comet Ikeya-Seki (C/1965 S1), attained a magnitude of −10 when it literally appeared as a dagger sticking out of the solar disk around sunrise on 21 October of that year.

The respect with which Honda, Seki and Ikeya were regarded in the Japan of the 1960s spurred more of their compatriots to spend hundreds of hours per year sweeping the night sky. The reader should take a deep breath at this point because Tomita, Tago, Yamamoto, Fujikawa, Sato, Kosaka, Daido, Suzuki, Kojima, Araya, Kobayashi, Mori, Saigusa, Kosai and Haneda all captured comets in the late 1960s and 1970s. Seki, while not discovering any more new comets after 1970, went on to become a prolific observer throughout the 1970s, 1980s and 1990s using a 21-cm reflector at first, a 40-cm reflector from 1977 to 1980 and then a 60-cm telescope made available to him at Geisei Observatory in Kochi prefecture. This 60-cm f/3.5 Newtonian was donated to Kochi observatory and education centre by Seizo Goto, the director of the Goto telescope company. Using this fine instrument Seki-san concentrated on measuring the positions of comets and asteroids, recovering twenty-eight periodic comets on their return to the solar system (a Japanese record) and discovering 223 asteroids between 1981 and 1998. At one point Brian Marsden described the middle-aged Seki of the 1980s and 1990s as the most important all-round amateur astronomer in the world. It is worth mentioning that Seki's talents were not restricted to astronomy either, as he was an accomplished classical guitarist, athlete and author! A superhuman no less!

As for Minoru Honda himself, well, after inspiring a nation to hunt for comets, and after his three final comet discoveries (all captured in 1968) Honda, like George Alcock, switched to nova hunting in his mid-fifties; he discovered a remarkable fourteen novae by photographic patrolling between 1970 and 1987. The new objects were discovered in Serpens (two), Vulpecula, Cygnus (two), Crater, Sagittarius (three), Aquila (three), Lacerta and Hercules; three were co-discoveries with other amateurs. Of course, George Alcock chose a different route for his nova discoveries; incredibly, he memorized the Milky Way down to eighth magnitude and spent hundreds of hours per year in his garden, sitting in a deckchair, armed with his 15 × 80 Beck Tordalk binoculars from the mid-1960s onward. Even the single-minded Japanese seem to have decided that memorizing 30,000 stars was a step too far in terms of dedication!

Figure 3. A meeting between the two famous amateur discoverers George Alcock and Kesao Takamizawa took place at the IWCA meeting in Cambridge, UK, on 15 August 1999. Alcock discovered five comets and five novae visually, whereas Takamizawa-san discovered five comets and three novae photographically. (Image by Martin Mobberley.)

AN ARMY OF NOVA PATROLLERS

Comets stand out in the eyepiece as soon as you spot them, simply because they are fuzzy. By comparison the novae, unless they are bright naked eye objects, just look like any other stars when they are fainter than fourth magnitude and below the normal observer's constellation memory. So the choice for the nova patroller is between a photo-graphic patrol (where each image is compared against a master image), or visually memorizing the sky; Honda-san chose the photographic approach.

So it was that the date of 13 February 1970, the day that Honda discovered the nova FH Serpentis, seems to have marked another turning point in Japanese astronomy, as his nova successes spurred his countrymen Kuwano and Wakuda to also photograph the night sky with basic photographic equipment and then spend thousands of hours checking negatives. Mitsuri Suzuki and Matsuo Sugano joined in the nova discovery game during Honda's final years. During the 1970s, 1980s, 1990s and into the twenty-first century, if a nova was discovered it was almost always by a Japanese photographer or by their main rival Bill Liller. In the four decades since Honda's very first nova discovery, he and the others he inspired would discover or co-discover more than 80 of the almost 200 Milky Way novae found since 1970, which equates to a Japanese discovery or co-discovery almost every six months! Including Honda himself some twenty Japanese amateur astronomers have discovered or co-discovered one or more novae. If not for the tireless American patroller Bill Liller (born in 1927), hunting the southern Milky Way from Vina del Mar in Chile, another forty novae may well have gone their way too. Honda died in 1990, but his legacy remains. In his seventies he was made the director of the local kindergarten Wakatake-no-sono which translates into 'garden of young bamboo'. Originating from Hiroshima prefecture it is hardly surprising that

Figure 4. The Japanese nova discoverer Katsumi Haseda of Aichi, Japan, with his Takahashi EM-200 equatorial mount and twin 100-mm aperture, f/4 patrol cameras. He also uses a 120-mm focal length f/3.5 lens for his nova patrolling. (Image by kind permission of Katsumi Haseda, communicated to the author by Seiichiro Kiyota.)

Honda detested nuclear weapons and weapons in space. A note in his observatory read 'I am against the Strategic Defense Initiative SDI which pollutes the space around the Earth.'

The switch to photographic patrolling using relatively inexpensive camera equipment inspired a whole new generation of Japanese photographic nova and comet hunters after Honda had departed. Taking another deep breath we can note that the observers Takamizawa, Kuwano, Wakuda, Sugano, Sakurai, Suzuki, Yamamoto, Tago, Haseda,

Figure 5. Nova discoverer Yukio Sakurai of Mito, Ibaraki-ken, with some of his astronomical equipment. (Image by kind permission of Yukio Sakurai, communicated to the author by Seiichiro Kiyota.)

Nishimura, Nakamura, Takao and Hatayama were all successful. The list is almost endless! Even today, with competition from automated patrol systems like ASAS (the All-Sky Automated Survey) which uses a 180-mm f/2.8 lens), the Japanese patrollers and Bill Liller still seem to just have the edge in claiming the discovery.

It should perhaps be emphasized that comet and nova patrolling can and could be a pretty demoralizing process, even in that era before automated machines patrolled the night sky for both categories of object. Nowadays much of the emphasis is on supernova patrolling where the real hurdle to be surmounted is simply the mind-numbingly

Table 1. Japanese nova discoverers and their tallies

Patroller	Patrol years	Discoveries	Equipment
Honda	1970–1987	14	150 mm f.l. lens + Tri-X
Nishimura	2003–current	9	200 mm f.l. lens + film
Sakurai	1994–current	7	180 mm f.l. lens + DSLR
Yamamoto	1993–2003	7	200 mm f.l. lens + film
Nishiyama	2008–current	7	105 mm f.l. lens + CCD
Kabashima	2008–current	7	105 mm f.l. lens + CCD
Kuwano	1971–1979	6	100 mm f.l. lens + film
Nakamura	2001–current	6	135 mm f.l. lens + CCD
Haseda	2000–current	6	135/400 mm lens + film
Tago	1994–current	5	105 mm f.l. lens + film
Wakuda	1983–1988	5	400 mm f.l. lens + film
Takao	2003–current	4	120 mm f.l. lens + CCD
Sugano	1987–1993	3	Lenses + Tri-X film
Takamizawa	1995–2000	3	400 mm f.l. lens + film
Kanatsu	1993–2000	2	200 mm f.l.lens + film
Kaneda	2007–current	2	105 mm f.l lens + DSLR
Itagaki	2004–current	2	0.21 m aperture reflector + CCD
Osada	1975	1	Naked eye; V1500 Cyg
Suzuki	1980s	1	200 mm f.l. lens + film
Hatayama	2001	1	100 mm f.l. lens + film

Bear in mind that many of the discoverers' totals were shared with other Japanese amateurs in the list because Japanese co-discoveries are quite common. This table is accurate to the end of 2009, but is likely to become out of date very quickly!

tedious chore of checking the 4,000 or 5,000 images needed, on average, to make each discovery. Supernova patrolling is a numbers game. If one takes the popular value of a supernova occurring in a reasonably large galaxy once per century, then if you patrol one hundred galaxies you might expect to discover a supernova every year (if no one else beats you to it). If you regularly check 5,000 galaxies then you might reasonably expect to spot a supernova in one of them each week. A tedious process, yes, but if you miss a supernova you can always hope to discover another one at some point; faint ones are discovered almost every day! However, with the much rarer nova and comet discoveries it

Figure 6. Yuji Nakamura of Kameyama, Mie, Japan, with his Takahashi EM-200 mount and Pentax camera. (Image by kind permission of Yuji Nakamura, communicated to the author by Seiichiro Kiyota.)

is very easy to be clouded out or to be distracted by work and family commitments such that you miss the best nova for years just by sheer bad luck. George Alcock, observing from the cloudy UK, discovered five comets and five novae in a 32-year time span. So he would, typically, go many years without a discovery; potentially a highly demoralizing state of affairs, unless you really love star gazing. If you simply crave becoming a discoverer with every fibre of your being, patrolling can be dangerous for your sanity: you need to love doing it too.

PATROLLING THE MILKY WAY

Although comets are rarely discovered by amateur astronomers these days, due to the relentless CCD patrols and the automated checking by systems like the Catalina Sky Survey and Rob McNaught, Japanese amateur astronomers are still at the forefront of nova and supernova discovery. There is also a healthy interest in detecting cataclysmic variable (CV) stars in outburst too; these CVs (or 'dwarf novae' as they are often called) have less dramatic outbursts but ones that recur on timescales from months to decades. Where the two categories of novae and CVs overlap we find the class of object known as recurrent novae. Finding a long-period recurrent nova in outburst is almost as prestigious as discovering a new nova, but with the distinct advantage that you know where the object lives before you start sweeping the sky.

Unlike with comet discoveries, where professional patrols tend to sweep up incoming objects as soon as they brighten above magnitude 17, amateur nova discovery is still possible. Yes, there are automated patrols here too but, essentially, the camera equipment used (typically lenses in the 100- to 200-mm focal length range) is no different to that available to amateurs. The only real difference is that software checks

Figure 7. Akira Takao of Kita-kyushu, Japan, is a doctor of medicine and yet another successful Japanese nova patroller. Takao uses an old LX200 Schmidt-Cassegrain fork with a wooden box slung between the tines to hold a 120-mm focal length f/3.5 lens attached to an SBIG ST8 CCD. (Image by kind permission of Akira Takao, communicated to the author by Seiichiro Kiyota.)

the images in the professional patrols, whereas a human checks the images in an amateur patrol. Also, unlike with amateur supernova patrolling, an outlay of thousands or tens of thousands of pounds on a computerized mount and a 35-cm telescope, plus a sensitive CCD camera, is not required. All you need is a digital SLR camera, a modest focal length lens, a basic equatorial mount, a PC and an enormous amount of patience!

Whereas new long-period comets can literally be discovered any-where in the sky, novae are, rather predictably, discovered in the most densely packed Milky Way star fields. Sagittarius and Scorpius are the most productive nova constellations and are just high enough in the Japanese summer months to make a nova patrol possible, but other constellations like Aquila, Scutum, Cygnus, Vulpecula and northern Ophiuchus can be patrolled even from UK latitudes in the summer months. The regions to the south and west of Altair are especially pro-ductive, as is the smaller region near to the 'Coathanger' asterism in Vulpecula.

No Japanese amateurs have yet surpassed Honda's impressive eleven comet and fourteen nova discoveries, but many have discovered or co-discovered significant numbers of novae and, with the days of film-based patrols now making way for purely digital patrolling, the 'bad old days' of having to wait for films to be developed, fixed, dried and exam-ined are well and truly over. Once images are in a digital form it is easy to align and blink them with a master patrol image. New objects in the field reveal themselves instantly as a blinking spot. However, much caution is needed as hundreds of bright variable stars in the Milky Way can masquerade as novae and where the ecliptic crosses the Milky Way (in Sagittarius, Ophiuchus, Scorpius, Gemini and Taurus) moving asteroids can impersonate novae too.

While the brightest naked-eye novae might seem likely to give the discover the greatest kudos, once a nova brightens to third magnitude or better it is likely to be discovered by dozens of visual amateur astronomers within twenty-four hours of its discovery. So, in many ways, a nova discovery of around fourth magnitude is probably the best any individual discoverer can hope for. However, such discoveries are very rare as they require the nova to be within a few thousand light years of the Earth, a relatively local distance within the Milky Way. In practice the Japanese nova discoverers of the past quarter-century have tended to discover novae that have been between seventh and eleventh magnitude (at maximum brightness) with the greatest number of these being either ninth or tenth magnitude and, perhaps, 20,000 light years away and nearer to the galactic centre. If anything the digital SLR camera revolution has tended to push the typical nova discovery magnitude nearer to tenth magnitude as CCD and CMOS sensors can go fainter than photographic film. While this might not be as exciting as a first-magnitude, 'once-in-a-lifetime' nova there can be as many as ten discoverable Milky Way novae down to eleventh magnitude every year, even if many will inevitably be in Sagittarius or Scorpius. By comparison you will be lucky to find a year where there are more than two seventh-magnitude novae within the Milky Way. It should also be borne in mind that many novae are fast faders and even if they might attain naked-eye brightness at discovery, they can fade by several magnitudes in the following weeks. The most memorable novae are those that hang around and do strange things at binocular magnitudes, sometimes for an entire year. Alcock's nova HR Del of 1967 was the classic example of this.

MORE JAPANESE COMETS

But before you start to imagine that after the 1970s the prolific nova patrolling in Japan totally replaced comet sweeping, think again! Remember, before the Shoemakers started their relentless Palomar Schmidt patrols in the 1980s visual comet hunting was popular throughout the world. In Honda's early years of comet hunting he was in competition with the likes of the American Leslie Peltier and the Czech astronomer Antonín Mrkos. Between 1959 and 1965 the UK's own George Alcock bagged four comets, capturing the fifth, Iras-Araki-Alcock, in 1983. From 1972, there was a new man setting the standard, namely Bill Bradfield of Dernancourt, near Adelaide, Australia, and, from 1982, Rodney Austin of New Zealand became the other Southern Hemisphere comet discoverer. Then, of course, the indefatigable North American comet sweepers David Levy, Don Machholz and Rolf Meier dominated the 1980s and 1990s. But the Japanese were still hunting comets during that time, even if Bradfield, Austin, Levy, Machholz and a few others were beating them to the discovery in many cases. However, the late 1980s and 1990s would produce a number of notable bright comet discoveries by the Japanese; comets that would prove memorable for their brightness and also for their tongue twisting names. For example, in January 1987 the comet Nishikawa-Takamizawa-Tago (C/1987 B1) was a splendid telescopic object and the bright Japanese comets Ichimura and Furuyama were also found later in the year. Yanaka bagged two comets in 1988 and 1989 and Okazaki also shared a bright comet discovery with Levy and Rudenko in 1989. The Russian comet sweeper Cernis shared a discovery with Kiuchi and Nakamura in March 1990 and Tsuchiya and Kiuchi swept up a bright comet in July of that year too. However, possibly the greatest find of Tsuruhiko Kiuchi's career was his discovery of an eleventh-magnitude comet in Ursa Major on 26 September 1992 while sweeping the skies with a pair of huge 25 × 150 Fujinon binoculars, so popular with the Japanese comet hunters. Kiuchi had swept up the enigmatic returning parent comet of the Perseid meteors, 109P/Swift-Tuttle: a comet not seen since 1862. Remarkably, despite the excitement associated with the comet's possible return, and Brian Marsden's prediction

Figure 8. The comet 109P/Swift-Tuttle was swept up in September 1992 by Tsuruhiko Kiuchi. It had not been seen for 130 years! (Offset guided 24-minute photograph by Martin Mobberley with a 36-cm f/5 Newtonian and gas hypersensitized Kodak 2415 film on 13 November 1992.)

that it would return in 1992, professional astronomers had failed to detect the returning comet. Tsutomu Seki had missed it purely by bad luck in his own photographic search.

At this point I cannot help mentioning an entertaining tale regarding 109P/Swift-Tuttle concerning the two editors of this very *Yearbook*! In early 1992 Patrick Moore had bet John Mason a bottle of whisky on his belief that Swift-Tuttle would not be recovered in 1992, on the basis that it had already returned and been missed by the patrols. John disagreed and was confident that Swift-Tuttle would be found that year. As it turned out John was right and, at the BAA annual general meeting in London on 26 October 1992, Patrick happily handed John his bottle of whisky to much amusement and applause from the audience.

On a similar theme, involving a comet recovery, on 18 September 1995, in the dawn skies over Japan, amateurs Yuji Nakamura, Masaaki Tanaka and Shougo Utsunomiya bagged a bright comet within twenty minutes of each other. Unfortunately for them the comet was the returning comet de Vico, last seen in 1846, so it would not be named after them, but the recovery was an important one and their discovery was highly significant. The veteran Seki had himself been trying to deliberately recover comet de Vico and succeeded just after his countrymen spotted the comet, making it a quadruple Japanese recovery of this long-lost object.

Then, of course, who can forget comet C/1996 B2 Hyakutake, discovered with 25×150 binoculars by Yuji Hyakutake of Kagoshima. This magnificent zero-magnitude comet made a close flyby of the Earth in March 1996 with the comet's head being three times the apparent diameter of the Moon and the tail stretching more than 70° across the sky. His previous fainter comet discovery, C/1995 Y1 Haykutake, is now largely forgotten. Hyakutake-san told the national media that he had been inspired to take up astronomy when seeing the magnificent comet discovered by his countrymen Ikeya and Seki in 1965.

Tragically, six years after Hyakutake's discovery, and only two months after that famous discoverer Karou Ikeya co-discovered the longest period 'periodic comet', 153P/Ikeya-Zhang, Yuji Hyakutake would die of a heart aneurysm, at the tragically young age of 51, in 2002. But, to quote the teenage Ikeya of the early 1960s, discovering a bright comet is the chance to 'write your name across the sky' and Yuji Hyakutake had certainly done that.

The Japanese patroller Kesao Takamizawa is worth a special mention

Figure 9. The awesome comet 1996 B2 Hyakutake, discovered by Yuji Hyakutake, showing 25° of tail on the night of 25 March 1996. (A three-minute exposure by Martin Mobberley with an 85-mm lens at f/1.8 and hypersensitized Kodak 2415 film.)

at this point as he discovered a staggering number of objects, including comets, during his photographic nova patrolling. Takamizawa, of Saku-machi, Nagano, Japan, used twin 400-mm focal length f/4 patrol lenses and 400 ISO film. He discovered the novae V1425 Aquilae and V2487 Ophiuchi, an outburst of the recurrent nova CI Aquilae, two supernovae, five comets and 900 variable stars! All of the major discoveries took place between 1987 and 2000.

INTO THE DIGITAL ERA

One of the most respected modern observers in Japan is Yukio Sakurai of Mito, Ibaraki-ken. Sakurai has been discovering novae since 1994 and has notched up seven discoveries. He is one of the few patrollers to survive the switch from photographic film to digital SLR camera patrolling. While this may sound a trivial matter, it is not, because dedicated patrollers build up a huge database of negatives covering the same regions of the sky during their hunting career. While digital cameras avoid the need for tedious film processing and provide instant results, a brand new library of master images also needs to be acquired. Of Sakurai's seven nova discoveries five were made in Sagittarius, with the other two being in Scorpius and Puppis. Possibly his most famous find was the 'nova' known as 'Sakurai's object' or V4334 Sagittarius, which he discovered in 1996. It is thought to have been an unusual 'asymptotic giant branch star' that has undergone a 'helium flash' relieving it of its atmosphere to become a white dwarf; quite a unique find!

In recent years Sakurai's countrymen Nishimura, Yamamoto, Nakamura, Haseda, Tago, Takao and Kaneda have been providing him with some serious competition and since 2008 the duo of Nishiyama and Kabashima have achieved seven nova discoveries at the time of writing. No doubt, by the time this *Yearbook* appears in print the numbers of their discoveries will have grown significantly. Most of these patrollers use relatively modest focal length lenses of, typically, 100 to 200 mm focal length, although longer lenses up to 400 mm are sometimes listed when film is used. Such lenses can record stars down to magnitude twelve in exposures of a minute or two and so novae down to magnitude eleven are clearly visible when the digital images are aligned and blinked. Being Japanese the patrollers can also take pride in using cameras, lenses and equatorial mountings (typically Takahashi models) made in Japan. Perhaps the only exception here is the patrol system of Akira Takao of Kita-kyushu, Japan. Takao-san is a doctor of medicine, but by night he patrols the sky, and he captured four novae between 2003 and 2005. He uses the fork mounting from an old Meade LX200 Schmidt-Cassegrain, with a wooden box slung between the fork tines holding a 120-mm focal length f/3.5 lens which is attached to an SBIG ST8 CCD. This gives him a field of view of 6.6° × 4.4°.

TRAWLING IN THE ASTEROIDS

In the Japan of the 1970s and 1980s some of the top discoverers were given access to professional equipment, well beyond their financial means as amateur astronomers, with which they could pursue less stressful patrol and measurement work. Searching for comets and novae can be very rewarding when a discovery is secured, but when cloud or other commitments mean a discovery is missed it all becomes very demoralizing and energy sapping. But with larger instruments and a photographic or CCD approach fainter objects like asteroids can be swept up on a regular basis. A missed discovery is far less painful when you know that, in the asteroid belt, there are plenty more faint objects just waiting to be discovered. In addition, the same equipment can be used to make valuable astrometric measurements of asteroidal and cometary positions helping to refine the database of known orbits. Lost periodic comets can be hunted down too.

Perhaps the best known Japanese amateur in this 'pro-am' regard, at least in the photographic era, was the aforementioned Tsutomu Seki. As mentioned earlier, in addition to his six bright visual comet discoveries of 1961 to 1970 Seki recovered 28 periodic comets between 1974 and 1995 and discovered 223 asteroids with the 60-cm reflector at Geisei observatory from 1981 to 1998. His discovery career spanned 37 years. Seki will be 81 this year and rose to be the director of Geisei Observatory as well as being the director of the Comet Section of the Oriental Astronomical Association. However, Seki was certainly not the most prolific Japanese asteroid discoverer. Takao Kobayashi, co-discoverer of the splendid comet Kobayashi-Berger-Milon in 1975, discovered a staggering 2,243 asteroids between 1991 and 2002, from Oizumi, Japan, averaging 17 asteroid discoveries *per month* using a 0.25-m f/4.4 reflector! This truly amazing feat places him as the ninth most prolific asteroid discoverer in history, and that includes robotic systems like LINEAR, Spacewatch, NEAT and LONEOS! In terms of human discoverers only the Belgian Eric Elst, using the ESO Schmidt camera at La Silla, and the team of van Houten, van Houten-Groeneveld and Gehrels working at Palomar Observatory have discovered more asteroids than Kobayashi-san. In addition the Japanese duo of Seiji *Ueda* and Hiroshi Kaneda discovered 705 asteroids from 1987 to 2000 from Kushiro observatory and Kin Endate working with Kazuo Watanabe at Kitami Observatory bagged another 571 from 1987 to 1997. The Japanese asteroid discovery story does not end there either, as from 1993 to 2000 Yoshisada Shimizu and Takeshi Urata, working at Nachi-Katsuura observatory, discovered 310 asteroids and, working alone, Urata found another 156 and co-discovered yet another 483 asteroids with other astronomers worldwide. In total some 5,000 numbered asteroids have now been discovered by Japanese amateurs or semi-amateurs. Remarkable!

SUPERNOVA HUNTING IN JAPAN

In recent years there has been a distinct tailing off in amateur comet discoveries and even in amateur asteroid discoveries across the globe, largely due to the fact that the discovery machines like LINEAR, NEAT and the Catalina Sky Survey team have become incredibly efficient at discovering objects of magnitude 17 moving at tens of arcseconds per hour against the stellar background. However, as comet and asteroid discoveries have become far more challenging, the new CCD and robotic telescope era has given amateurs the ability to patrol as many as a thousand galaxies per night in the hope of beating the professionals to the brightest supernova discoveries.

I have already mentioned Kaorou Ikeya in respect of his five comet discoveries of the 1960s and his sixth in 2002. However, in the 1980s Ikeya had already changed his focus from comet to supernova hunting, no doubt inspired by the successes of the Australian Robert Evans from 1981 onwards. On 2 December 1984 Ikeya-san bagged the bright, magnitude 13 supernova 1984R in NGC 3675. His second visual supernova discovery, made with a 250-mm reflector on an alt-azimuth mounting, was secured on 16 January 1988. On that date, along with Evans, Pollas and another Japanese amateur named Horiguchi, he co-discovered another magnitude-13 supernova, the first of 1988; this was supernova 1988A in the galaxy NGC 4579. In fact, between 1983 and 1985 four supernovae were discovered photographically by Japanese amateur astronomers, two by Okazaki (already a comet discoverer) and two by the aforementioned Horiguchi. Okazaki-san would eventually co-discover his third supernova in 1996. On 9 February 1992 another Japanese amateur, Shunji Sasaki, made a photographic supernova discovery which turned out to be the brightest of that year. The object, supernova 1992g, was found in the galaxy NGC 3294 at magnitude 14. But by late February, when it had been determined to be a valuable Type Ia supernova, it peaked in brightness at twelfth magnitude.

At this point it is worth mentioning the unique husband and wife Japanese discovery team of Yoshio and Reiki Kushida. Yoshio (born in 1957) is the discoverer or co-discoverer (with Muramatsu-san) of 49 asteroids as well as being the discoverer and co-discoverer of the two periodic comets 144P/Kushida and 147P/Kushida-Muramatsu. His wife Reiki is the co-discoverer of the asteroid named 4875 Ingalls and between 1991 and 2004 she discovered an impressive twelve super-novae making her the most successful Japanese supernova discoverer up to 2004. However, in 2001 Koichi Itagaki would embark on his own supernova patrol and by 2004 he had quickly overhauled Reiki Kushida's total of twelve supernovae and he just kept on going. At the time of writing Itagaki has discovered more than 50 bright supernovae and is on track to have at least 60 by the time this *Yearbook* appears in print: so watch out, Tom Boles![1]

Figure 10. Supernova 2008ij, the forty-third supernova of Koichi Itagaki. This was a fifteenth-magnitude object in NGC 6643. (Image taken by Martin Mobberley on 26 December 2008 with a Celestron 14 and SBIG ST9XE CCD. A stack of seven 120-second exposures.)

Most of Koichi Itagaki's supernova patrolling has been made with a huge 0.6-m f/5.7 reflector, but during additional relentless patrolling with a 21-cm f/3 astrograph having a wide 2.2° field Itagaki-san has discovered other objects too. He bagged two novae in Aquila and Ophiuchus, recovered (with Hiroshi Kaneda) the returning comet P/1896 R2 (Giacobini) which had been lost for 111 years and then discovered a comet of his own, C/2009 E1 (Itagaki). He has also discovered a number of unusual variable stars as well. In 1968 Itagaki-san had

1. Britain's leading discoverer of supernovae.

narrowly missed out on being a co-discoverer of the triple-barrelled Japanese comet Tago-Honda-Yamamoto but, unfortunately, four names are not allowed and so he was never credited with that find. Now aged 64, Koichi Itagaki shows no sign of reducing his prolific discovery output. There have been other determined Japanese supernova hunters in operation too, such as Yuji Hirose who discovered the supernova 2002ap in M74 after 22 years of hunting with five different telescopes! He then quickly bagged three more, namely 2002bo, 2005W and 2007uy. However, Itagaki-san is by far the most successful Japanese supernova hunter and many of his discoveries have been as bright as fifteenth or sixteenth magnitude. His supernova 2004dj, discovered in NGC 2403 reached a spectacular eleventh magnitude!

So, in conclusion, more than eighty years after Honda picked up Shigero Kanda's book *On Comets* and realized that he should try to discover some comets himself, to put Japan firmly on the astronomy map, Koichi Itagaki and the other supernova and nova hunters are making sure that the land of the rising sun still plays a huge rôle in the world of amateur astronomical discovery. Maybe there are some lessons to be learned here for observers in the West?

Digging Up the Ruins of the Galaxy

FRED WATSON

Home is where the heart is. So goes the old saying, and I guess it is still true, even in this age of unprecedented mobility. But I wonder how many of the sages who delighted in trotting out such gems ever stopped to think about exactly what they meant by 'home'?

Well, it is where you live, of course. Yes, but does not that depend on your viewpoint? For example, if you were a stray bacterium, a valiant survivor of NASA's pre-launch sterilization, stowed away aboard the New Horizons spacecraft en route to Pluto, would not 'home' be the Earth?

From the perspective of an interplanetary traveller, home is definitely our planet rather than 22 Acacia Avenue, or 7 Gasworks Lane. But curiously, even this definition of home is a moveable feast. I have noticed that scientists studying stars and gas clouds within a few hundred light years of the Sun tend to think of home as the Solar System as a whole – not even our particular planet. It seems that for astronomers, warm and fuzzy thoughts of 'home' can equally well be about their street, their planet, their Solar System, or – taking things up a notch – their Galaxy.

Of all the definitions of 'home' that we can imagine, the Milky Way Galaxy must surely rank as the grandest. This gigantic agglomeration of a hundred billion or so stars, plus copious helpings of gas and dust and an embarrassing amount of something whose identity is still unknown – dark matter – represents the ultimate in terms of our home in space. And I guess the reason we identify with it so strongly is that beyond our Milky Way, other galaxies are ten a penny, numbering perhaps a hundred billion in the observable universe, and who knows how many beyond our reach. It does make our Galaxy seem rather special.

GALACTIC PORTRAIT

So there you have it. Home is where the heart is, and home is the Milky Way Galaxy, splendid in its spiral structure and prolific in its star-formation. Would not it be nice to have a photo of it to hang over the mantelpiece, where some folk have aerial photos of their houses? But there is a problem. Because we are permanently embedded in the flattened disk of our Galaxy, and see its grandeur only as the gossamer band of the Milky Way, we are effectively blind to its structure. You could no more take a photo of the whole of our Galaxy from Earth than you could of Great Britain from the London Eye.

It is only within the last century or so that we have had any clue as to what our Galaxy might look like from the outside. Until 1918, most astronomers believed the Solar System was somewhere near the centre of a flattened disk of stars, an idea that owed its origins to the work of William Herschel more than a hundred years before. Herschel had based this notion on the fact that to a first approximation, the Milky Way contains a similar density of stars (the number of stars per square degree) all the way round.

Those of us who watch the sky from one season to the next know, of course, that the Milky Way is very patchy, and varies greatly in star density over relatively small distances. However, when you look at the big picture, the density variations are relatively small, and Herschel could be forgiven for imagining that we are somewhere near the middle.

Then, as the First World War drew to a close, a paper was published that turned this picture completely on its head. Written by an American astronomer called Harlow Shapley, it drew some startling conclusions from the way globular clusters are distributed around the sky. These mysterious objects – spheroidal aggregations of tens (or hundreds) of thousands of stars (Figure 1) – were still poorly understood. Most of what was known about them had come, again, from William Herschel. Even the term 'globular cluster' had been coined by him back in 1789. More importantly, though, Herschel had noticed that most of the then-known clusters were in the southern sky, particularly around the constellation Sagittarius, where the brightest portion of the Milky Way lies. Perhaps that had caused him a few niggling doubts about the Sun's central position in the Galaxy.

Figure 1. One of the most prominent globular clusters in the southern sky, 47 Tucanae contains well over a million stars and is easily visible to the naked eye. Globular clusters played an important rôle in our understanding of the Sun's position in our Galaxy. (Image courtesy of Anglo-Australian Observatory and David Malin Images.)

Shapley's breakthrough was to estimate the distances of 69 of these clusters, by measuring the brightness of 'standard candles' in the form of pulsating variable stars he had found in them. When he did that, and then plotted out the distances, he found that the clusters formed a roughly spherical distribution around a point in the direction of Sagittarius. Shapley recognized that the globular clusters must congregate in a swarm – or halo – around the galactic centre, so that they can be seen above and below the starry haze defining the plane of our Galaxy. What he had effectively done was to find a way of cheating the obscuration, thereby discovering the true centre of our Milky Way Galaxy.

From the distribution of the clusters, Shapley was able to deduce that our Galaxy is much, much bigger than Herschel had suspected, and that the Solar System is about halfway from the centre of the Galaxy to the edge. That finding still holds good today, but Shapley's estimate of the actual distance to the galactic centre – some 65,000 light years – is about three times greater than the modern value. That is because he was unaware that our view through the Galaxy is seriously impaired by dust in the Sun's neighbourhood, making distant objects appear dimmer than they should. The dust also accounts for the relatively uniform appearance of the Milky Way, as observed by Herschel. In fact, most of the stars we see when we look at the Milky Way are quite close by, and in our local neighbourhood.

For all his remarkable insight, Shapley got one thing completely wrong. 'With the plan of the sidereal system here outlined,' he said, 'it appears unlikely that the spiral nebulae can be considered separate galaxies of stars.' Controversy over the true nature of the so-called spiral nebulae was the hot topic of the era. Were they smallish objects within our Galaxy, or gigantic systems of stars at unimaginable distances beyond? Shapley believed they were nearby, famously taking that position in the 'Great Debate' with fellow astronomer Heber Curtis in Washington in 1920. The final answer was not long in coming; in 1925, Edwin Hubble presented overwhelming evidence that they were distant 'island universes' – galaxies like our own.

From that time on, astronomers assumed that the flattened disk of the Milky Way would be graced with the beautiful spiral arms they could see in other galaxies. It was not until the advent of radio astronomy, however, with its ability to reveal the signature of cold hydrogen lurking in spiral arms, that they were finally detected, and the first rudimentary maps of our Galaxy drawn. Today, our ability to map the disk of the Galaxy has been enhanced not only by modern radio telescopes and their 8-metre counterparts in the optical (visible) waveband, but also by new instruments sensitive to infrared radiation – light that is redder than red. Infrared radiation is much less susceptible to the dimming effect of interstellar dust. Thus, orbiting telescopes like the Spitzer Infrared Observatory are able to see at great distances the tell-tale aggregations of young stars that define our Galaxy's spiral structure.

Infrared astronomy also brought a surprise in the 1990s. Astronomers had long known that spiral galaxies usually have a spheroidal bulge of old (yellowish) stars at their centres, and, since the Milky Way in Sagittarius is broadened above and below the galactic plane by similar old stars, they assumed that our own Galaxy would also have a nice symmetrical bulge if it could be seen from the outside. But infrared observations revealed that our Galaxy's bulge is actually a so-called 'boxy' bulge (yes, that really is the technical term for it). And boxy bulges are found in spiral galaxies that have a bar in the centre.

Before your mind runs off to picture a row of beer-swilling aliens propping up the bar at the centre of a galaxy, let me explain that this, too, is a technical term for a linear feature that occurs in the centres of many spiral galaxies. It is made up, like the bulge, of old stars, but they circulate around the galactic centre in such a way as to form an elongated structure looking a bit like a bar magnet. The spiral arms in such galaxies are typically connected to the ends of the bar (Figure 2).

Figure 2. A spectacular barred spiral galaxy, NGC 1300, captured in a mosaic image by the Hubble Space Telescope. The galaxy's central bar is much more prominent than the bar of our own Galaxy would be if we could see it from the outside, and contains an intriguing whirlpool of spiral structure at its centre. (Image courtesy of Hubble Heritage Team, ESA and NASA.)

Recent observations of the radial velocities (line-of-sight speeds) of stars in the bulge of our own Galaxy have confirmed the presence of a bar tilted at about 20° to our line of sight. And the latest findings are that yes, the two major spiral arms of our Galaxy (known as the Scutum-Centaurus and Perseus arms) do connect with the ends of the bar. This is extraordinary detective work on the part of astronomers in a number of institutions, including the universities of Cambridge,

California and Wisconsin, and at last gives us the ability to hang a pretty detailed portrait of our Galaxy over the mantelpiece – even though it is not an actual photograph.

There is one more thing I should tell you about this portrait. Its subject – our Galaxy – is very big indeed by any earthly standards. You probably know that we estimate the diameter of its disk to be something in the region of 100,000 light years. That translates to 9×10^{17} kilometres, or almost a billion billion kilometres, as the crow flies. Like me, you probably have trouble getting to grips with such a distance. It is just a big number, and does not really mean very much.

But we can use our imaginary portrait of the Galaxy to get a feel for just how big it is. The picture is, perhaps, half a metre across, nicely framing the graceful spiral arms of our home in the universe. But now, imagine this portrait expanded to be the size of the Earth – a planet-sized depiction of our Galaxy. On that scale, what would be the separation of the Earth and the Sun? I will tell you, before you dash off for your pocket calculator – it is two millimetres. Absolutely minuscule. I cannot think of any more cogent indicator of the difference in scale between planetary systems and galaxies. Galaxies are *huge.*

GALAXIES VIRTUAL AND REAL

When we gaze out from the confines of our Galaxy to its near neighbours and beyond, we find galaxies in a profusion of different shapes – or morphologies, to use the official term. Even if we ignore elliptical (oval) and so-called irregular galaxies, and look at only the spirals, the variety is startling. Some have tightly wound spiral arms, some are loosely wound; some are dominated by a huge central bulge, some have almost no bulge at all. And as we have seen, some have a distinct bar across the centre.

It was Edwin Hubble who, in 1926, made the first attempt to categorize galaxies, producing his famous 'tuning fork' diagram. At the base of the fork are smooth, almost spherical elliptical galaxies, whose shapes become steadily more flattened as one progresses up the handle, until the diagram divides into the two prongs of the fork – which are populated by barred and non-barred spiral galaxies, respectively. At the tips of the prongs are the most loosely wound spirals in each category. What Hubble depicted was a gradual progression from the most symmetrical and uniform galaxies – the ellipticals – to the loosely wound, almost fragmentary form of the extreme spirals.

Hubble thought he was seeing an evolutionary sequence in this diagram, a series of similar galaxies captured at different eras in their development. Thus, he called the ellipticals 'early type' galaxies and the loose spirals 'late'. We now know that this interpretation is incorrect, but still use his terminology. You have to admire Hubble's thinking: his speculation about the evolution of objects whose true nature had been only so recently discovered is a measure of his innovation in the field.

Things have moved on a great deal in our understanding of the evolution of galaxies since Hubble's time. With the advent of computers from about the 1960s, astronomers have been able to build ever more sophisticated models of the physical processes that result in today's galaxies. They begin with instabilities in the primordial clouds of hydrogen that populated the early universe, and wind up with computer representations of galaxies that look strikingly similar to the ones we are surrounded by – spiral arms and all.

A little more than a decade ago, the astronomers who build these models (who are known in the trade as 'theorists') found that their computers were now so powerful that they could simulate galaxies almost one star at a time, making highly detailed representations. They found, for example, that the bars in barred spiral galaxies are probably the result of so-called 'buckling instabilities' in the underlying circulation of stars. They also discovered that galaxy evolution has some rather sinister aspects, with strong hints that large galaxies grow by cannibalizing their smaller neighbours. Naturally, the theorists wished to compare their models with the real thing, to determine how accurately they understood the physical processes at work in galaxy evolution. In particular, they wanted to be able to compare the details of their models with the best-observed of all galaxies – our own. And it was not just in our Galaxy's appearance that they were interested, but in the motions and chemistry of its constituent stars.

Sadly, the theorists were in for a disappointment. While they could build models simulating millions – even billions – of stars, the number of stars for which observational astronomers had detailed information was paltry in comparison, perhaps only twenty or thirty thousand. The data were principally radial velocities, gathered over decades by analysing the barcode of information revealed when the light of a star is spread into its rainbow colours in the instrument known as a spectrograph. Such velocities are essential for understanding the motions of stars in our Galaxy, but the same technique (spectroscopy) also has the potential to show the physical and chemical condition of a star's atmosphere, giving tell-tale pointers to its age and place of origin. Those measurements, however, had been made for an even smaller number of stars. 'Well,' said the theorists to the observers, 'you'd better get on with it, hadn't you . . . ?'

Fortunately, the wherewithal for 'getting on with it' was already at hand. Previous generations of observational astronomers had had no alternative but to observe one star at a time if they wanted spectroscopic details – which is why such information was so sparse. But in recent years, a new technique has been developed, utilizing optical fibres to observe many stars simultaneously. The idea is to exploit the flexibility and light-transmitting efficiency of fibre optics, allowing the random distribution of stars in the field of view of a telescope to be rearranged into a neat straight line – the ideal configuration for a spectrograph.

This 'multi-fibre' technique was originally developed to observe distant galaxies dozens at a time for studies of the wider universe, but it could equally well be applied to stars. Indeed, one of my few claims to fame is that back in 1982 I became the first person in the world to observe stars rather than galaxies with a multi-fibre system, using a pioneering device called FOCAP, built by engineers and scientists at the Anglo-Australian Observatory (AAO). That instrument required the fibres to be plugged into a brass 'field plate', a time-consuming operation necessary before each observation. The plates were peppered with accurately drilled holes representing the positions of the stars or galaxies in the focus of the telescope, and were themselves quite expensive to make. Moreover, a new one was required for each set of target objects. Thus, it was not long before FOCAP was superseded by robotic devices that could position the fibres to the same 0.01-millimetre accuracy, without the need for drilled plates.

Over the years, the AAO has built a number of robotic instruments of this type, both for its own telescopes and for those of other observatories. Most notable, perhaps, is the 400-object 2dF (2-degree field of view) system for the 3.9-metre Anglo-Australian Telescope (AAT), the largest optical telescope in Australia. That instrument was commissioned in the mid-1990s, and had an immediate impact on survey astronomy, in which population census-style statistics are gathered on very large numbers of celestial objects. The instrument has undergone one major upgrade – it is now called AAOmega – and, as we shall see, will have another in 2011.

With the advent of 2dF and other fibre-optics systems on the world's great telescopes, the stage was set for a revolution in our understanding in the mechanics of our Galaxy. Suddenly, we had the potential to collect spectroscopic data not on handfuls of stars, but on hundreds of thousands – or even millions.

GALACTIC ARCHAEOLOGY

The idea of using observations of large numbers of stars to probe the evolutionary history of our Galaxy has come to be known as 'galactic archaeology'. In some ways, this is a poor metaphor, since what we are looking for are fossils from past events in the Galaxy's history. 'Galactic palaeontology', however, does not quite have the same ring to it, and I suppose it is true that one of the things we are doing in galactic archaeology is attempting dig up the ruins of the past, often in the form of other galaxies that have been swallowed by our own.

Once again, studies of this kind have their roots in the last century. Shapley's 1918 paper on globular clusters, for example, contained a hint that he was thinking along evolutionary lines. He speculated that perhaps the globular clusters he had observed above and below the plane of our Galaxy might, if they crossed the plane, be gravitationally disrupted so that they would begin to fall apart. Specifically, he wondered if the tightly formed globulars would end up looking like loose, open star clusters, typified by the Pleiades and the Hyades. With the benefit of almost a century of hindsight, we now know this is not true. The open clusters are actually composed of stars that are very much younger than those in the globulars, and are themselves sites of recent star formation. However, full marks to Shapley for trying.

It was already known in 1918 that certain groups of stars – for example most of the stars in the Plough – had a common velocity through space. This suggested that these 'moving groups' were the recently dispersed remnants of open clusters, representing a later stage in their evolution. Moving groups were first observed during the nineteenth century, but were studied much more thoroughly during the 1960s by a well-known American astronomer, Olin Eggen. In particular,

Eggen noted that the best way to find moving groups is to look in what we now call 'phase space', rather than real space. Phase space simply replaces the three coordinates of distance found in normal three-dimensional space with the equivalent three components of velocity. Thus, a star's position in phase space will relate to how fast and in what direction it is moving, rather than its position in the Galaxy.

The great thing about this is that if you plot the positions of a large number of stars in phase space, those that group together in the same region are, by definition, moving with similar velocities. They therefore constitute a moving group, irrespective of whether they cluster together in the same part of the sky. This gives astronomers the capability of identifying groups of stars that are moving together through the Sun's neighbourhood, even though there is no obvious connection between them.

Further confirmation of this connection comes from other parameters that can be determined from the spectrum of a star. Certain features in this barcode of information relate to a star's temperature and surface gravity, quantities that do vary from star to star. However, other parameters like age and metallicity (the curious term used by astronomers to quantify the presence of elements other than hydrogen and helium) will be common to all members of the cluster, and can also be detected in the spectrum.

This technique is extremely powerful. As an example, consider a well-known group of stars with velocities similar to that of Arcturus, identified as the 'Arcturus Moving Group' by Eggen. Since Eggen's time, this group has been thought to be the dissipated remnants of an open cluster, rather like the Plough Moving Group mentioned above. But more recently, its advanced age (about 10 billion years), slow rotational velocity about the galactic centre and low metallicity suggest that it does not belong to the youthful population of our Galaxy's disk – which is where open clusters are found. Rather, it belongs to something now called the 'thick disk', a tenuous extension of older stars above and below the Galaxy's 'thin disk'. So, where has it come from?

A recent suggestion is that in the Arcturus Moving Group we are actually seeing a stream of stars not from a local cluster formed in our Galaxy, but from the remnants of a dwarf galaxy that has been accreted – or gobbled up – by our own. This ties in with the phenomenon of star streams, which are seen both in our own and in other nearby galaxies (Figure 3). According to the latest models of galaxy evolution, large

Figure 3. Some 40 million light years distant, the edge-on galaxy NGC 5907 shows evidence of galactic cannibalism in the faint streams of stars that encircle it. These are almost certainly the débris of a dwarf galaxy being ripped apart by the tidal effect of its giant neighbour. The streams will eventually be absorbed into NGC 5907's stellar halo. (Image courtesy of R. Jay Gabany, Blackbird Observatory, via NASA APOD.)

galaxies begin their mature lives surrounded by scores of smaller galaxies – dwarf galaxies. These, however, gradually spiral inwards under the gravitational influence of their giant neighbours. As they do, they are tidally disrupted to leave behind them (and project in front of them) trails of stars. Essentially, they are forcibly spread out along their orbits as they circulate in their death throes.

The best known star-streams in our Galaxy are the Magellanic Stream, originating in the Large and Small Magellanic Clouds (and first detected by radio astronomers), and the Sagittarius Stream, originating in the Sagittarius Dwarf Galaxy. Other known star streams represent the débris of various dwarf galaxies or ancient globular clusters that have succumbed to the tidal attraction of our Galaxy.

We have known for many years that the tenuous, spheroidal haloes of galaxies are populated not only by globular clusters, but by old stars, too – indeed, we can see them in other galaxies as well as our own.

What has emerged only recently, however, is the idea that perhaps most of these old halo stars began their lives as members of other, dwarf galaxies circulating around their voracious companions. If that is true, then all galaxies – and ours in particular – should retain the fossilized evidence of accreted dwarf galaxies in the stars of their haloes. While we are just beginning to detect such fossil streams visually in our own and other nearby galaxies, the potential of galactic archaeology – with its large-scale velocity surveys – is to reveal many more.

There is one other important component of the haloes of galaxies that we have barely mentioned, and this, too, falls within the province of the galactic archaeologist. We know that galaxies must be embedded in spheroidal blobs of something massive, but invisible, for their disks to remain intact as they spin. This mysterious stuff – the enigmatic dark matter – is thought to outweigh normal matter by about four to one, and to have played a vital rôle in the formation of galaxies in the early universe.

At present, we still do not know what dark matter is, but suspect it is made up of massive subatomic particles that do not interact in any way with normal matter – other than by gravity. Still-to-be-discovered particles like neutralinos and axions seem to be the prime candidates, and experiments under way at the Large Hadron Collider and elsewhere are designed to reveal them in the not-too-distant future.

But galactic archaeologists, too, can play their part in the hunt for dark matter, since their stars are tugged not only by the gravitation of visible objects, but by dark matter itself. For example, one early result from astronomers at the University of Strasbourg has confirmed that dark matter is real, and its perceived effects are almost certainly not due to some undiscovered quirk of Newtonian gravity. As time goes on, the joint efforts of particle physicists, galactic archaeologists and other astronomers will undoubtedly narrow down the possibilities for this unseen component of our Galaxy.

BREAKING DOWN THE BARRIERS

So what are the hot topics today in galactic archaeology? Perhaps the best way to get a feel for them is to do a bit of virtual eavesdropping on a recent international workshop. I am particularly fond of this one, since I chaired its Local Organizing Committee. It took place in May

2009 in an iconic (some might say clichéd) location – Palm Cove, on the Great Barrier Reef in northern Australia.

If you are going to hold a workshop in a clichéd location, you might as well give it a clichéd title, so we called it 'Overcoming Great Barriers in Galactic Archaeology'. Groan. But the meeting itself threw clichés out of the window, and got on with some serious business in understanding the archaeology of our own Galaxy and its near neighbours in the Local Group of galaxies.

Organized by the AAO in association with the Astrophysical Institute Potsdam, the Australian National University (ANU) and the University of Sydney, the workshop aimed to provide a forum in which our current knowledge could be assessed and future strategies mapped out for both observers and theorists. It was attended by 40 of the world's leading practitioners in the field. In keeping with the

Figure 4. Optical fibres terminated with magnetic buttons populate a six-degree-diameter field plate in the UK Schmidt Telescope's 6dF system. Positioned by a robot, the fibres enable more than a hundred stars to be observed in a single spectroscopic image. Each image contributes to the growing database of the international RAVE project (RAdial Velocity Experiment), which aims to measure a million stars. (Image courtesy of Fred Watson.)

tranquillity of Palm Cove, its format was relaxed – which was just as well, since it rained every day. However, the workshop unashamedly reverted to cliché on its final day with a hugely popular cruise to one of the sunny islands of the reef, Michaelmas Cay.

Everyone agreed that the timing of the workshop was most appropriate. Two of the ongoing spectroscopic mega-surveys that had been made possible by fibre-optics technology had now reached significant totals in the number of stars for which they had gathered data. These were RAVE (the RAdial Velocity Experiment), being carried out on the AAO's 1.2-metre UK Schmidt Telescope with an instrument called 6dF (Figure 4), and SEGUE (the Sloan Extension for Galactic Understanding and Exploration), which utilizes the 2.5-metre Sloan Telescope in New Mexico. At the time of writing (February 2010), both these surveys have exceeded 400,000 spectra in the datasets they have accumulated, and are starting to produce significant findings in galactic archaeology.

The workshop was also intrigued to hear about stellar surveys still on the horizon. New ground-based instruments such as the ANU's SkyMapper telescope, the LAMOST telescope in China (Figure 5) and HERMES – the third incarnation of 2dF on the AAT – will have a major impact on galactic archaeology. Space missions such as Europe's GAIA and Japan's JASMINE will also yield massive new datasets within the next decade. GAIA, scheduled for launch late in 2011, is especially ambitious, and is expected to yield the positions, distances and motions of up to a billion stars in our Galaxy with unprecedented precision.

We clearly stand at a significant moment in the development of observational galactic astronomy. It rivals the recent achievements in 'precision cosmology', the study of the history and evolution of the universe as a whole, which have resulted from large-scale galaxy surveys and the detailed exploration of the remnant flash of the Big Bang (the cosmic microwave background radiation).

So where are the great barriers that still need to be overcome? Principally, they lie at the interface between our best theoretical understanding of the formation and evolution of galaxies, and what we observe. While it is true that on the broadest scale, standard theoretical models will produce galaxies a lot like our own, the devil is in the detail. And in contrast to the situation only a decade ago, when, as we have seen, radial velocities and physical parameters were known for only twenty or

Figure 5. Perhaps the world's most unusual large telescope, the 4-metre-aperture LAMOST is a recent project of the Chinese Academy of Sciences. Located at Xinglong, near Beijing, the telescope is capable of observing 4,000 targets simultaneously, and will be a major contributor to galactic archaeology. (Image courtesy of Fred Watson.)

thirty thousand stars in our Galaxy and a mere handful beyond, we are now data-rich – and getting richer – in this field. Thus, the challenge has been passed back to the theorists, who are now having to build galaxies using much more sophisticated models. These so-called chemo-hydrodynamical models incorporate not only the motions of stars and gas, but the evolution of their chemical constituents, too.

In recent years, our understanding of the overall structure of our own Galaxy has gone through a revolution. The traditional components of disk, bulge and halo have fragmented into thin and thick disk populations (with a systematic change in the metallicity of the latter as one looks further away from the galactic centre), and inner and outer halo components that have quite different kinematics (systemic motion). Complexity is clearly the name of the game in today's view of the Galaxy.

From the overall properties of our Galaxy, the workshop turned its attention to the individual stars and star clusters contained within it, and here the great barriers seemed to get significantly more reef-like. Questions ranged from whether the Sun is, in fact, a 'solar-type' star (in terms of our understanding of its chemical composition) to the failure of calculations of the by-products of the Big Bang in reproducing the observed amount of a particular isotope of lithium in ancient halo dwarf stars. Few clues seem to be available to solve this 'lithium problem', but they are currently being explored in detail.

Chemical clues that disintegrating ultra-faint dwarf spheroidal galaxies may indeed have fed stars into the outer halo of our Galaxy were also explored, and found plausible. These virtually invisible dwarf galaxies have been discovered by clever analysis techniques around both our own Galaxy and the Andromeda Galaxy, and their metallicity signatures closely match those found in the outer halo. Some of their stars are very metal-poor indeed (i.e. virtually unpolluted by elements heavier than hydrogen and helium).

The idea of 'chemical tagging' to reveal common origins in disparate groups of stars in our Galaxy also found favour in discussions of stellar streams in the solar neighbourhood. With the new data sets, much more structure in the local velocity field (in phase space) is revealed than was possible in Eggen's time. How many of these streams really are the débris of tidally disrupted globular clusters and dwarf spheroidal galaxies? Or are some of them simply due to the effects of resonance between the rotation of the stars about the galactic centre, and the rotation of the galactic bar and disk?

As we have already seen, the detailed measurement of the physical properties of very large numbers of stars is essential to help in disentangling such problems. Metallicity, surface gravity, effective temperature and so on are all required for us to understand the origin of individual stars. This will allow us to build up a population census of the Sun's neighbourhood that is entirely unprecedented. To do this requires sophisticated instrumentation, and the workshop ended with the promise of exactly that being provided – most notably by HERMES on the AAT. A rather lively discussion as to exactly what individual chemical elements should be probed by this exciting new instrument inspired confidence in the community's ongoing zest for a better understanding of every single nook and cranny of our Galaxy.

As Tim Beers of Michigan State University and Daniela Carollo of the ANU concluded in their *Nature Physics* wrap-up of the workshop, 'May the great barriers to Galactic Archaeology continue to fall, and the magnificent Great Barrier Reef, from which the conference drew its name, continue to live on.' Clichéd or not, I think we can all drink to that.

HOME SWEET HOME

Perhaps it seems a bit odd that our home in the universe – the Milky Way Galaxy – should be one of the last places to succumb to detailed probing by astronomers. Arguably, both our Solar System and the universe at large are better known to science. The former is within our reach for physical examination with spacecraft, while the latter presents views that are unimpeded by the dusty disk of the Galaxy.

But this exploration of our cosmic home is a difficult mission whose time has come – by courtesy of innovative astronomical instruments and sophisticated computer models. I feel privileged to have been involved in this study in a small way, starting with observations of stars in the galactic bulge in the late 1970s (when anything that was not extragalactic astronomy was terribly unfashionable), and culminating in my present involvement with the RAVE survey.

Like the hypothetical microbe on its way to Pluto thinking homely thoughts about planet Earth, those of us in the field of galactic archaeology feel warmed by the knowledge that we are learning ever more about our true home in space – the Milky Way Galaxy. Even if we will never be able to take a photograph of it from the outside, at least we will know how it got to be the way it is.

And finally, just in case you do happen to be a Pluto-bound microbe, here is a word of advice. Watch out for the 10.9 kilograms of radioactive plutonium dioxide with which you are sharing the spacecraft. As you will discover in a few years, solar panels are not much use in an environment that receives only a thousandth as much heat and light as Earth. Do let us know how you get on.

ACKNOWLEDGEMENTS

As always, it is a pleasure to acknowledge the support of the former Anglo-Australian Observatory, now known as the Australian Astronomical Observatory, and a division of the Department of Innovation, Industry, Science and Research. I should also like to thank all my colleagues on the international RAVE project for their continuing support of galactic archaeology, and for freely sharing their expert knowledge. I am also grateful to the delegates of the Palm Cove workshop (Figure 6) for their enthusiastic and energetic participation.

Figure 6. Trying hard not to look as though they are on holiday, participants in the Overcoming Great Barriers in Galactic Archaeology Workshop at the Angsana Resort, Palm Cove, Queensland, contemplate the future of galactic archaeology with due stoicism. (Image courtesy of Fred Watson.)

FURTHER READING

http://www.spitzer.caltech.edu/Media/releases/ssc2008-10/release.
shtml (recent news on galactic structure).
http://antwrp.gsfc.nasa.gov/diamond_jubilee/papers/trimble.html (the
Shapley–Curtis 'Great Debate').
http://sci.esa.int/science-e/www/area/index.cfm?fareaid=26 (the ESA
GAIA mission).
http://www.rave-survey.aip.de/rave/ (RAdial Velocity Experiment
homepage).
http://www.aao.gov.au/conf/palmcove/ (Overcoming Great Barriers in
Galactic Archaeology Workshop, 2009).
http://www.aao.gov.au/conf/palmcove/Participants.htm (workshop
presentations; click on participants' names to download).

The Norman Lockyer Observatory

JACK WICKINGS

Sir Joseph Norman Lockyer was a prominent member of the Victorian scientific community. He was the founding editor of the international scientific journal *Nature*. He had been secretary and later a deputy commissioner of the Devonshire Commission looking into scientific education. That commission led to the unification of science colleges in London leading to the founding of the Royal College of Science, where Sir Norman became the country's first professor of astronomical physics from 1890 to 1901. (He was knighted in 1897.) The commission also recommended the setting up of the Solar Physics Observatory in South Kensington with Sir Norman as its director. The aim was to further his research into the Sun and its effect on world weather patterns. He had already discovered the true nature of sunspots, had shown that the Sun was made from hydrogen and then gone on to discover and name the element helium in the Sun's atmosphere. (Lockyer had successfully identified the spectral line, which was among those observed by the French astronomer Pierre Jules Janssen during the 1868 total eclipse, as being that of an unknown element (found, he believed, only in the Sun), for which he proposed the name helium from the Greek word, *helios*, for Sun.) He had also led many solar eclipse expeditions. When he retired from his professorship he remained director of the Solar Physics Observatory.

In 1907, the Royal College of Science became Imperial College of Science and Technology. The Solar Physics Observatory had become a world centre for solar research, but the smoky atmosphere of London was affecting the efficiency of its operation. Sir Norman proposed that it should be re-sited to a hilltop in Surrey, but a decision was delayed until 1911, when it was finally decided that the observatory should move to Cambridge where there was a Chair of Astronomy. There was no place for Sir Norman. With the move, much of his work linking solar activity to the world's weather was abandoned.

Figure 1. Portrait of Sir Joseph Norman Lockyer. (Image courtesy of Norman Lockyer Observatory Archives.)

Perhaps Sir Norman had a suspicion of the fate of his observatory. At any rate, in 1909, the Lockyers started to build a new house at Sidmouth in Devon on the west-facing slopes of a steep hill called Salcombe Hill. The flints for its construction were quarried on top of the hill and transported down on a railway system. Of course, the new house was equipped with a dome to house Sir Norman's original 6¼-inch telescope.

In 1911, the Lockyers retired to Sidmouth but even at the age of 76 years Sir Norman was not ready for the fireside chair and slippers; he had one more observatory to build.

THE HILL OBSERVATORY, 1911–1920

The hilltop that had provided the building materials for the Lockyer house was also the ideal place to build an observatory. At about 550 feet above sea level, it was large in area and covered in gorse and heather, with few trees – an ideal covering for an observatory because the ground cover would minimize the distortion of the telescopic images caused by rising currents of warm air. In addition, the high elevation would free it from the mists and fog of the valley. Sir Norman was not without rich and powerful friends and very soon an appeal was started to raise funds for the building of a privately funded observatory which was to be known as the Hill Observatory. Prince Arthur of Connaught was president of the appeal committee. Sir Norman contributed

Figure 2. The Kensington telescope was built by Thomas Cooke & Sons for the Solar Physics Observatory at South Kensington, where it was set up in 1885 to apply Lockyer's spectrographic methods to the measurement of the temperature of stars. Today, it is used by the public on clear nights to view the planets and brighter night sky objects. On sunny days it is used to show Fraunhofer lines in the solar spectrum. It is in essence an equatorially mounted refractor, but clamped to the main viewing tube is a large objective-prism spectrograph. In this second telescope starlight is split by a prism in front of the objective lens into its component colours so that at the other end of the tube, where the light falls on a photographic plate, the separate colours are drawn out into a narrow strip, i.e. a spectrum. The telescope is mounted on a German equatorial mount and driven by a mechanical clock, controlled by a centrifugal governor, turning the instrument at constant speed about the polar axis. (Image courtesy of Norman Lockyer Observatory Archives.)

£4,000, Lady Lockyer £1,000 and their close friend Lieutenant Colonel Francis McClean £9,000. Francis McClean also contributed his father's 10-inch Grubb refractor and his brother Captain W. N. McClean designed the domes that were to house the McClean telescope and a 10-inch Cooke refractor (the Kensington telescope) that Sir Norman had brought with him from the Solar Physics Observatory in London. Sir Norman had hoped to obtain the 36-inch reflecting telescope, but this was moved to Cambridge. Nevertheless there was his 30-inch telescope and it was intended that this too would be installed at the Hill Observatory. By 1913 the observatory was operational with the 'Long House' containing a library and laboratory to back up the work carried on in the domes. It had its own water supply and power house.

Sir Norman was its director with his son James as second in command. The Research Committee included Sir Frank Dyson, Astronomer Royal, Prof. Eddington of Cambridge, Prof. Fowler, President of the Royal Astronomical Society, and Prof. Turner of Oxford. Foreign members included leading American astronomers, Dr G. E. Hale, Director of the Mount Wilson Observatory and Prof. Frost, Director of the Yerkes Observatory. The main work of the observatory was now in the characterization of stars and for this purpose the telescopes were fitted with large prisms placed in front of the main lens of the telescope. Plans were in hand in 1914 to build the Connaught Dome that would house the 30-inch reflector, but the onset of hostilities caused the observatory to be closed for the duration of the First World War. During the war, James Lockyer saw service with the Royal Naval Air Service and then as a major in the RAF.

Sir Norman was not idle during the war years. Once more he was pressing the government to spend more on scientific research and the adoption of scientific methods. During the war this led to a body being set up, which eventually became the Department of Scientific and Industrial Research. The Hill Observatory became a corporation in 1916 with Professor Richard Gregory as Vice Chairman of the Council. Gregory had been one of Sir Norman's assistants at South Kensington and in 1919 he took over as editor of *Nature* and was knighted in the same year.

Sir Norman Lockyer died peacefully in his garden on the side of Salcombe Hill. The date was 16 August 1920. So ended the life of a man who had dedicated himself to the furtherance not only of astronomy, but of science in all its forms. His early work on the Sun pioneered

Figure 3. The Hill Observatory in 1913. (Image courtesy of Norman Lockyer Observatory Archives.)

experimental methods which eventually led to a greater understanding of the universe. He had been involved in the setting up of new government departments, had founded the early Science Museum and had a formative rôle in the creation of Imperial College of Science and Technology. Despite these great works, his greatest gift to the world's scientific community was the journal *Nature*. This publication provided a means whereby the scientists of the world could communicate their findings to one another. This act alone has greatly influenced the advancement of science throughout the world.

THE NORMAN LOCKYER OBSERVATORY, 1920–1997

James Lockyer took over as director of the observatory on the death of his father and it was renamed the Norman Lockyer Observatory in memory of its founder. The work on the classification of stars continued; of particular interest was the study of new stars or novae. Bright novae which appeared in 1920 and 1934 (V476 Cygni and DQ Herculis, respectively) allowed the changes in the spectra of these stars to be recorded, giving clues to the way in which such stars develop. The observatory had a large collection of stellar spectra and these were used to deduce the distances of stars, a line of research proposed by Prof.

Adams, Director of the Mount Wilson Observatory. This library of photographic plates is held under controlled conditions at the Norman Lockyer Observatory to this day.

Sir Robert Mond had been a supporter of the observatory from its founding. In 1932 he provided the funds to build a third telescope at the observatory. This new instrument was, in fact, four telescopes in one. Each tube had a different focal length and their prime use was photographic. It could be used to photograph large areas of the sky, aiding the observatory's work on stellar classification. It was known as the Mond Astrograph.

In 1936, the observatory suffered a severe blow with the untimely death of James Lockyer. The post of director was given to his assistant Mr D. L. Edwards who continued the programme of research. Astronomy was changing. Observatories were being built on top of high mountains and astronomers were calling for larger and larger telescopes to look ever deeper into space. The Norman Lockyer Observatory continued to do good work but it no longer attracted the funds needed to keep it going. In 1945, the University College of the South West of England took over the day-to-day running of the observatory. While the college was conducting basic research on the Earth's magnetism and the composition of the upper atmosphere, there was no

Figure 4. Aerial view of the Norman Lockyer Observatory in the 1970s. (Image courtesy of Norman Lockyer Observatory Archives.)

Chair of Astronomy. Mr Donald Barber had taken over as superintendant in 1955 on the death of Edwards, but on his retirement in 1961 no replacement was appointed. Astronomical research at the observatory ceased and maintenance of the instruments stopped.

The university continued to use the site for research and in 1975 there came a request from the newly formed Sidmouth and District Astronomical Society for the use of a meeting room and one of the telescopes. This was granted and the society set about the renovation of the McClean telescope. At about the same time the Sidmouth Amateur Radio Society also asked if they could use a disused building to house their radio equipment and this request was also granted. A new period of activity started at the observatory and once more the McClean telescope was in use, if only by amateurs.

This phase was to be short-lived. The university had no further use for the site and in 1983 the decision was made to close it down. The instruments were to be dispersed and the domes demolished. The site would then be ripe for development. The citizens of Sidmouth were appalled, particularly as a plot of land on Peak Hill to the west of Sidmouth had also come on to the market. Too many Devon clifftops had been covered in housing or, worse still, caravan parks. This was not to happen in Sidmouth. There started a protracted round of negotiations, which resulted in East Devon District Council purchasing the 46-acre observatory site. Forty acres of farm and woodland were sold to the National Trust. The people of Sidmouth collected £250,000 to cover the purchase of the land both on top of Salcombe Hill and on top of Peak Hill. The Council sold Sir Norman's 'Long House', which was converted into a private dwelling and a tumble-down bungalow was sold for demolition and the construction of a new bungalow. These properties must have one of the finest views in East Devon.

East Devon District Council used the proceeds of these sales to renovate the observatory. The McClean telescope was sent away to Newcastle-upon-Tyne for complete renovation. New lenses had to be made as the originals had been stolen. Fortunately, Sinden Optics of Newcastle had all the original records of the telescopes, so that exact copies could be made.

The Mond Astrograph had been badly vandalized and was thought to be beyond repair. It was disposed of to amateur astronomers who have now reconstructed the telescope and it is functioning at an observatory in Lancashire. The 14-foot-diameter Mond Dome was converted

Figure 5. Built in 1895, the McClean telescope was given to Norman Lockyer when he was setting up the Hill Observatory in 1912, having vacated the Solar Physics Observatory in Kensington. The twin-tube arrangement betrays the origins of this instrument – an international project, conceived in Paris in 1887, to map the entire heavens photographically. This *Carte du Ciel* would require 10,000 large glass negatives. The photographic tube is the wider of the two. As photographic emulsions were then sensitive only to blue light, the optics for this tube are blue-corrected, whilst those for the narrower viewing tube are yellow-corrected. (Image courtesy of Norman Lockyer Observatory Archives.)

into a small planetarium seating about twenty people. An additional building was attached to the Mond Dome and this housed a meeting room for the societies as well as a radio room. The Sidmouth Amateur Radio Society and the Sidmouth and District Astronomical Society were allowed to use the premises on an annual licence, on the understanding that the observatory would be opened to the public on nine occasions during the year. Four trustees from the societies took responsibility for the site which was formally reopened by Patrick Moore in October 1989.

From the start, the observatory attracted many visitors to its programme of open evenings and afternoons. Many visitors from Sidmouth were amazed to find such a place on their doorstep. Visits by school parties flourished, but all too often these groups had to be split up in order to fit them into the small planetarium. The meeting room became too small to cope with the increased membership of the Astronomical Society, which had to hold its lecture meetings in the Arts Centre in Sidmouth. It became clear, by 1993, that a major building programme was needed to cope with the increased popularity of the observatory.

Proposals were put to East Devon District Council for a major extension to the premises, to include a 25-foot-diameter 60-seat planetarium and generally improved facilities. A far-sighted Council agreed to back the proposals and construction started in January 1995. The two societies played their part, taking on the responsibility of equipping the new buildings so that in September of that year Patrick Moore again visited the observatory to open the new planetarium, which was named the James Lockyer Planetarium in honour of the observatory's second director.

The Mond Dome was returned to its original function and in it was installed Sir Norman's faithful 6¼-inch telescope (the Lockyer telescope). A book could be written about the adventures of this telescope, which was lovingly renovated by the society. The reward was to

Figure 6. Aerial view of the Norman Lockyer Observatory in 1995. (Image courtesy of Norman Lockyer Observatory Archives.)

Figure 7. The Lockyer telecope. Dating from 1871, this 6.25-inch refractor is the oldest telescope on the site. Like the other historic refractors it is on a German equatorial mount. It has a special place in scientific history in that as an amateur astronomer Lockyer borrowed the superb objective lens from Thomas Cooke, fitted it to an improvised papier mache tube and fixed a specially made prism spectroscope to the eyepiece end. Examining the solar chromosphere with this in 1868, he discovered and named the element helium. The instrument has been restored as near as possible to its original condition except that the weight-driven clock has been replaced by an electric RA drive. The only controls are clamps for declination and RA, focusing and the drive advance/retard. The Lockyer telescope is housed in the Mond Dome. (Image courtesy of Norman Lockyer Observatory Archives.)

discover that the optical quality of the 135-year-old lens was of the highest order. One feels that Sir Norman would approve that the telescope, which he first used to explore the Sun, is still in constant use. A fourth telescope dome was built to house an Orion Optics reflecting telescope whose wide field of view complemented the refracting telescopes on the site.

Lockyer's observatory had taken on a new lease of life. The two societies that reopened the observatory joined together to form the Norman Lockyer Observatory Society, a company limited by guarantee and a registered charity. The membership of the society now exceeded 230 and its interests expanded beyond the original radio and astronomical interests to include the reception of images of the Earth from weather satellites, meteorology, information technology and the history of science.

Once more accommodation had become a problem. The monthly lectures were now held in the 60-seat planetarium which from the very first lecture could hardly contain the number of members who wanted to attend. It was clear that a larger venue was needed and in 1998 thought was given to a purpose-built lecture theatre. Early plans were too ambitious and failed to attract funding. Finally a new design was agreed which added a 100-seat theatre on to the side of the original meeting room. Folding doors allowed the seating capacity to be increased to 120. Equipment was to include a data projector and computer, an audio system with a floor loop for the hard-of-hearing as well as efficient air conditioning. Thanks to two significant bequests and the unstinting aid of local councils and charities this dream came into being and the Donald Barber Lecture Theatre was officially opened in December 2005.

The new theatre ushered in a new phase in the development of the observatory. The monthly lectures were vastly improved, where the lecturer could throw his/her slides on to a seven-foot-square screen. The excellence of the facility was soon recognized by local concerns who have booked it for many different purposes from staff training to

Figure 8. Aerial view of the Norman Lockyer Observatory in 2005. (Image courtesy of Norman Lockyer Observatory Archives.)

annual general meetings and even wedding receptions. The planetarium was greatly improved by the gift of a Spitz projector from the Old Royal Observatory, Greenwich.

The observatory had become a very busy place with an extended programme of open events, school and group visits as well as classes in astronomy. In 2006, it was decided to have a special open day and so the annual Astronomy Fair was born, taking place on the first Saturday in August. Trade stands are housed in a marquee set up in the extensive grounds while leading speakers lecture in the theatre. Visits to the planetarium make it a memorable day for some 500 visitors. There have now been five such events and their popularity has increased both with the public and with exhibitors.

Plans have been laid to further advance the possibilities at this unique observatory with its southern aspect over the sea and hence its freedom from light pollution. A gift of a 20-inch reflecting telescope has set the society on another search for funds to build a dome to house it. When complete it is intended that the telescope will be computer-driven from the lecture theatre so that a large audience will be able to view the heavens.

There can be no doubt that the Norman Lockyer Observatory has come a long way since its near destruction in 1983, its reopening in 1989 when membership stood at about forty, to the present day where several thousand visitors are welcomed to this historic site every year. It must be remembered that the observatory is not subsidized in any way and owes its success to the voluntary efforts of its members. It is fortunate that some members are retired professional astronomers whose advice has been invaluable. Members have benefited from this and they cheerfully welcome the host of visitors to the observatory, presenting to them science with a smile on its face. Something, it is believed, of which Sir Norman Lockyer would heartily approve.

Meteors from the Dragon's Head

JOHN MASON

The Giacobinid (or October Draconid) meteor showers were among the most spectacular of the last century. Two outstanding Giacobinid outbursts were seen on 9 October 1933 and, thirteen years later, on 10 October 1946 when visual rates were greater than one meteor every second, but the total duration of each display was only about an hour. Lesser Giacobinid showers were also observed in 1926, 1952, 1985, 1998 and 2005 but none in other years. All the observed showers occurred when the parent comet, 21P/Giacobini-Zinner passed close to the orbit of the Earth. This has led to the suggestion that the stream is young with meteoroids mostly located close to the parent comet. Now there is the possibility of another fine Giacobinid display on 8 October 2011 – not at the level of the great storms of the past, but still likely to produce a noteworthy shower.

COMET 21P/GIACOBINI-ZINNER

As long ago as 1915, the Revd. Dr Martin Davidson wrote that there was the possibility of a meteor shower on about 9 or 10 October, caused by débris from the short-period comet discovered in December 1900 by Michel Giacobini at Nice Observatory. The comet was independently discovered in October 1913 by Ernst Zinner at Bamberg, and is now known as comet 21P/Giacobini-Zinner.

This comet currently has an orbital period of about 6.5 years, so that although the Earth crosses the plane of the comet's orbit every year, the comet will be nearby at the same time only about once every 13 years. The comet crosses the plane of Earth's orbit, moving from north to south, at the descending node, about six days after perihelion passage (its closest approach to the Sun), as shown in Figure 1. It is not until about 8, 9 or 10 October that the Earth passes closest to the descending node of the comet's orbit, and this will usually be some time either

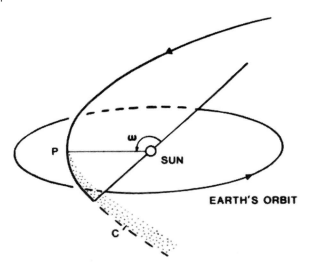

Figure 1. Schematic diagram showing a portion of the orbit of comet 21P/Giacobini-Zinner. Perihelion is marked with the letter P, and 6 days after passing through perihelion the comet dives down through the plane of the Earth's orbit around the Sun at the descending node. It is when the Earth passes close to this position that displays of Giacobinid meteors may be seen. The meteoroid stream associated with the comet is shown here as a dotted band.

before or after the comet passes the same point. For a meteor shower associated with this comet to be observed, the Earth must pass close to the comet's orbit at the descending node (i.e. within about 0.04 AU or 6 million kilometres[1]) and only a relatively short time (ideally less than 100 days) before or after the comet has passed the same point.

But there is an additional complication. At the other end of the comet's orbit, near aphelion (its greatest distance from the Sun), the ascending node of the comet's orbit lies relatively close to the direction of Jupiter's aphelion. Consequently, the comet makes frequent close approaches to Jupiter, and because of the low inclination of the comet's orbit it may remain under the influence of the giant planet's gravitational pull for a fairly long period of time. Such Jovian perturbations

---

1. An astronomical unit (abbreviated to AU) is a unit of length equal to about 149.6 million kilometres. It is defined as the average distance between the Earth and the Sun over one Earth orbit.

may considerably alter the comet's perihelion distance and hence they will have a considerable effect on the potential visibility, or otherwise, of the associated meteor shower. Prior to 1898, the comet's perihelion distance was 1.222 AU. A very close approach to Jupiter then decreased this to 0.932 AU, and a later encounter in 1910 increased it to 0.976 AU. This brought the descending node of the comet's orbit close enough to Earth's orbit for meteor showers to be observed at four out of the next eight returns of the comet – in 1926, 1933, 1946 and 1952.

EARLY DRACONID OBSERVATIONS

In 1920, Davidson revised his earlier predictions and suggested that a meteor shower associated with comet Giacobini-Zinner would most likely occur on 9 October with its radiant (the point in the sky from which the meteors would appear to emanate) located not far from the distinctive quadrilateral of stars marking the 'head' of Draco, the Dragon. Comet Giacobini-Zinner had passed perihelion in the spring of 1920 and that October the great meteor observer William Frederick Denning made the first definite observations of meteors belonging to the 'new' shower; from 6 to 9 October, he observed five slow meteors emanating from a radiant close to that calculated by Davidson.

The comet next returned to perihelion at the end of 1926 and both Davidson and Andrew Claude de la Cherois Crommelin made predictions for an associated meteor shower on 9–10 October that year, with a radiant between RA 17h 24m and 17h 40m, Dec. +54°. On the evening of 9 October, at 22h 16m UT, the shower was suddenly brought to the attention of observers in the UK in quite dramatic fashion when a spectacular fireball, of zenithal magnitude −7, appeared. Denning described it as follows:

> . . . it gave a brilliant illumination of the sky and left a streak remaining visible to the eye for about thirty minutes, during which time it underwent curious changes of form and exhibited a considerable drift amongst the stars. . . . There were 53 observations of the meteor, but not more than one-third were found available for ascertaining the radiant point, which was found at 262° (RA 17h 28m), +55° both by myself and Mr King.

That night, the indefatigable John Philip Manning Prentice was observing from Stowmarket in Suffolk, and out of 36 meteors seen in magnificently clear but rather windy conditions between 20h 20m and 23h 20m UT, he noted sixteen which emanated from a rather diffuse radiant centred on 17h 32m, +54°, including five within a 40-minute period. The meteors were all slow and Prentice thought that the hourly number of meteors visible would have been 17 had his attention been directed without interruption to the sky. The close coincidence of the radiants of the fireball and of the meteors recorded by Prentice with the predictions of Davidson and Crommelin established, beyond doubt, the association of the meteor shower with the comet. This connection was announced in a paper entitled 'A New Cometary Meteor Shower', published by Denning in November 1926 (*Monthly Notices of the Royal Astronomical Society*, vol. 87, pp. 104–6). Thereafter, the shower became known as the October Draconids or the Giacobinids.

THE GREAT DRACONID METEOR STORMS

It was computed that in 1926 the encounter distance was only 0.0005 AU (74,800 kilometres), with the Earth passing inside the comet's orbit, only 69 days before the comet reached the node. Given that the period of the comet was 6.5 years, calculations were made for the next return in 1933, which showed that the nodal passage would be 80 days after the comet on this occasion, with the Earth passing inside the comet's orbit at a distance of 0.0054 AU (807,800 kilometres). Since only negative results had been obtained in the intervening years, Prentice and his colleagues in the British Astronomical Association (BAA) Meteor Section awaited the 1933 return with very considerable interest. As it happened, most of the UK was cloud-covered on the night of 9–10 October 1933, but from Armagh Observatory in Northern Ireland the Rev. William Frederick Archdall Ellison observed a great meteor storm, and was quoted in the *Belfast Telegraph* of 11 October 1933:

> Between 7 and 7.35 p.m. I counted 300 meteors . . . and occasionally there were brilliant flashing fireballs which lighted up the landscape like sheet lightning...called indoors for an evening meal at 7.35, I was out again at 7.58. Then it was apparent that a really great

meteoric storm was in progress. I counted 200 meteors in two minutes and then counting became impossible. The firestars became as thick as the flakes of a snowstorm . . .

Apart from a brief glimpse of the shower, during a break in the clouds, by W. B. Housman at Seaton in Devon, Prentice, in his report of the great shower (*Journal of the British Astronomical Association*, 1934, vol. 44, p. 110), could refer only to the observations made elsewhere in Europe. These showed that 'the stream returned in very great abundance, giving a meteor storm comparable to the classic meteor storms of the last century'. When all of the observers' reports had been gathered in, it became clear that the visual rate at maximum approached 100 per minute, or about 6,000 meteors per hour, around 20h 15m UT on 9 October. The meteors were slow, mostly faint (with the majority being only third to fifth magnitude) and were generally described as yellow. As will be seen from the rates curve in Figure 2, the peak of the shower was very

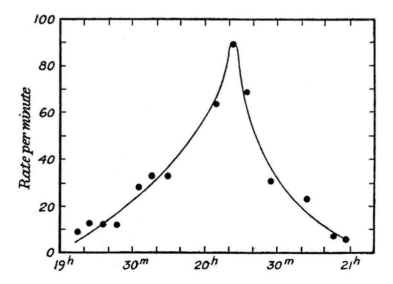

Figure 2. Rough plot showing the brief, but spectacular, Giacobinid meteor outburst on 9 October 1933. Maximum activity was at 20h 15m UT, when rates approached a hundred meteors per minute, but the width of the entire peak lasted only a little over three hours.

narrow; the time during which the rate was greater than one half of the maximum value was just 35 minutes.

The relation of the meteor stream to the comet was now placed beyond doubt and the next returns were expected in 1939 and 1940. In October 1939, the Earth reached the node of the comet's orbit 136 days ahead of the comet, but neither on that occasion, nor in October 1940, did Prentice or his fellow Meteor Section members observe any associated meteors. It is highly likely that daylight interfered with the watches, since the predicted time of maximum fell after dawn in 1939 and during the afternoon in 1940, from the UK, so the negative observations are not surprising in view of the established short duration of the shower.

The next return in October 1946 was predicted to occur as the Earth crossed inside the cometary orbit at a distance of only 0.0015 AU (224,400 kilometres), only 15 days behind the comet, and the expectations of another short-lived intense meteoric storm were fulfilled. On this occasion the peak of the shower occurred as dawn was breaking from Europe, so observers in Canada and the USA had the best uninterrupted view, although observations were seriously hampered by bright moonlight (the Moon was full on 10 October), which considerably reduced the number of meteors seen. In his account of the shower (*Popular Astronomy*, 1946, vol. 54, pp. 475–7), Charles P. Olivier, President of the American Meteor Society, describes the well-organized watches at the University of Oklahoma Observatory led by Professor B. S. Whitney. Taking counts every 10 minutes, his team estimated that the peak of the shower occurred between 03h 50m and 04h 00m UT on the morning of 10 October; during this interval 475 meteors were seen, giving an equivalent hourly rate of 2,850 meteors per hour. When the effects of bright moonlight and of a thin layer of cirrostratus cloud are taken into account, it is estimated that the recorded counts should be increased by a factor of about two. This would indicate a fairly similar level of peak activity for the 1946 Giacobinid shower to that found thirteen years earlier.

At the Skalnaté Pleso Observatory in Czechoslovakia, a team of observers had to contend with cloud, bright moonlight and dawn twilight to monitor the shower's visual activity at the time of the peak. These observations were described and analysed by Lubor Kresák, nearly thirty years after the event (*Bulletin of the Astronomical Institute of Czechoslovakia*, 1975, vol. 26, no. 6, pp. 327–42). Due to the approach of sunrise, the curve of meteor rates obtained at Skalnaté Pleso on the early morning of 10 October 1946 is well defined on the ascending branch only, with observations terminated shortly after 04h 15m UT, as shown in Figure 3. The main peak at about 03h 53m UT is well seen, together with two transient increases around 03h 23m and 03h 40m UT. Inspection of the observing records revealed that both of the secondary maxima were accompanied by the appearance of conspicuous groups of bright meteors. Indeed the transient increase between 03h 20m and 03h 25m UT may have been considerably higher than indicated because there was some cloudiness at the time which cleared shortly afterwards. The peak of the shower was again extremely narrow; the time during which the rate was greater than one half of the maximum value was only about 25 minutes.

Prentice gave an account of his own observations at Stowmarket and in summarizing the work of the BAA Meteor Section (*Journal of*

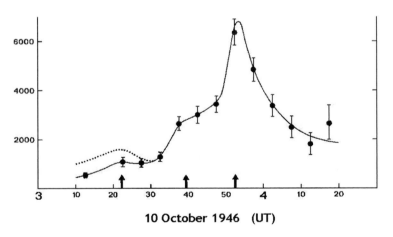

10 October 1946 (UT)

Figure 3. The hourly rate of the Draconid meteor storm on 10 October 1946, derived from visual observations at the Skalnaté Pleso Observatory in Czechoslovakia. There was a sharp peak at 03h 53m UT, when rates were again close to a hundred meteors per minute, but observations were hampered by cloud, bright moonlight and dawn twilight. (Plot courtesy of Lubor Kresák, *Bulletin of the Astronomical Institute of Czechoslovakia*, 1975, vol. 26, no. 6, pp. 327–42.)

the British Astronomical Association, 1947, vol. 57, p. 86) he concluded that at maximum the equivalent visual zenithal hourly rate[2] (ZHR) was 2,250 meteors per hour. However, the radiant was very low in the north from the UK at the time of the peak and there is no doubt that many fainter members of the stream would have been drowned out by bright moonlight.

In August 1946, during the annual Perseid meteor shower, Prentice had worked on a vitally important collaboration with the radio astronomers at Jodrell Bank. They had established the coincidence between radio echoes observed using the ex-army trailers of radar equipment at Jodrell Bank with the occurrence of visually observed meteors. In the event, the 1946 Giacobinid storm was the first one to be extensively observed using radio techniques and it firmly established the validity of radio echo observations of the ionized trails of meteors. Such radar equipment operated at Jodrell Bank and elsewhere confirmed that the majority of all meteor activity on 10 October 1946 occurred between 03h 00m and 04h 30m UT, with the radio peak occurring slightly earlier than the maximum noted by visual observers.

Estimating the peak ZHR for major outbursts of meteoric activity such as the Giacobinid meteor storms of 1933 and 1946 is fraught with difficulty, and there is still very considerable debate as to the absolute and relative activity levels of the shower in these two years. The situation is made even more difficult by the fact that the observational circumstances pertaining in the two years were so different. The 1933 outburst occurred in the mid-evening from Europe when the radiant was located at a respectable altitude above the north-western horizon with little interference from the waning gibbous Moon, which was only just rising as the shower reached its peak. By contrast, the 1946 outburst occurred near full Moon where even very thin layers of cloud led to increased scattering of the moonlight, causing many of the fainter shower members to be missed. On this occasion, observers in North America witnessed the shower with the radiant at a respectable altitude and no interference from twilight compared with those in Europe.

2. The zenithal hourly rate (ZHR) of a meteor shower is the number of meteors that would be seen by a single observer in one hour under a clear, dark sky (limiting magnitude 6.5) if the radiant of the shower were at the zenith. The observed rate (the rate that can effectively be seen) is virtually always lower than the ZHR and decreases the lower the radiant is above the observer's horizon.

Some older references give an estimated peak ZHR of 5,000 meteors per hour for 1933 and 4,000 meteors per hour for 1946. However, Peter Jenniskens in his summary of the different options (*Astronomy and Astrophysics*, 1995, vol. 295, pp. 206–35) quotes peak values of 10,000–12,000 meteors per hour for the two years. The arguments will surely continue in the best traditions of scientific research.

ACTIVITY IN 1952 AND 1972: LOW AND VERY LOW!

On 9 October 1952, radio observations from Jodrell Bank showed that a moderate shower took place during daylight hours from the UK, with estimated peak rates approaching 180 meteors per hour. According to the Jodrell Bank team, the Draconid rate first rose above that of the sporadic background at 14h 20m UT on 9 October. Meteor radar echoes were counted in 10-minute intervals: three were noted at 15h 00m UT, there were 6 at 15h 10m, 10 at 15h 20m, 11 at 15h 30m and 17 appeared at 15m 40h. The highest rates occurred at 15h 50m, when a 10-minute rate of 29 was reported – equivalent to an hourly rate of 174. The fall from maximum activity was rapid, and 30 minutes after the peak, the 10-minute rate had declined to three. The last definite signs of Draconid activity occurred at 16h 40m UT, when the rate was just two. The Jodrell Bank observers concluded that the radiant of the shower was at RA 17h 28m, Dec. +54°. One or two meteors at the tail end of the shower were observed visually in the early evening as darkness fell. On this occasion, the Earth reached the node 195 days before the comet, with the Earth passing outside the comet's orbit at a distance of 0.0054 AU (807,800 kilometres).

The next close approach of the parent comet to Jupiter took place in 1958. The comet's perihelion distance was decreased to 0.934 AU, and so no Giacobinid showers occurred between 1952 and 1972. However, in 1969 another close approach to Jupiter increased the comet's perihelion distance to 0.994 AU. This brought the orbit very close to the Earth's once again, increasing the chances of a shower. The orbital period of the comet was now 6.52 years, so major showers were most likely every 13 years.

Observers looked forward to the possible Draconid shower on 8–9 October 1972 with great anticipation. Not only was the Earth crossing outside the comet's orbit only 58 days after the comet had passed the descending node, but also the miss distance was a mere 0.00074 AU (110,700 kilometres), far closer then in either 1933 or 1946 – and the Moon was only just past new! The whole situation could hardly have been more promising. In the event, the shower was a massive let-down! The author remembers only too well sitting out in a park in North London as darkness fell on the early evening of 8 October 1972, filled with excitement as to the spectacle which might unfold that evening. Although conditions were far from ideal, the sky was fairly clear, with the radiant high in the north-western sky. Observing from dusk until the mid-evening, the author saw no more than 1–2 Draconid meteors per hour – very disappointing to say the least.

Maximum in 1972 had been predicted for around 17h 00m UT on 8 October, which made Japan and the Far East the best bet for observations. Unfortunately, visual observers had to contend with fog and low clouds, but the Hiraiso Branch, Radio Research Laboratories, Nakaminato, Ibaraki, Japan, operated a 27.1 MHz radar, recording a peak of 84 echoes in 10 minutes at 16h 10m UT on 8 October, followed by a secondary peak of 69 echoes in 10 minutes at 21h 00m UT.

In 1981, an approach to within 1.6 AU of Jupiter took place, and this further increased the perihelion distance to 1.028 AU. The next opportunity for a Giacobinid display was on 8 October 1985 and, once again, the shower was to spring some surprises on unsuspecting observers. In 1985, the Earth reached the comet's descending node at about 13h 15m UT on 8 October, passing 0.0329 AU (4.92 million kilometres) inside the comet's orbit only 26 days after the comet itself had passed the same point.

RADIO OBSERVATIONS OF THE 1985 DRACONID SHOWER

Predictions for a Giacobinid display in 1985 were generally based on the assumption that peak activity would coincide with the Earth's arrival at the comet's descending node. In this instance, a shower would take place centred on the time of the nodal crossing (13h 15m UT), but only if the radius of the meteoroid swarm was at least 0.033 AU. Previous observations indicated that the stream was not that wide, and so activity was expected to be only modest or even non-existent. Interestingly, Yu. V. Evdokimov of the Engelhart Astronomical

Observatory in Kazan had predicted maximum activity to be some eight hours earlier, at about 05h 00m UT on 8 October. Given the likelihood that any Giacobinid shower activity would peak during daylight hours from the UK, the author decided to monitor the shower using the forward-scatter radio technique.

Meteor trails were detected by the forward-scattering of VHF radio waves over an extended path; the frequency employed was 70.31 MHz. The transmitter was located at Radio Gdańsk (lat. 54°.4N, long. 180.7E.), an FM station transmitting as part of the Polish Home Service. The receiver was located at Barnham, England (lat. 50°.8N, long. 0°.6W). The path length between the two sites was 1,360 kilometres, and the bearing of the transmitter from the receiver was 065° measured from true north. The transmitter at Radio Gdańsk had a power of 40 kW. The station broadcast continuously from 05h 30m UT until midnight. A four-element folded dipole yagi antenna was used at the receiving station, with a 3 dB beamwidth of about 58° in azimuth. This antenna was directed along the great-circle path towards the transmitting station. It was elevated at an angle of 5°.2 to the horizontal, thus directing the principal lobe towards the 100-kilometre level, vertically above the mid-point of the transmitter–receiver path.

At the receiving station an SX-200 scanning monitor receiver was used to pick up the VHF radio signals scattered from the meteor trails. This receiver had a sensitivity of 0.4 microvolts and a signal-to-noise ratio of 12 dB, with a selectivity of more than 60 dB at ±25 kHz of the set frequency. The signal was taken from the external output of the receiver and fed via a high-stability amplifier, having a voltage gain of 100, to a twin-channel chart recorder. One channel was used to display the output from a crystal-controlled clock oscillator, which produced a narrow pulse every minute, and was used as an accurate timing reference. The second channel was used to display the output from the receiver. The chart feed-rate was set to either 120 or 60 millimetres per minute depending on the observed meteor rate. Great care was taken to eliminate sources of external mains-borne or radiofrequency interference. An audio output was available for aural monitoring of the received signal.

Continuous recordings were made at the receiving station on 7, 8 and 9 October 1985 between 06h 00m and 23h 00m UT. The chart records displayed the usual array of spiky signals attributed to scattering from individual meteor trails. A measure of the meteor rate was obtained by determining the number of signals having amplitudes exceeding some arbitrarily chosen threshold level. The level selected was that corresponding to 2 mV above the mean noise level of the receiver output. The number of spikes exceeding this counting level was determined for each 5-minute interval throughout the period in question. These data provided an observational record of Giacobinid shower activity. A correction was applied to the observed data to compensate for the 'dead-time' introduced by the method of recording.

The number of meteor events, corrected for 'dead-time', observed in 5-minute intervals between 06h 00m and 12h 00m UT on 8 October 1985 is shown in Figure 4a. The background level, as determined by observations with the same equipment on 9 October 1985, is shown in

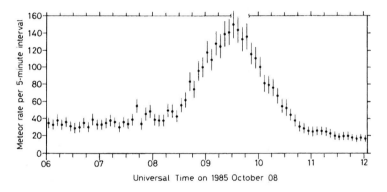

Figure 4. (a, top panel) Total radio meteor rates (five-minute counts) recorded on 8 October 1985 using the forward scattering of radio waves at 70.31 MHz. (b, bottom panel) Background (sporadic) meteor rates (five-minute counts) recorded on 9 October 1985 using the forward-scatter technique. Comparing the data for the two days, it is clear that a significant meteor display occurred on 8 October between about 07h 40m and 12h 00m UT. It is also evident that no meteor shower was observed during the same period on the following day. (Plots courtesy of the author.)

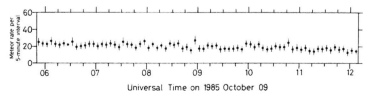

Figure 4b as a comparison. It is clear from Figure 4a that a significant meteor display occurred on 8 October 1985 between about 07h 40m and 12h 00m UT. Peak observed rates occurred in the 5-minute interval between 09h 30m and 09h 35m UT. In this period an observed total count of 91 meteor events was recorded. After correction for 'deadtime', this gave a total corrected count of 150 events. It is evident from Figure 4b that no meteor shower was observed during the same period on the following day. Indeed, recordings made throughout 7 and 9 October 1985 showed no evidence of any unusual meteor activity.

Various observational factors affect the number of shower meteors which can be detected, in a given time period, by the scattering of radio waves from ionized meteor trails. The relevant factors in the case of forward scattering, where the transmitter and receiver are widely separated, are expressed approximately as functions of the position of the shower radiant. In combination, they provide an observational weight factor (called the *observability function*), which may change appreciably as the radiant moves in the course of a day. The consequent predictable variation in the occurrence rate of scattered signals, caused by the method of observation, may then be determined, and distinguished from the variations actually caused by fluctuations in the incidence rate of shower meteors.

At 15-minute intervals throughout 8 October 1985, the altitude and azimuth of the theoretical Giacobinid radiant were calculated for a location on the Earth's surface at the mid-point of the transmitter–receiver path. The derived altitudes were then corrected for zenithal attraction,[3] which is a significant factor for the Giacobinid shower on account of the low geocentric velocity of the incoming meteoroids (20.4 kilometres per second). Using the corrected radiant altitude, and the difference between its azimuth and the azimuth of the transmitter from the mid-point of the transmitter–receiver path, it was possible to calculate the observability function for the shower. This was found to maximize just after 19h 35m UT and to be near zero between about 12h 15m and 15h 45m UT. During this latter period the azimuth

3. Zenithal attraction causes the observed radiants for meteors to appear closer to the zenith than their true position. It occurs because meteoroids entering the upper atmosphere are subject to the Earth's gravitational pull, which increases their geocentric velocities. The change in apparent orbital velocity is most evident for slow meteoroids, such as the Giacobinids.

of the apparent shower radiant was very nearly equal to the azimuth of the transmitter from the transmitter–receiver path mid-point. At this time very few meteor trails were potentially observable.

The net Giacobinid meteor flux was estimated by subtracting from the total meteor counts obtained on 8 October (Figure 4a) the sporadic meteor counts observed on 9 October (Figure 4b). The sporadic meteor data were smoothed by using a running mean of six 5-minute intervals. For each 5-minute period, the net shower count was divided by the relevant value of the observability function to obtain the estimated true shower count. These values are shown in Figure 5. The large error bars on the shower counts approaching 12h 00m UT are due to the fact that the observability function is becoming small, and the shower counts are based on only small net numbers of shower meteors. No meaningful values could be obtained between about 12h 15m and 15h 45m UT, because the observability function was either extremely small or zero. The chart record for 8 October showed that after 16h 00m UT, when the observability function had once again risen to an 'acceptable' value, Giacobinid meteor activity had fallen to a very low level, and total meteor counts were comparable with the background levels of 7 and 9 October.

DRACONID ACTIVITY IN 1985

It is clear from Figure 5 that, contrary to many expectations, a short-lived outburst of Giacobinid meteoroids took place on 8 October 1985. Although in no way comparable to the meteor storms of 1933 and 1946, it was probably similar to the display in 1952. In 1985, a steady rise in Giacobinid activity began shortly after 08h 15m UT, reaching a maximum in the 5-minute interval between 09h 30m and 09h 35m UT. Near the peak, the variation in Giacobinid rates was rapid. This means that peak rates calculated by averaging over short time periods are greatly affected by the length of time period chosen. In the present work the shower rate at maximum was determined by averaging over a 5-minute interval centred on 09h 32.5m UT. After subtraction of the sporadic flux, a maximum net shower count of 131 was obtained. On dividing this number by the derived value of the observability function, a calculated peak count of 186 ± 22 Giacobinid meteors over the 5-minute period was determined. This is equivalent to a peak hourly rate

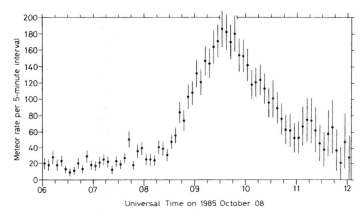

Figure 5. Calculated Giacobinid (Draconid) radio meteor rates (five-minute counts) recorded on 8 October 1985 using the forward scattering of radio waves at 70.31 MHz. These data have been corrected for 'dead time' in the recording apparatus, the sporadic background has been subtracted and the observability function for the given transmitter–receiver path applied to the data. The shower peaked at 09h 35m UT, but a number of smaller, sub-peaks may be discerned in the data. (Plots courtesy of the author.)

of 2,232 meteors per hour. The sporadic meteor rate at this time found by observations with the same equipment was 228 meteors per hour. This indicates that the peak shower rate was roughly ten times the level of background meteor activity.

The Giacobinid maximum in Figure 5 is slightly asymmetric, with the rise to the peak being slightly more rapid than the decline. Owing to this skewness, the time of shower maximum was calculated from a weighted mean of the eight shower counts made between 09h 15m and 09h 55m UT. This gave the time of the peak as 09h 35 ± 1m UT, equivalent to a solar longitude of 195°.255 (epoch 2000.0). There is some evidence for a double peak with a noticeable dip in activity between 09h 40m and 09h 45m UT, followed by a slight recovery in the next 5-minute interval, and then a steady decline. By 12h 00m UT shower rates had subsided to a level comparable with the background level.

Prior to 08h 30m UT there were a number of very short-lived bursts in shower activity, lasting 1–3 minutes. The most significant was in the interval between 07h 41m and 07h 44m UT, when a total observed count of 31 meteors was obtained. This corresponded to a 5-minute count of 52 meteors (65 after correction for 'dead-time') and an estimated Giacobinid 5-minute count of 67 meteors. The values plotted in Figures 4 and 5 are counts over the full 5-minute period.

A characteristic of Giacobinid activity in 1933, 1946 and 1952 was the remarkably short total duration of the showers. For these three cases the estimated duration of the display was 3h 15m, 3h 30m and 2h 30m, respectively. The 1985 shower lasted from about 08h 30m to 11h 45m UT, an interval of 3h 15m, in good agreement with earlier returns. All these results indicate that the densest part of the Giacobinid meteoroid stream is no more than about 375,000 kilometres across.

At the time, the 1985 Giacobinid shower was unique among the observed displays of this stream in that shower maximum did not occur when the Earth reached the descending node of the parent comet, but 3h 40m earlier, corresponding to a difference in solar longitude of 0°.15. This displacement of the core of the meteoroid stream out of the plane of the comet's orbit must have resulted from perturbations at an earlier close approach of the particles to the planet Jupiter. It is clearly important that during future expected returns of this stream, would-be observers monitor its activity for a reasonable period both before and after the Earth reaches the nodal point.

Radar observations of the 1985 Giacobinid display were made from stations at Ottawa, Onsala, Ondrejov and Dushanbe. Results of investigations at Onsala have been reported by Bertil-Anders Lindblad of the Lund Observatory, Sweden, who obtained a maximum zenithal Giacobinid rate of 667 meteors per hour in the 5-minute interval from 09h 30m to 09h 35m UT on 8 October, in excellent agreement with the author's work. Studies at the Ondrejov Observatory have been summarized by Milos Simek. Unfortunately, owing to various difficulties, no observations were made between 05h 30m and 09h 55m UT on 8 October, and it seems that the main peak was missed.

Maximum in 1985 occurred during daylight hours as seen from Europe, but the fall from the peak was witnessed by visual observers in the Pacific area and Japan, although hampered initially by twilight. Observations communicated by Masahiro Koseki of the Nippon Meteor Society and others show that an extensive display was visible from Japan shortly after dusk (local time) on 8 October. Results indicated that Giacobinid rates fell from about 300 meteors per hour at 09h 45m UT to 20 meteors per hour by 12h 15m UT. The radio observations show that the main peak occurred before 09h 45m UT, but earlier visual observations were seriously hampered by the brightness of the evening twilight sky.

DUST TRAIL MODELS: A RADICAL NEW APPROACH

In the years between the 1985 Giacobinid outburst and the anticipated display thirteen years later, in 1998, there was a very significant change in our view of how the dust is distributed around a periodic comet. In the older view, the dust was considered to be spread around the comet in a sort of inhomogeneous 'cloud', both behind and ahead of the parent comet's nucleus, and some way inside and outside of the comet's orbit. Such a view suggested that major Giacobinid meteor showers occur if (1) the Earth closely follows the comet to the comet's descending node; (2) the Earth passes very close to the comet's orbit; and (3) the Earth passes inside the comet's orbit at the node. Although all three of these criteria were satisfied in the 'storm' years of 1933 and 1946, this rather simplistic model could not explain certain anomalies, such as the lack of any significant shower in 1972, and the unexpected outburst in 1985.

In 1985, during investigations of another meteor shower which produces great outbursts in activity when the parent comet is nearby – the Leonids of mid-November – E. D. Kondrat'eva and E. A. Reznikov of Kazan State University put forward a new idea for predicting the sharpest storms and outbursts in meteor showers – the dust trail model. Each time that an active comet returns to perihelion, meteoroids are released into a range of orbits with parameters close to, but not identical to, those of the parent comet. The range in orbital periods of the ejected dust particles soon causes them to stretch out into a long, narrow dust trail, successive trails being created at each perihelion passage of the comet. Even during a single revolution, the orbits of the individual meteoroids are subject to gravitational perturbations. The key idea in these dust trail models is that these perturbations are a function *only* of position along the dust trail, being the same for all particles within the trail cross section at a given position along the trail.

A set of particles at a particular location along a trail will have the same orbital periods, but their other orbital elements can differ owing to the range of ejection velocities from the cometary nucleus. This leads to broadening of the trail, but its width will still be much less than the trail's length, although greater than the diameter of the Earth. A single trail will also be much narrower than the width of the entire meteoroid stream produced by the parent comet. Consequently, after a comet has returned many times to perihelion, the stream will consists of a large number of separate individual dust trails. It depends upon which (if any) of these trails the Earth intersects, near to the nodal crossing point, as to the strength of the outburst that will be observed. It should also be noted that older dust trails have a tendency to be broader, more diffuse and consequently yielding lower meteor rates than younger, narrower and more concentrated trails.

It was Kondrat'eva and Reznikov's breakthrough paper in 1985 that tied particular meteor storms to dust ejected at specific returns of the parent comet. Some time after the publication (in Russian) of this paper, several other workers quite independently came up with the same idea, most notably David Asher of Armagh Observatory, Northern Ireland, and Robert H. McNaught, Research School of Astronomy and Astrophysics, Australian National University, who applied the theory with stunning accuracy to the Leonid meteor storm

Figure 6. Proof of the accuracy of the dust trail model was provided in dramatic fashion when the Leonid meteor storm of 18 November 1999 peaked within ±5 minutes of the time predicted by David Asher and Robert McNaught. Here, above the Sinai Desert in Egypt, Leonid meteors radiate out from the Sickle of Leo. (Image courtesy of Dr Nigel Evans.)

of 18 November 1999 (Figure 6), predicting the time of the outburst to within ±5 minutes – a really quite remarkable achievement and a clear demonstration of the power of the dust trail model.

According to Asher, to determine when an outburst might occur one needs only to know the time when the particles were ejected from the parent comet and a later time when the Earth passes through the stream. The trail will produce an outburst at this later time if the result of planetary perturbations has been to bring the node of the trail particle precisely to Earth intersection, rather than the node being inside or outside Earth's orbit. Only one value of the orbital period allows particles to reach their node at the time when the Earth passes through the stream. The trick with dust trail calculations is to iteratively find the value of this period and then calculate the perturbations on just one representative particle with that period.

THE DRACONIDS IN 1998 AND 2005

In 1993, Reznikov applied the dust trail theory to the return of the Giacobinids in 1998. On this occasion, the Earth was expected to pass 0.0383 AU (5.7 million kilometres) inside the descending node of the comet's orbit at about 20h 50m UT on 8 October, some 92 days after the comet had passed the same point. (Figure 7 shows the parent comet at its return in 1998.) Reznikov boldly predicted that an outburst would occur at a time very different from the nodal crossing of the comet's orbit and therefore quite distinct from many other people's forecasts. Also in 1993, Lubor Kresák had estimated the time of the peak to be 17h 45m UT. As it turned out, there was no peak at this time, nor at the time the Earth was closest to the descending node; the peak actually occurred between 13h 10m and 13h 20m UT, very close to Reznikov's prediction. The dust trail model had notched up another success, with most of the activity in 1998 being due to dust released at the 1926 return of the comet.

The timing of the peak once again favoured observers in the Far East, as had been the case thirteen years earlier, but moonlight was a problem from mid-evening onwards with a waning gibbous Moon in Taurus. Visual and intensified video observations from Japan and China indicated a peak ZHR of 500–700 meteors per hour at around 13h 15m UT. Milos Simek and P. Pecina reported backscatter radar

Figure 7. Comet 21P/Giacobini-Zinner imaged on 25 October 1998 by Martin Mobberley from Suffolk using a 30-cm LX200 and ST7 CCD camera. The field of view is 16 × 11 arcminutes. North is up.

observations using the meteor radar at the Ondrejov Observatory. Meteor activity started to become more pronounced at about 11h UT, rising steeply after 12h 30m UT. A maximum hourly echo rate of 492 meteors per hour for durations greater than 0.4 seconds was recorded in the ten-minute interval centred at 13h 15m UT. Activity then initially declined but there appeared to be a secondary peak (with an hourly echo rate of 320 meteors per hour) at around 14h 15m UT. As darkness fell over Europe that evening, visual observers reported Draconid ZHRs of only about ten meteors per hour, so the display had greatly subsided by then. The shower was reported to be rich in faint meteors, mostly in the 3rd to 4th magnitude range.

In October 2005, the Earth again passed through the Giacobinid meteoroid swarm, ninety-two days after the comet reached the descending node, but the 'miss' distance was not particularly close, being 0.043 AU (6.4 million kilometres) inside the comet's orbit. In fact, this geometry was only slightly worse than that pertaining in 1985 – lagging farther behind the comet and slightly farther inside the orbit – so a shower was certainly possible. Calculations made using the dust trail model did not turn up any encounters with dust released during any fairly recent perihelion passages of the parent comet, so no major outburst seemed likely. In the event, only very modest activity was detected by meteor radars and visual observers between about 14h 30m and 18h 00m UT on 8 October 2005, with peak activity occurring at around 16h 05m UT. The equivalent ZHR for the meteoroids detected by radar was about 160 meteors per hour, while visual observers in Asia, Europe and North America observing during the same period recorded a peak ZHR of around 40 meteors per hour. In essence the shower was similar to that seen by radar in 1952 and visually in 1926. Calculations by Jeremie Vaubaillon of the Institut de Mécanique Celeste et de Calcul des Ephemerides (IMCCE), Paris, and colleagues at the University of Western Ontario in Canada showed that the 2005 Draconid shower was due to the 1946 dust trail, the shower being rich in faint meteors producing higher activity in the radar data than in the visual observations.

AND WHAT OF THE FUTURE?

Table 1 below summarizes the eight Giacobinid showers observed to date. The values given for the peak ZHR are only approximate, particularly for the great Draconid 'storms' of 1933 and 1946.

Table 1. Observed Draconid showers or storms

Date	C-E (AU)	Earth at node	ZHR (metres per hour)
9 October 1926	+0.0005	69.1 before	~17
9 October 1933	+0.0054	80.2 after	~6,000
10 October 1946	+0.0015	15.4 after	~5,000
9 October 1952	−0.0057	195.5 before	~180
8 October 1972	−0.00074	58.5 after	very low!
8 October 1985	+0.0329	27.2 after	~700
8 October 1998	+0.0383	49.5 before	~500
8 October 2005	+0.043	91.8 after	~160

'C-E' is the minimum distance between the comet's orbit and the Earth's orbit at the descending node (denoting the Earth outside, and + inside the comet's orbit). 'Earth at node' is the number of days before or after the comet that the Earth passed the node. (Reproduced courtesy of Nick James of the BAA.)

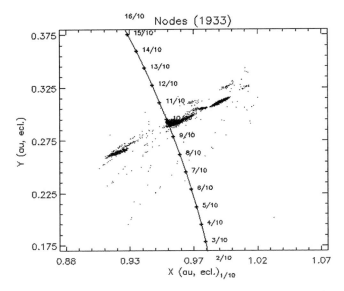

Figure 8. Plots showing dust trails produced by meteoroids ejected by comet 21P/Giacobini-Zinner in the vicinity of Earth's orbit as it traversed the region close to the descending node of the comet's orbit in early/mid-October 1933 and 1946 – a (panel above) and b (panel on opposite page), respectively. The path of the Earth through the dust trails is shown by the line curving from bottom to top, with tick marks showing the date at daily intervals. The outbursts in these two years were primarily due to the 1900 and 1907 dust trails. (Plots courtesy of Jeremie Vaubaillon, Institut de Mécanique Celeste et de Calcul des Ephemerides (IMCCE), Paris; numerical simulations supported by CINES and CNRS.)

Studies of all the significant Giacobinid displays have been carried out by Jeremie Vaubaillon using the dust trail theory (see http://www.imcce.fr/en/ephemerides/phenomenes/meteor/predictions_request.php ?name=Draconids). He found that it is essential to include a large enough number of old dust trails to be able to explain all of the observed Giacobinid showers using the model. In his studies he includes all dust trails going back to the 1596 return of the parent comet. Reznikov determined that the 1900 and 1907 dust trails were responsible for the 1933 and 1946 Draconid outbursts, each of which is a narrow expanse of dust now displaced from the current position of the comet (Figures 8a and 8b). Reznikov could not explain the unexpected 1985 shower, but that

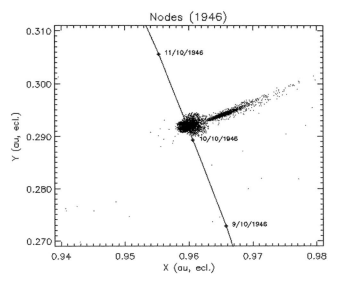

Nodes (1946)

was simply because he did not include old enough dust trails. It turns out that the 1887 and 1894 dust trails (and maybe even older filaments) were mainly behind the 1985 outburst, with a contribution from the very thin 1946 trail also detected. Trails with a different perturbation history have a quite different width; some are very thin, while others are quite broad.

In October 2011 there is, once again, the likelihood of a Giacobinid shower. The parent comet returns to perihelion on 11 February 2012 and reaches the descending node 6.06 days later on 17 February. On 8 October 2011 the Earth will pass close to the node 132 days before the comet and on the face of it the chances of a great shower do not seem particularly high. However, calculations using the dust trail model, by many different workers, have indicated that there is a very good chance of a significant outburst that day, with the Earth coming close to a group of rather old trails (Figure 9). The closest encounters will be with the 1880, 1887, 1894 and 1900 dust trails, with miss distances of between 0.0009 AU (1887) and 0.00136 AU (1900).

Overall, Draconid activity is likely to peak somewhere between 16h and 22h UT on 8 October 2011, with the period between 19h and 21h most likely to yield the greatest activity. This means that longitudes in Eastern Europe and the Middle East will be favoured, although it will

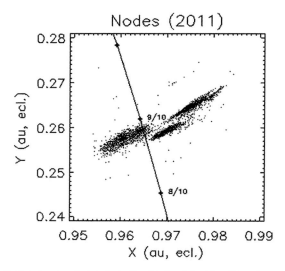

Figure 9. Plot showing dust trails in the vicinity of Earth's orbit as it traverses the region close to the descending node of comet 21P/Giacobini-Zinner on 8 and 9 October 2011. The tick marks are at 00h UT on the dates in question. It can be seen that the Earth is likely to encounter the dust from several rather old trails between 16h and 22h UT on 8 October. (Plot courtesy of Jeremie Vaubaillon, Institut de Mécanique Celeste et de Calcul des Ephemerides (IMCCE), Paris; numerical simulations supported by CINES and CNRS.)

be essential for would-be observers to be far enough north to ensure that the radiant is at a respectable altitude above the horizon during the period of potential activity. Interestingly, there is a very considerable spread in the predicted peak rates for the October 2011 Draconids spanning over an order of magnitude, with the maximum ZHR ranging from a few tens of meteors per hour to several hundred, as viewed by a single observer. The only way to find out what happens is to go out and look for yourself!

Unfortunately, there will be a waxing gibbous Moon in Aquarius, less than four days from full, so there will some interference from moonlight. Observers are therefore advised to direct their gaze to the northern half of the sky, keeping the Moon behind them. The radiant of the shower will be centred on RA 17h 32m, Dec. +55.5°, not far from the star Nu Draconis in the 'head' of Draco. Throughout the period of likely activity of the shower (16h to 22h UT), the radiant will be at a respectable altitude above the north-western horizon – and it is on a Saturday evening. Let us hope for clear skies across northern and eastern Europe on 8 October 2011.

EPILOGUE

And, whatever happens in 2011, Earth will be passing the descending node of comet 21P/Giacobini-Zinner in 2018, only 22.7 days after the comet itself has passed by this same point. On this occasion, the minimum separation between the respective orbits of Earth and the comet will be 0.017 AU, which is somewhere between the situation that produced the great storm over Europe in 1933 and the outstanding shower over Japan in 1985. But we shall have to await accurate predictions using the dust trail model for a clearer view of what might happen then.

The Librations of the Moon

PAUL G. ABEL

The Moon is our nearest neighbour in space. Its orbit is gravitationally tidally locked to the Earth; this means that the same face is always turned towards us as it orbits the Earth. What many people do not realize is that, surprisingly, we can see more than 50 per cent of the lunar surface from Earth; in fact a total of 59 per cent (although no more than 50 per cent at any one time) of the lunar surface is visible due to an effect called *libration*. Libration has the effect of bringing objects on the far side of the Moon on to the limb of the near side, and although these features appear foreshortened in a telescope, they can be observed and studied. These objects lie in the so-called *libration zones*, and until the advent of spacecraft, provided tantalizing hints as to what lay on the far side of the Moon.

The libration zones have almost exclusively been the domain of the amateur astronomer, and one astronomer in particular, Patrick Moore, spent much of the 1950s and 1960s mapping these regions. While it is true that, thanks to spacecraft, Moon mapping is now essentially complete, this does not mean that there is nothing for the lunar observer to do. As we shall see, the amateur can embark on long-period studies of the features in the libration zones, and make a real contribution to our understanding of our nearby neighbour.

I have split the rest of the article into four sections. In the next section we shall look at what librations are and why they occur, and this is best done by looking at the orbit of the Moon. In the section after that, I have given some ideas for the sort of long-term studies on which the amateur may wish to embark. This is not an exhaustive list by any means, and examples of many good programmes of study can be found in the British Astronomical Association (BAA) Lunar Section observing programme. In the last section I have included maps of the libration zones. I am most grateful to Peter Grego of the BAA's Lunar Section who compiled and provided the libration charts. There are eight charts in total covering all of the libration areas, and I have given a brief discussion of various features in each of these charts.

Let us now look at some simple celestial mechanics and try to understand why the librations of the Moon occur.

THE LUNAR ORBIT

The Moon orbits the Earth once every 27.3 days. This is known as a *sidereal month*. During this time, it travels along or very near to the ecliptic – the path marked out by the Sun as it moves through the various constellations of the Zodiac.

In Figure 1, the Moon's orbit about the Earth is given. The orbit is not quite circular; it has a small eccentricity (the amount an ellipse deviates from a circle) of 0.05. In the diagram, the sunlight is coming in from the left, and the Moon's position at various points in the orbit is shown.

Starting at Position 1, the Moon is effectively between the Sun and the Earth and the Moon is said to be *new* and is not visible. The Moon then moves around in its orbit to Position 2, during which time it appears in the evening sky as a *waxing crescent*. This continues until Position 3 is reached; we have a *half-moon* in the evening sky (this

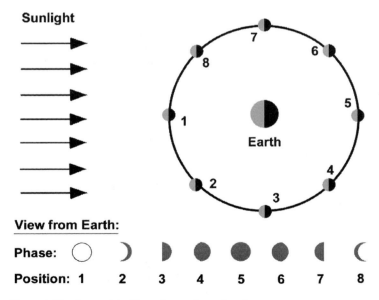

Figure 1. The phases of the Moon. See text for explanation.

phase is also known as the *first quarter* since, as viewed from Earth, a quarter of the lunar surface is illuminated). At Position 4, the Moon is now in its *waxing gibbous* phase which continues until *full moon* at Position 5. After this the phase starts to decrease, and at Position 6 it is a *waning gibbous* until the phase arrives at the *last quarter* where it is at Position 7. The phase continues to decrease still further and the Moon appears to Earth as a *waning crescent* in Position 8, and this continues until it becomes *new* again and the whole cycle is repeated.

Although a sidereal month is 27.3 days long, it takes slightly longer that this for the phases given in Figure 1 to occur. In fact, it takes a total of 29.3 days for the phases 1 to 8 to occur and this period of time is known as a *synodic month*. The reason a synodic month is longer than a sidereal month is because the Earth is not stationary in space; it moves around the Sun and so the direction of the sunlight shown in Figure 1 is not constant. This means that we have moved around the Sun a little by the time we have passed from one new moon to the next, and so it takes a little longer than the 27.3 days to get from one new moon to the next.

So, what of librations? There are three types of libration: *longi-tudinal*, *diurnal* and *latitudinal*. Diurnal librations are brought about by small oscillations in the Earth's orbit and latitudinal ones are the result of the Moon's axis rotation and the fact that its orbit is inclined to the ecliptic by more than 5°. It is the longitudinal librations that are of interest to us, and these librations are the direct result of the Moon's orbit around the Earth being slightly eccentric rather than perfectly circular.

As mentioned earlier, the Moon's orbit is gravitationally tidally locked so its rotational period is the same as its orbital period, and if its orbit was completely circular, there would be no librations. Now, imagine a lunar crater on the central meridian (CM) – an imaginary line running down the centre of the Moon's disk from pole to pole. If the Moon's orbit was perfectly circular, then the crater would always be in exactly the same position on the CM as the Moon went around the Earth. However, the eccentricity of the lunar orbit means that there are sometimes lags or leads in the rotation and so the crater would appear to wobble to and fro about a mean position, and it is during these 'wobbles' that we get to see parts of the far side of the lunar surface. The effect can be quite noticeable; just watch how the position of the Mare Crisium can vary over the course of a year: sometimes it is near the limb and other times it can be well placed on the lunar disk.

Although the mathematics which models librations is rather complex, it is nonetheless well understood and so librations are entirely predictable; such predictions can be found in the *Handbook of the British Astronomical Association*, the WinJUPOS program and elsewhere. In a general prediction you will find the date on which a libration occurs, the size of the libration (given in degrees) and the position angle/direction of the libration. This is usually measured eastwards (anticlockwise) from the north point of the lunar disk.

OBSERVATIONS OF THE LIBRATION REGIONS

There are many types of observation the amateur can carry out, and I shall give an overview of some of them here. These observations are essentially topographic in nature and are primarily concerned with observing specific regions or features over long periods of time to determine how they appear under different angles of illumination. Broadly speaking, we have the following classes of observation.

Low-Light Studies. In general lunar observers tend to make observations of craters and other surface features when the terminator is on or near the feature in question. In the case of low-light studies, the Sun makes a low angle to the feature to be observed. This means the object will cast long shadows (i.e. if it is a crater, the floor will be filled with shadow cast by the crater walls). Spacecraft data are rather poor in this area since spacecraft tend to image lunar features when the Sun is high above them with very little or no shadow. Much useful information can be gleaned about the topography of features during low-light studies; trenches and the like can be put into sharp relief under such lighting.

High-Light Studies. During high-light observations of a feature, the Sun is practically overhead and so little or no shadow is cast. Of course this is absolutely the worst time to learn your way around an unfamiliar lunar feature or region since everything will be bleached out and the details of features will be rather difficult to discern. Certain features, however, actually come out rather well under such lighting. In particular, rays and albedo features show up well under this lighting, and if they have been missed previously, their existence will be revealed.

Transient Lunar Phenomena (TLP). TLP are short-lived glows (often reddish), obscurations, brightenings or other changes in the appearance of the lunar surface. TLP are somewhat controversial although reports of such phenomena on the Moon go back over 1,000 years, with some events being observed independently by multiple witnesses or reputable scientists. Nevertheless, the majority of TLP reports are irreproducible and there is insufficient data to distinguish between alternative hypotheses. On the near side of the Moon, the crater Aristarchus seems to be a particularly active region for reported TLP. It is worth monitoring the features within the libration zones to see if there are any TLP 'hotspots' there.

MAKING AN OBSERVATION

Clearly, observing features in the libration zones is more difficult than observing near-side lunar features. Probably the best method is to choose a region or feature which interests you and work out when a suitable libration will carry it round on to the near side of the disk. This can be done by checking the *BAA Handbook* or using the WinJUPOS program. You can then make a detailed observation of the feature concerned, and observe it under various conditions of lighting, thus becoming completely familiar with its appearance at all angles of illumination.

Remember when you make an observation to include the date, time, telescope and magnification used, along with the seeing conditions. It is also a good idea to put on the co-longitude at the start and end of your observation as this tells you where the terminator is located during your observations. If you are going to make a drawing of a feature, it is best to start with a small feature. Often newcomers start with a massive area; this is a mistake simply because of the very considerable amount of detail that will be observed! Do not make your drawing too small either; draw it fairly large on a piece of A4 paper to make sure you get the proportions and details correct. I have a notebook for lunar observations as it is handy to have them all in one place; loose sheets are bound to become lost!

One more thing: there is little point in your observations just taking up room on your hard-drive or in a bookcase. Send them in to the BAA Lunar Section and the ALPO where they can be put to good use. Let us now go on to look at the lunar libration zones in detail.

MAP 1: NW LIMB

85°N to 45°N

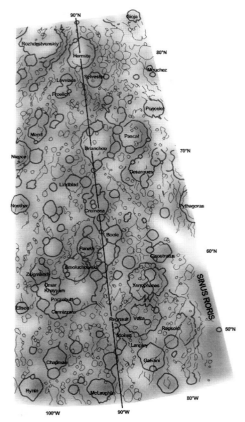

Brianchan Crater. This crater is 145 km wide and like Xenophones crater, is badly eroded due to violent impacts which have occurred after its formation. Many small craters can be found on its floor.

Rozhdestvenskiy Crater. A large crater classified as a walled plain. If you look to the north-west you will observe a series of small craters which forms a valley encroaching on the rim of this crater.

Sinus Roris. Only part of this bay is in the libration zone and the only way to view it completely is from spacecraft data. Its boundaries are rather indistinct.

Xenophones Crater. A crater some 125 km wide and around 3.2 km deep. It is clearly an old structure which has been badly worn and eroded. The floor is composed of dark basaltic lava.

MAP 2: NE LIMB

85°N to 45°N

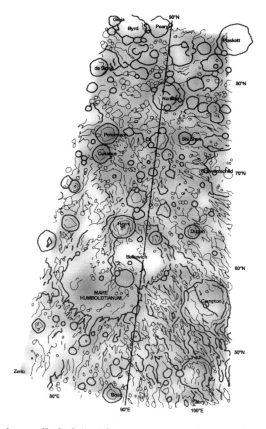

Belkovich Crater. Another walled plain. The crater encroaches on the north-east edge of the Mare Humboldtianum.

Compton Crater. A rather prominent, roughly circular crater 162 km wide. A formation of mountains marks the centre of the crater, which has partially terraced walls.

De Sitter Crater. This crater forms an unusual crater cluster consisting of satellite craters De Sitter L and M. The interior of De Sitter is rather irregular and hilly.

Mare Humboldtianum. An interesting mare located in the Humboldtianum basin. The floor is rather dark.

MAP 3: NE LIMB

45°N to 0°N

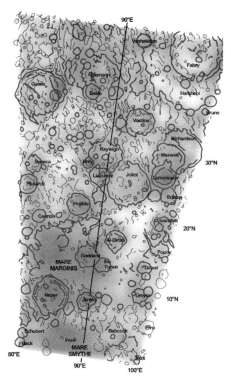

Gauss Crater. Another large walled plain which has no central hill or mountain.

Joliot Crater. A huge impact crater 164 km wide. Part of the floor contains ray material from Bruno crater off to the north-east.

Mare Marginis. A different mare to the rest in that it is rather irregular in shape. The surface of this mare displays some unusual bright spiral albedo markings, whose origin is still not understood.

Maxwell Crater. Interesting crater whose floor has been partially flooded by the encroaching Lomonosov crater. Maxwell itself is part of the larger Richardson crater.

MAP 4: SE LIMB

0°S to 45°S

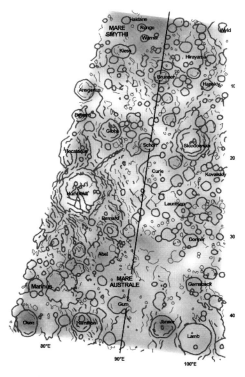

Gibbs Crater. An interesting shaped crater which has a distinctive 'bulge' on the north wall.

Humboldt Crater. An impressive crater some 207 km wide. The floor contains a number of fascinating features such as clefts and cracks which seem to form a series of radial spokes.

Mare Australe. Another unusual mare with a rather uneven floor which contains a number of impact craters including Lyot crater (Map 5).

Mare Smythii. This is located on the equator within the Smythii basin and is fairly well defined.

MAP 5: SE LIMB

45°S to 85°S

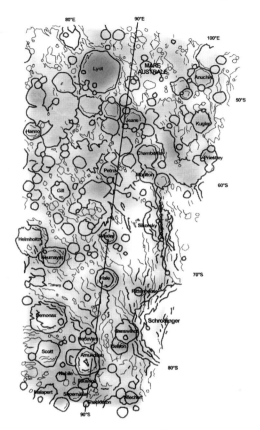

Hale Crater. A well-defined lunar crater whose lack of erosion on the wall suggests this is a relatively young lunar crater.

Lyot. A large impact crater within the Mare Australe. Its floor is rather dark and the rim of the crater is eroded. A number of small craters are present in the south-west floor.

Schrödinger. A vast walled plain, only partially visible from Earth. Spacecraft have revealed it to be a large impressive structure with a well-defined rim, terraced walls and an irregular outer rampart.

Sikorsky. Lies just to the north-west of the huge walled plain Schrödinger. There is a 310-km gorge in the middle of the crater known as the Vallis Schrödinger.

MAP 6: SW LIMB

45°S to 85°

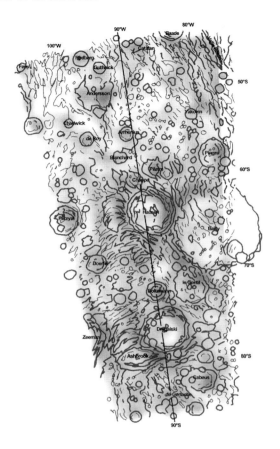

Bailly. The largest crater on the visible side of the Moon, some 300 km in diameter. The floor of the crater is rather uneven and contains a number of small craters.

Drygalski. A large impact crater lying close to the eternally dark southern polar craters. The outer rim of the crater is rather mountainous and eroded due to impacts.

Guthnick Crater. This crater is situated in a large portion of the ejecta material which surrounds the vast Mare Orientale basin. Just to the north-west lies the crater Rydberg.

Hausen. Another vast crater. The walls of this crater are terraced and the centre is marked by a series of complex peaks.

MAP 7: SW LIMB

0°S to 45°S

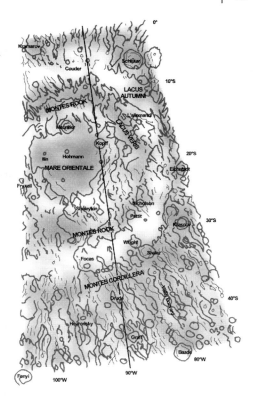

Montes Cordillera. A large mountain range which surrounds the Mare Orientale.

Mare Orientale. A stunning, vast, ringed formation only partially visible from Earth, and some 900 km wide at its widest point. It is clearly the result of a large asteroid impact on the lunar surface.

Montes Rook. A vast ring of mountains which completely encloses the Mare Orientale. Closer inspection will reveal the range to be a double-ringed formation.

Schulter Crater. A nearly circular crater with a dark floor. A small rille can be found close to the inner north-west wall.

MAP 8: NW LIMB

45°N to 0°N

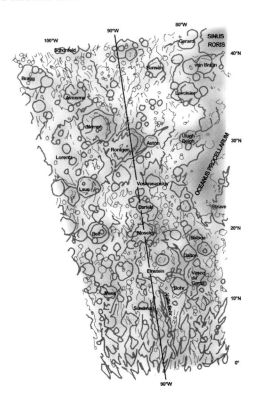

Einstein Crater. Discovered by Patrick Moore in 1952. This crater is a large walled plain whose rim has been almost completely destroyed. Several small craters can be found on its floor.

Lavoisier. This is a fairly eroded crater formation with many satellite craters situated on the rim. The floor contains a notable curving ridge along with several rilles.

Nernst. A large impact crater situated in the Lorentz walled plain.

Vallis Bohr. A long valley located south of Einstein crater, extending for about 810 km.

FURTHER READING

BAA Lunar Section website: http://www.baalunarsection.org.uk/
Handbook of the British Astronomical Association:
  http://www.britastro.org/
WinJUPOS program: http://www.grischa-hahn.homepage.
  t-online.de/astro/winjupos/index.htm.
P. Moore, *Patrick Moore on the Moon*, Cassell & Co, 2001.

Astronomy and the Early Royal Society

ALLAN CHAPMAN

On 28 November 1660, a body of scientific friends came together at Gresham College, in Bishopsgate, in the City of London. They were already, in many ways, an established group, for most of them were members of a 'Philosophical', or scientific, 'Club' that had been meeting regularly in Oxford for the past ten years. What they shared, however, was a belief that all branches of the natural world, from medicine to cosmology, could be opened up and advanced by the 'experimental method', using refined instruments such as telescopes, microscopes, vacuum pumps, barometers and clocks, and new laboratory techniques, instruments which Robert Hooke in 1665 described as 'artificial organs', that strengthened our natural organs of sight and perception.

One science in particular was high on their agenda, however, not only because it was already the most advanced of the then known sciences, and was moving forward faster than all the others, but because it offered enormous practical benefits if it could be developed further. And that science was astronomy.

In November 1660, the country was beginning to find its feet again after 18 years of civil war and political chaos, the execution of King Charles I and an unpopular spell of rigid Puritan rule. For in May 1660, the monarchy had been triumphantly restored, with the thirty-year-old King Charles II ascending the throne. Charles II was clearly going to do his best to stabilize and unify the nation, and, among other things, he had a good brain and a genuine interest in science. The scientific friends turned to the new king for support and possible patronage, and soon after, His Majesty granted them two Royal Charters of Incorporation, some ceremonial regalia (but no money, as His Majesty was broke) and the right to call themselves the Royal Society.

Few people today would recognize the names of most of the astronomers who helped to make up the Royal Society's first Fellowship:

men like the Revd Drs John Wilkins, Seth Ward and John Wallis, and Sir Jonas Moore and Sir Paul Neile. Yet everyone knows Dr Christopher Wren (knighted in 1673), who was already an astronomer of Europe-wide reputation before his subsequent fame as an architect eclipsed it. For in 1660, Wren was Professor of Astronomy at Gresham College, London, and soon after would return to Oxford to become the university's Savilian Professor of Astronomy: a post which he held in tandem for years with that of Surveyor, or Architect, to the king. And soon after the Society was constituted, Wren's younger friend, Robert Hooke, became its Curator of Experiments and a Fellow, and then, in 1677, the man who had recently become the first Astronomer Royal, the Revd John Flamsteed, would be elected to the Fellowship.

Sir Jonas Moore (knighted in 1673), however, was a pivotal figure in the astronomical and mathematical world of the day, and was elected to the Royal Society in 1674. As a young man in his native Lancashire, Moore had been a mathematical teacher, and played a major rôle in helping to preserve the papers of those celebrated three north-country astronomers Jeremiah Horrocks, William Crabtree and William Gascoigne, all of whom were, tragically, dead by 1644, and was also connected with Charles, Christopher and Richard Townley of the same county. During the Civil War Moore had worked as a civil engineer, draining the Norfolk fens, and had in addition been Tutor in Arithmetic to the Duke of York, the future King Charles II's younger brother; and at the Restoration in 1660 he was a figure of some importance and a friend of His Majesty. Yet he still retained an active interest in astronomy, ensuring that the highly original work of Horrocks, Crabtree and Gascoigne was recognized both by the early Royal Society and by continental astronomers after 1660; he also observed an eclipse of the Moon with Hooke on 1 January 1675, and played a decisive rôle in the founding of the Royal Observatory, Greenwich, in the same year.

Long before 1660, indeed, astronomy had been a thoroughly international science, with its roots lying in ancient Greece. Tycho Brahe and Galileo, who died respectively in 1601 and 1642, had enduring formidable reputations as exponents of the 'new' type of research astronomy. Central to this 'new' astronomy was original observation of the heavens with precision instruments, and in the case of Galileo and his successors, with telescopes. And on the contemporary European scene in the 1660s there were several major figures such as Christiaan Huygens in Holland, Johannes Hevelius in Poland, Olaus Rømer in

Denmark, Giovanni Domenico Cassini in Italy (and later in France) and the Frenchman Adrien Auzout, not to mention the recently deceased Father Pierre Gassendi in France, who had first observed a Mercury transit by telescopic projection in 1631. What is more, astronomy, like the other newly advancing sciences, knew no national boundaries, with people corresponding with each other and comparing instruments and observations across the length and breadth of Europe: Catholics with Protestants, and republicans with monarchists. The celebrated Johannes Kepler (died 1630), the man whose laws of planetary motion had helped revolutionize theoretical astronomy between 1609 and 1620, was a devout Lutheran Protestant, though this did not prevent him from becoming astronomer to the staunchly Catholic Holy Roman Emperor, Rudolf II, in Prague. And what made this possible was a common culture, for while English, Dutch and French might fight like cats and dogs in their wars, what they all shared was an education that was grounded in classical Greek learning, and in the international scholarly language: Latin.

WHAT WERE ASTRONOMERS DISCUSSING IN 1660?

To put the astronomical achievements of the early Royal Society into context, it is first necessary to look at what were the dominant intellectual and technical concerns of both British and European astronomers around 1660. And to understand that, we must realize that astronomy, and the wider repercussions of astronomical discovery, had moved ahead more rapidly during the years between 1609 and 1660 than over any other half-century in history. And that, strange as it may seem, includes any 50-year period during the twentieth century as well. For while twentieth-century astronomy developed at an amazing speed, it has not had such a profound set of implications for our broader cultural understanding as had that of the half-century leading up to 1660.

And central to this transformation was the introduction of the telescope into astronomy in 1609. For while telescopes in 2011 are very much more powerful and versatile (including radio and microwave telescopes) than they were in 1900, we have nonetheless become so accustomed to the wonders of telescopic discovery that we expect them and almost take them for granted. Yet when Thomas Harriot in London, his friends at Trafenti (also Traventi), South Wales, and

Galileo in northern Italy first turned their ×6 magnification telescopes to the Moon in 1609, what they saw was without precedent in human history or experience.

And then two things happened. Firstly, they, and a rapidly growing body of telescope users across Europe, found that not only the Moon, but also the Sun, planets and stars looked radically different through telescopes than they did to the ancestral vision of the naked eye. And secondly, they soon found, after Galileo and probably Harriot had independently discovered the optical principles that lay at the heart of the telescope's ability to magnify images, that it was possible to make a succession of better and more powerful telescopes. Indeed, they had come across a principle that underlies the whole of modern science: namely, improve the technology and you will make fresh discoveries. We take this technologically assisted discovery process so much for granted today that it is hard for us to envisage a time when our five natural and unaided senses imposed an insurmountable limit upon what we could ever know.

One radically new discovery made by the early telescopic astronomers was that the planets were not mere points of light, as they all look to the naked eye, but *spheres*, and even worlds. Even the smallest telescopes showed the Moon to be a world-like place with many features similar to the earth, for as Galileo in particular was at pains to show, it had mountains, plains and a rough, broken surface. It might even have *seas*, containing water; and let us not forget that our modern usage of the word *maria* for the flat, darker areas of the lunar surface comes from the Latin word for sea, first given to them by Galileo. And as Galileo was fascinated by the roughness of the lunar surface, so Harriot made meticulous drawings of the relative positions of what he called the Moon's 'round valleys', or craters. Yet to the naked eye, the Moon looked like the tarnished silvery ball that the ancients thought it was.

And in addition to the Moon, Venus, Jupiter and Saturn all appeared as spheres (Saturn sometimes like a rugby ball) in even the feeblest of telescopes, while Jupiter, the biggest of the spheres, was shown to have four moons rotating around itself, and *not* around the Earth, around which all things were supposed to rotate.

And what about the starry realm itself? When Galileo looked at the Milky Way – which to the naked eye from time immemorial had resembled a faint milky glow – he found it to be made up of countless thousands of individual stars. The seven stars of the Pleiades cluster in

Galileo's telescope suddenly became 36 stars, while Robert Hooke in 1664, using a much more powerful 12-foot-focus telescope, could make out 78 small stars, and with a 36-foot-focus telescope, numerous stars, in the same cluster.

These and other discoveries begged at least three very important questions. Firstly, if the Moon and planets really were spherical worlds, just like the Earth, then were they inhabited? For surely, God would not create habitations without inhabitants, any more than a builder would build houses if there were no one to live in them? But what manner of creatures could they possibly be? Could they even have invented telescopes and be busy looking at us, as the astronomical brothers Christiaan and Constantijn Huygens in Holland speculated? For let us not forget that the fascination with extraterrestrial intelligence is not modern, but goes back almost 400 years.

Secondly, how vast was the stellar universe? For even the earliest telescopes showed starfields upon starfields receding to infinity, as it became clear that the constellations were not all at the same distance from the Earth, and not fixed to the inside of a black sphere, but that this was only a line-of-sight effect caused by the scattering of stars throughout the three-dimensional boundlessness of space. The boundlessness of space, indeed: what a radically different concept of the universe from the enclosed sphere of Aristotle and Ptolemy, which had dominated astronomical thinking from Greek times to the telescopic era.

And thirdly, in the midst of this new cosmological vastness revealed by the telescope, was it still realistic to think of the Earth as the centre around which the Sun, Moon and planets rotated, especially as Galileo had discovered that even the planet Jupiter had four moons rotating around it, and not around the Earth? So did the telescope provide unexpected support for the Copernican theory, as Galileo believed? And could our Sun perhaps be no more than an ordinary star, and could the stars themselves have their own spherical worlds rotating around them?

This is what I meant when I said that astronomy had gone through more profound changes in understanding between 1609 and 1660 than it ever passed through in the twentieth century, for among other things, in this period the Greeks were shown to have got a great deal wrong. And while medieval and Renaissance theologians and philosophers, such as Archbishop Thomas Bradwardine, Cardinal Nicholas of Cusa and Thomas Digges, had speculated about infinity and a 'plurality' of worlds and stars, they had done so imaginatively, within the conventions of theological and philosophical deduction. Yet the telescopic universe was there for the viewing, and while seventeenth-century astronomers wrestled mightily with trying to make sense of, and interpret, what they were seeing, the planetary spheres, the vast starfields and a couple of mysterious misty 'nebulae' (or clouds), in Orion's Sword and in Andromeda in particular, simply begged an explanation.

THE REVD DR JOHN WILKINS AND FLYING TO THE MOON

Without the scientific, and especially the inspirational, genius of John Wilkins, the Royal Society would probably never have come into being. For Wilkins was, in many ways, a larger-than-life figure who, in 1648, had become Warden of Wadham College, Oxford. He was a born communicator, and a true visionary of science, who clearly had the power to captivate and inspire people.

As a young man, Wilkins had become fascinated by astronomy and by the implications of Galileo's telescopic discoveries, and at the age of 24 in 1638 he had published his *Discourse Concerning a New World and Another Planet*. This was the first full-scale treatment and interpretation of Galileo's work to be written in English: written, moreover, in a very straightforward and readable English that was meant to get through to as many people as possible, and not just Latin-literate academics. For in the *Discourse* Wilkins discussed many of the points mentioned above. He took it as axiomatic that the Copernican theory was scientifically correct. On the frontispiece of the book, moreover, Wilkins not only depicted the Sun at the centre of the Solar System, with the Earth and planets turning around it, but included figures of Galileo – holding a telescope – and Copernicus jointly demonstrating the truth of the heliocentric system. And then, in this picture, instead of the stars being drawn upon a sphere, in accordance with the conventional iconography, he showed them as rising forever upwards, to a possibly infinite universe.

But the idea of the planets as *worlds* like our own received a full treatment in the final chapter, or 'Proposition', No. 16. And, so he plausibly argued, could not the ingenuity of modern humans devise a

'Flying Chariot' that might bear intrepid sky-voyagers through the air, and on to the Moon? Indeed, this Chariot or conveyance could be like a small ship, inside of which was a powerful clockwork engine which would operate great wings, to take the machine aloft. What is more, Wilkins's Chariot was not science fiction, but a brilliant exercise in lateral thinking, based on the best science and technology of the age. For geared machines were coming into increasing use in the mid-seventeenth century, and Wilkins was intrigued by the potential of powerful springs. Sailing ships fitted with large wheels were already exceeding speeds of twenty miles per hour across the flat polders of Holland, so why, if they had sufficiently powerful spring-operated wings, should they not take off – and fly on to the Moon? After all, this was the age of great oceanic discovery, when navigators were routinely crossing vast and hitherto unknown oceans in long voyages: so was not flying to a 'world in the Moon' any more than an extension of sailing to China? And when they got to the Moon, would they find 'Selenites' (from the Greek Moon goddess Selene) living there, and could we even *trade* with them?

We know that several of Wilkins's friends in the Oxford Philosophical Club were actively interested in astronomy. In particular, there were the Revd Drs Seth Ward and John Wallis, who between them occupied Oxford's Savilian Professorships in Astronomy and Geometry. Both were first-class mathematicians, while we know that it was Professor Ward who taught Robert Hooke how to make telescopic observations, as well as how to use a simple pendulum to time things accurately. And also part of Wilkins' circle, of course, was the young Dr Christopher Wren. Wren and Hooke had established a lifelong friendship as young men at Oxford, though the slightly older Wren had left Oxford in 1657 to become Professor of Astronomy at Gresham College, in the City of London. However, he came back to Oxford to succeed Seth Ward as Savilian Professor of Astronomy in 1661, when Ward became Bishop of Exeter. And let us not forget that mathematics and geometry were as fundamental to astronomical research in 1660 as they are today. For while the telescope produced a body of thought-changing discoveries in the universe, mathematics, nonetheless, had always been essential to astronomical advancement, for it provided the proofs that gave observations a context within the wider body of knowledge, and an irrefutable foundation that set mathematical astronomy apart from mere interesting speculation. It is not for nothing, therefore, that all of these men – Wilkins, Ward, Wallis, Wren, Hooke and many more – were not only advocates of the 'new', post-Galilean astronomy but also mathematicians of international standing.

THE FIRST 'BIG TELESCOPE' ASTRONOMERS

It took only a few magnifications beyond the power of the naked eye to set in motion the telescopic revolution that began in 1609. For all of these early instruments had very small lenses, with object-glasses rarely more than 1.5 inches across, and 'Galilean' concave eye lenses giving a field of view restricted to 10 arcminutes or so. Magnifications as low as ×6 were common in the early days, though Thomas Harriot had a ×50 magnification by 1611. Yet it was these relatively feeble instruments that first transformed mankind's understanding of the cosmos. These spectacle-lens telescopes, however, had soon revealed to observers everything that could be seen in the sky with such instruments, and major new discoveries had effectively ground to a halt by 1615. What is more, they stayed there until the late 1640s, when new techniques of glass manufacture made it possible to produce good blanks for object-glasses that were two, three or more inches in diameter.

During the 1650s and 1660s the refracting telescope was transformed. The driving intellectual concern among European astronomers at this time was to see planetary surfaces in greater and greater detail. Were there mountains on Venus? Were there continents on Mars? Could one detect signs of life on the Moon? And what were the odd projections (originally styled *ansae*, or 'handles') that made Saturn look sometimes like a rugby ball, and sometimes like a sphere? The only way forward was to improve the telescope.

In consequence, the new breed of master-opticians who started to specialize in big telescope objectives – Eustachio Divini and Giuseppe Campani in Italy, Christiaan and Constantijn Huygens in Holland, and Richard Reeves in London – began to experiment with thick pieces of clear glass, sometimes almost as big as a saucer. They devised accurate hand-operated polishing machines that could impart the gentlest of curves to the glass to throw back the focal point to 12, 15, 25, 36, 60 or more feet away from the lens. And they did this not to reduce chromatic aberration – as is popularly assumed – but to obtain the biggest possible prime-focus image. For the bigger the original prime-focus image, the easier it was to get a very high magnification when that image was 'charged' (as they said in the 1660s) with a short-focus Keplerian or new Huygenian eyepiece.

Then all of a sudden new discoveries began to be made thick and fast. Christiaan Huygens, in the Hague in Holland, and using a 23-foot-focus refractor, which came into use in March 1655, was able to announce four major discoveries, in his *Systema Saturni* (1659). Firstly, that the odd shape of Saturn was caused by its being surrounded by a 'thin, flat ring, that nowhere touched the planet': Saturn's ring had been discovered. Secondly, that Mars seemed to have an axial rotation of just over one Earth day, and that there was a coloured marking on its surface – the Syrtis Major – the first 'continental' object to be found on any planetary surface. Thirdly, that the planet Saturn had a satellite, subsequently known as Titan. And fourthly, that the Orion Nebula resembled a faintly glowing, slightly curved mass, with a dozen stars in the same field. Could it be a hole in the stellar fabric through which an even more distant light was shining?

Already by his mid-twenties Huygens possessed an international reputation as an astronomer and as a deviser of instruments. And very soon after the Royal Society was founded, in 1661, he was invited to become part of its Fellowship. Indeed, the electing of distinguished for-eign Fellows to the Society was established right from the start, and clearly proclaimed the international character of the whole of science. It was, in fact, when Huygens was visiting London and the Royal Society in 1661 that he came upon a manuscript by that deceased young astronomer Jeremiah Horrocks, describing his observation of the Venus transit of 1639, as was mentioned above in relation to Sir Jonas Moore. Huygens wanted to see Horrock's manuscript published, and passed a copy on to the great Polish astronomer Johannes Hevelius, who, in recognition of Horrocks's genius, published it at his own expense in Danzig in 1662. Hevelius himself and Parisian astronomer Adrien Auzout were also elected overseas Fellows of the Royal Society, as were a number of others.

Several of the early Fellows of the Royal Society either owned, or else had access to, those remarkable long refracting telescopes. Wilkins seems to have had one with an object-glass of 80 feet focal length – and was faced with the problem of getting its long tube from Oxford to Cambridge when, in 1659, he was made Master of Trinity College, Cambridge. Sir Paul Neile, Dr Jonathan Goddard and Samuel Pepys each owned telescopes of a dozen or more feet focal length – all probably made by Richard Reeves, the foremost English object-glass grinder in the early 1660s, or perhaps by his rival Christopher Cocks. Wren mentions using telescopes of 6, 12, 22 and 35 feet focal length, while the Devonshire brothers Peter and William Ball, both Fellows of the Royal Society, reported to the Society their observations of Saturn with a 38-foot-focal-length refractor from their estate at Mamhead, near Exeter, in 1666.

Saturn, of course, was an object of great fascination to the astronomers of the 1660s, for what could those rings be made of, and how were they suspended around the planet? For quite simply, they were unique in the heavens. The Ball brothers suggested that Saturn had two, asymmetric rings, 180° apart from each other across the body of Saturn (looking a bit like a sideways-on figure-of-eight to a terrestrial observer). And then, in 1675–6, Giovanni Domenico Cassini, using a state-of-the-art long refractor and working near Paris, a slightly more southerly latitude than any available in England, and in clear country air, solved the rings riddle. He found that Saturn did indeed have two rings, but instead of being asymmetric, as the Ball brothers thought, the smaller ring was fitted exactly and symmetrically inside the larger ring, but with a slight gap between them: the Cassini Division.

Cassini, of course, had a slight latitude advantage over the English astronomers, for the new Royal Observatory outside Paris was 2½° nearer to the Equator than London, with the resulting effect that the ecliptic band through which the planets move is 2½° higher in the sky than in London: five whole lunar diameters higher, in fact. And not only had Cassini got a latitude advantage – crucial when trying to resolve tiny details on the surface of the planets – he also had cleaner and more stable air. Robert Hooke, on the contrary, working with 36- and 60-foot-focal-length telescopes from the Royal Society's meeting place, Gresham College, in Bishopsgate, was in the thick of the City of London, on the north bank of the Thames. When he looked south he had not only the coal smoke of thousands of chimneys to contend with, but also the hot air effluent of the tallow chandlers, soap boilers and other industrial enterprises which nestled along the banks of the river half a mile away.

In spite of these disadvantages, however, Hooke was a remarkable telescopic astronomer. Between about 1664 and 1678, indeed, he reported an astonishing body of original observations to the *Philosophical Transactions* journal and other publications of the Royal Society. For instance, he made detailed telescopic studies of the big, conspicuous comets of 1664 and 1677. He realized that inside the head of a comet was a bright nucleus, from which streamers poured out, to form the tail and *medulla* or stem: his fine drawing of the comet of 1677 was probably the first detailed physical case study of an individual comet, drawing attention to its nucleus, streamers and structural parts. So why, Hooke asked, did comets appear as fuzzy patches when well out in the Solar System, and then sprout a tail and structural detail only as they approached the Sun? Knowing nothing of radiation or energy physics, he suggested that the inner Solar System perhaps contained some sort of solvent (or in contemporary chemical terminology, a *menstruum*) which consumed or burnt up the Sun-bound comet, producing its streamers. Indeed, cometary nuclei, he deduced, must be self-luminous, for even the side of the nucleus pointing away from the Sun and into space glowed just as brightly as the Sun-facing side. But what kind of combustion could take place in airless space, and without flame?

Then Hooke became the first scientist to take astronomy into the laboratory, when he successfully simulated the tails of comets by suspending iron-filing-encrusted wax balls inside long glass cylinders of weak acid, and studying the resulting flow-pattern of the escaping (hydrogen) bubbles.

Comets were not the only heavenly bodies that Hooke tried to model in the experimental laboratory: he also attempted to re-create lunar craters. Though not a lunar cartographer, like his contemporaries Hevelius and Riccioli, Hooke does have the distinction of making the first high-magnification study of a single lunar formation. For in 1665, he published in his book *Micrographia* a detailed drawing of the single crater Hipparchus and its immediate vicinity. Yet how, Hooke argued, are craters formed? He then suggested that they may have been formed (a) by projectiles from space hitting the Moon, or (b) by lunar volcanic activity. Both of these were, of course, astonishingly advanced and original ideas for 1665, for no one at that date had any coherent idea of the existence of space débris or asteroidal matter. (Meteorites, for example, were thought to be the returning ejecta from terrestrial volcanoes.) Nor was there anything to suggest that the Moon had volcanoes. But Hooke went on with his modelling.

Firstly, he dropped lead pistol balls from a great height into a tub containing a thick, viscous pipe-clay mixture. The impacting balls formed astonishing lunar-like craters, with ramparts, and occasionally central elevations. Secondly, he used a pair of bellows to blow air beneath another thick, viscous mixture, and found that when the surface bubbles burst, they produced beautiful crater-like depressions. No one before had thought of astronomical bodies as being formed, and perhaps re-modelled, by slow, accumulative changes, and in this, as in many other things, Hooke was an amazingly original, lateral-thinking scientist.

It has been calculated – from the optical information contained in his reported observations – that the 60-foot-focus long telescope to which Hooke had access in 1665–6 had a magnification of ×173: a very respectable power, in fact. And with this, and with a 36-foot telescope having an object-glass of 3.5 inches in diameter, he made successive observations of Jupiter and Mars. He was able to identify six polar and belt zones on the surface of Jupiter, and may, with Cassini, have discovered that object later named the Great Red Spot in 1664. Hooke also recorded seeing the shadows of Jupiter's satellites move across the planet. Mars, however, he found a confusing object, for he could see no permanent marks on its surface, in spite of the fact that Huygens, whom Hooke knew, had already identified what we now call the Syrtis Major. This, however, led Hooke to wonder if, instead of having a clear axial rotation in a fixed plane, Mars had a 'turbinated' or rolling motion, in which it presented ever-changing appearances to the terrestrial observer.

Of course, we now know that Hooke was wrong, though what is likely – though it cannot be proven – is that when he was observing it in the spring of 1666, one of the Red Planet's global dust storms was raging, and obscuring the permanent detail.

Hooke also made active attempts to improve telescopes, for he was acutely aware by the 1660s that astronomical like all scientific progress depended on the quality and accuracy of available research instruments. He invented an ingenious, yet not ultimately practicable, 'Engin' or machine for figuring lenses. He even proposed – rather optimistically – the building of giant refracting telescopes with focal lengths of 1,000 or even 10,000 feet, but was brought sharply down to earth by Adrien Auzout, a Fellow of the Royal Society, in Paris, who wrote to the Royal Society saying that such monsters were utterly beyond technological feasibility, and would need object-glasses nearly two feet in diameter! Auzout was right, though Hooke still held out hopes that if we could make telescopes big enough, then we might be able to see signs of life on the Moon. At one point, he even suggested that the area around the crater Hipparchus reminded him of the fair rolling grasslands of Salisbury Plain! Hooke was a truly great scientist, but his imagination could, on occasion, run away with him!

THE THEORY OF GRAVITY

One area where Hooke's feet were much more securely on the ground, however, was the theory of gravitation. Although it was Sir Isaac Newton, elected to the Fellowship in 1672, who produced the definitive mathematical formulation of the laws of universal gravitation in 1687, the problem of *attraction* across space had long been a pressing problem for astronomers by 1660. Indeed, ever since astronomers had abandoned the classical idea that the planets and stars were attached to rotating crystalline spheres, soon after 1600, the cause of the 'gravitating principle' that pulled things to a centre had become an object of investigation for scientists. Johannes Kepler, by 1620, wondered whether it might be related to magnetism. After all, Galileo's discovery of sunspots had shown that the Sun rotated on its axis in 28 days, so could not the Sun be a giant magnet, emitting some kind of spinning flux across space, which made the planets move as part of a great, invisible whirlpool? A whirlpool which, nonetheless, moved in accordance with very exact physical principles, as Kepler had demonstrated in his three laws.

Between 1620 and the 1680s, many people worked on the gravity problem. Galileo's experiments with accelerating objects in free fall, and with the exactly equal, or 'isochronous', swings of simple pendulums, had shown that it was not the weight (Latin *gravitas*) of an object that mattered, but its proportionate relationship with the Earth. And was the force that made bricks fall from houses in any way connected with the force that made the planets orbit the Sun?

The young Englishman Jeremiah Horrocks, in the late 1630s, was experimenting with the 'precession of apsides', or the tendency of the major axis of a conical pendulum to gradually creep back upon itself. He used a simple pendulum, such as a weight hanging from a piece of string, and the weight was made to move in an elliptical orbit, which it does naturally when released (just try it). What was the invisible relationship between the weight, the suspension point and the Earth? Were forces similar to those acting between the Sun and planets in the Solar System at work? Indeed, many people – Galileo in Italy, Kepler in Austria, Gassendi in France, Huygens in Holland, and Horrocks and Hooke in England – were all working on the gravity problem long before Newton began to get interested after 1666.

And broadly speaking, all these scientists attacked the problem from two different research directions. One direction was that of controlled physical experiments, using falling, rolling or rotating objects. The other direction was the taking of precise angular measurements of the changing positions of the Sun, Moon, planets and comets against the fixed stars, to quantify their mutual speeding up and slowing down, in the hope of establishing how attractive forces might act at different distances in space. Yet was terrestrial attraction caused by the same invisible force as celestial attraction? No one could be really sure in 1660, but what could not be denied was the fact that *all* of these forces behaved with an amazing mathematical exactitude.

From the late 1650s to the mid-1670s, Robert Hooke was conducting a wide variety of researches into gravity: some were physical laboratory experiments in dynamics, others were based on the analysis of accurately measured planetary and cometary orbits. In 1669 he had attempted – unsuccessfully – to prove the Earth's yearly rotation from a hoped-for star parallax using a 36-foot zenith telescope, and by 1674 had marshalled an enormous amount of experimental and mathematical data. And in that year, he published, through the Royal Society, three demonstrable principles of gravity.

1. That all bodies possessed gravity, and had a gravitational effect upon each other's movements in space.
2. That all originally impulsed bodies would move in a straight line until another body deflected them into a circular or an elliptical curved motion.
3. That the mutual attraction between bodies increased with their closeness (though in 1674 Hooke had not yet been able to calculate in what ratio).

There was nothing secret in any of this, for not only was it published in his *An Attempt to prove the Motion of the Earth* (1674), but copies would have been sent to the learned societies of Europe. It is also impossible to believe that the young Isaac Newton was unfamiliar with it, and with Hooke's previous gravitation researches, for both men were Fellows of the Royal Society.

Hooke and Newton had really fallen out for the first time in 1673, when Hooke challenged Newton's theory of light and colours. But Hooke, who was at heart a convivial man, tried to patch up their relationship. Newton, as he himself was to record, first became interested in the force that made the Moon go around the Earth in 1666, though abandoning the study, as it made his head 'ake'. Yet as we have seen above, there had already been a great deal of work done on gravity by that date – and not secretly, but circulating freely among the astronomers and mathematicians of Europe.

Then in 1679 Hooke and Newton began to correspond about gravity. The letters still survive, and were even published in the twentieth century in Newton's *Correspondence*. Their chronology makes it clear not only that Hooke provided Newton with some rather significant ideas, but that, at this point, Newton abruptly broke off the correspondence. Had the correspondence with Hooke – particularly that pertaining to the free fall of bodies around a centre of attraction in space – suddenly cleared an obstruction in Newton's thinking, enabling him to proceed, and give no acknowledgement?

When Newton's monumental *Principia Mathematica* came off the presses in 1687, Hooke was furious. Furious *not* because of any reluctance to acknowledge the undoubted mathematical brilliance of the work, and the crucial inverse square law of gravitation which it contained, but because Newton refused to give him credit for his own contributions to its intellectual architecture.

The sad collapse of relations between Hooke and Newton after 1687 was one of the low points of the Royal Society's brilliant formative period. It was in part the product of a major personality clash, but stemmed largely from Newton's refusal to pay his intellectual debts. For in 1687 Hooke was no obscure third-rate pretender trying to steal Newton's undoubted glory, but a man of 52 who, for the past quarter-century, had earned and enjoyed a formidable, Europe-wide reputation as an astronomer and a physical scientist, and who simply wanted to be acknowledged for the contributions which he had made.

Nonetheless, the elucidation of the laws of gravitation by 1687 was not only one of the great astronomical achievements of the early Royal Society, but one of the great triumphs of the scientific method.

THE ROYAL OBSERVATORY, GREENWICH

One of the leading agendas of the early Royal Society was the use of the new science and technology to improve the human condition. Indeed, this had lain at the heart of that vision for the new, experimental science as advocated by Sir Francis Bacon around 1620, which would become a formative principle of the Society's creation in 1660. And one of Bacon's perceived goals for the new science was the improvement of navigation and practical seamanship.

Early seventeenth-century navigators had little difficulty in fixing their exact *latitude*, or north–south position, on the Earth's surface, between the equator and the poles: they could use the Pole Star, or the Sun. Yet what proved very hard to measure correctly was the east–west, or *longitude*, position of a ship on the high seas, such as how many degrees and minutes of arc it was west of Bristol, or east of the Cape of Good Hope. And as both sea-going trade and naval sea-power were growing rapidly by 1670, the problem of the longitude was coming to be acutely felt.

The solution lay in astronomy, for as the Moon is so much closer to us than the stars, the position of the Moon with relation to any given bright fixed star will be slightly different in Greenwich than it will be in Ireland, America or China, due to the lunar parallax angle.

The Royal Society was actively discussing this problem in 1674, largely at the suggestion of Sir Jonas Moore, and a young astronomer from Derby, the Revd John Flamsteed, was consulted. As one of the leading practical astronomers of his time, Flamsteed told the Royal Society that the only reliable way to fix a ship's position using the Moon was to totally re-observe the entire heavens from one base observatory, and measure the positions of the Sun, Moon and stars to a new level of accuracy employing the latest astronomical technology. This included large telescopic quadrants for measuring angles, and the new precision pendulum clocks which could be accurate to less than a minute of time per day.

King Charles II was impressed, and decided to found a Royal Observatory on top of Greenwich Hill. Sir Christopher Wren designed the buildings, the great Lancashire courtier-astronomer Sir Jonas Moore stood the cost of the newly designed instruments out of his own pocket and Flamsteed was warranted as the first Astronomer Royal in 1675.

Flamsteed worked night in, night out at the Royal Observatory for the next 46 years – dying while still in office on 31 December 1719. And while even his meticulous observations proved to be insufficiently accurate to make the 'lunars' longitude method viable, the vast body of astronomical data which he accumulated, and which his formidable widow Margaret published in three big volumes in 1725, immediately set new standards of angular measurement in astronomy. Yet it would take another half-century of observation, further major improvements in instrument technology, four subsequent Astronomers Royal and additional observations by Tobias Mayer at Göttingen in Germany before the 'lunars' method became practicable after 1767. And only shortly after that, the young Horatio Nelson would be getting ready to go to sea as a midshipman, and learning how to take 'lunars' as part of his navigation training.

But the Royal Observatory was to become an international benchmark for astronomical accuracy, and its creation in 1675 was one of the great achievements of early Royal Society astronomy. It was also the beginning of the Greenwich Meridian, which became the accepted international meridian in 1884.

CONCLUSION

Without doubt, the creation of the Royal Society in 1660 would turn out to be one of the great achievements in scientific history. Nor can it be denied that its contributions to astronomy were, and have continued to be, enormous, from Wilkins' flying chariot to Hooke's long-telescope observations, and on to the establishment of the Royal Observatory in 1675.

The Royal Society came to embody many of those characteristics that we now take for granted in a learned society. It was self-electing and self-regulating and under no outside control, seeing scientific originality as its chief criterion. It also invited distinguished foreigners to join its Fellowship. It initiated key lines of research among its self-funded members, and pioneered modern science journalism. The Society's *Philosophical Transactions* is probably the longest-running serial publication in history: its first number was issued in March 1665, and it is still going strong. This journal introduced the concept of a modern scientific forum, with original research articles, book reviews and letters sent in by Fellows reporting their observations and discoveries.

For while there had been societies of poets, writers and philosophers before 1660 in France and Italy, those bodies had all been relatively short-lived, and invariably under the direct patronage of a monarch or great noble. But the Royal Society, in its stress upon experimental and instrumental science, was unique. What is more, its independence from external control created a major precedent for the future of how science – especially British and American – would develop, while one has only to look at the preserved copies of its *Philosophical Transactions* to see how very prominently astronomy figured in the work of the Royal Society's founding Fellows.

FURTHER READING

Primary Sources

Note. Many of the English scientific books of this period are available on the website English books online. Books available in modern facsimile reprints are indicated.

John Flamsteed, *The 'Preface' to John Flamsteed's Historia Coelestis Britannica* (1725), ed. Allan Chapman, based on a translation by Alison Dione Johnson. National Maritime Museum Monographs No. 52 (1982).

Francesco Fontana, *New Discoveries made with his own telescopes and microscopes* (Naples 1646), translated by Sally Beaumont and Peter Fay (Reading, 2001).

Robert Hooke, *Micrographia* (1665): for astronomical observations see pp. 237–46 [reprint available].

The Diary of Robert Hooke 1672–1680, transcribed and edited by H. W. Robinson and W. Adams (London, 1930).

Robert Hooke, *An Attempt to prove the Motion of the Earth* (1674).

Robert Hooke, *A Description of Helioscopes* (1676).

Robert Hooke, *Cometa, or remarks about Comets* (London, 1678).

The Correspondence of Sir Isaac Newton, 1676–1687, II (1960), ed. H. W. Turnbull; for correspondence between Hooke and Newton, 1679.

Philosophical Transactions of the Royal Society, 1665–1668, contain detailed accounts of long telescope observations by Hooke and others. The journal is also available online via the Royal Society. See in particular vol. 1 (12), 2 April 1666, p. 198 (Hooke's Mars observations); 1 (14), 2 July 1666, pp. 245–6 (Jupiter observations) and p. 247 (Saturn observations); 11 (128), 1676, pp. 689–90 (Cassini Division report); 1 (1), 1665, pp. 3, 69 (improving telescopes); 2, 1667, pp. 541–4 (micrometer); 1 (9), 1666, pp. 152–3 (Ball brothers' observations of Saturn).

Thomas Sprat, *History of the Royal Society* (1667) [reprint available].

Richard Waller, *The Posthumous Works of Robert Hooke, M.D., F.R.S.* (1705) [reprint available].

Secondary Sources

Allan Chapman, *Dividing the Circle. The Development of Critical Angular Measurement in Astronomy 1500–1850* (Praxis-Wiley, 1990, 1995).

Allan Chapman, *England's Leonardo. Robert Hooke and the Seventeenth-Century Scientific Revolution* (Institute of Physics, 2005).

Allan Chapman, 'Hooke's telescopic observations of Solar System bodies', in Paul Kent and Allan Chapman (eds), *Robert Hooke and the English Renaissance* (Gracewing, 2005), pp. 95–123.

Stillman Drake, *The Discoveries and Opinions of Galileo* (Doubleday, 1957); contains translations of Galileo's principal astronomical tracts.

Eric G. Forbes, *Greenwich Observatory 1: Origins and Early History (1675–1835)* (Taylor and Francis, 1975).

Michael Hoskin (ed.), *The Cambridge Illustrated History of Astronomy* (Cambridge University Press, 1997).

Derek Howse, *Greenwich Observatory 3: The Buildings and Instruments* (Taylor and Francis, 1975).

Henry C. King, *The History of the Telescope* (1955).

John D. North, *The Measure of the Universe: a History of Modern Cosmology* (Oxford University Press, 1965; Dover, 1990).

Margery Purver, *The Royal Society: Concept and Creation* (1967).

Albert Van Helden, 'Christopher Wren's "De Corpore Saturni"', *Notes and Records of the Royal Society* 23 (1968), 221.

Albert Van Helden, 'The invention of the telescope', *Transactions of the American Philosophical Society* 67 (4) (Philadelphia, 1977), 1–64.

Part III

Miscellaneous

Some Interesting Variable Stars

JOHN ISLES

All variable stars are of potential interest, and hundreds of them can be observed with the slightest optical aid – even with a pair of binoculars. The stars in the list that follows include many that are popular with amateur observers, as well as some less well-known objects that are nevertheless suitable for study visually. The periods and ranges of many variables are not constant from one cycle to another, and some are completely irregular.

Finder charts are given after the list for those stars marked with an asterisk. These charts are adapted with permission from those issued by the Variable Star Section of the British Astronomical Association. Apart from the eclipsing variables and others in which the light changes are purely a geometrical effect, variable stars can be divided broadly into two classes: the pulsating stars, and the eruptive or cataclysmic variables.

Mira (Omicron Ceti) is the best-known member of the long-period subclass of pulsating red-giant stars. The chart is suitable for use in estimating the magnitude of Mira when it reaches naked-eye brightness – typically from about a month before the predicted date of maximum until two or three months after maximum. Predictions for Mira and other stars of its class follow the section of finder charts.

The semi-regular variables are less predictable, and generally have smaller ranges. V Canum Venaticorum is one of the more reliable ones, with steady oscillations in a six-month cycle. Z Ursae Majoris, easily found with binoculars near Delta, has a large range, and often shows double maxima owing to the presence of multiple periodicities in its light changes. The chart for Z is also suitable for observing another semi-regular star, RY Ursae Majoris. These semi-regular stars are mostly red giants or supergiants.

The RV Tauri stars are of earlier spectral class than the semi-regulars, and in a full cycle of variation they often show deep minima and double maxima that are separated by a secondary minimum. U Monocerotis is one of the brightest RV Tauri stars.

Among eruptive variable stars is the carbon-rich supergiant R Coronae Borealis. Its unpredictable eruptions cause it not to brighten, but to fade. This happens when one of the sooty clouds that the star throws out from time to time happens to come in our direction and blots out most of the star's light from our view. Much of the time R Coronae is bright enough to be seen in binoculars, and the chart can be used to estimate its magnitude. During the deepest minima, however, the star needs a telescope of 25-cm or larger aperture to be detected.

CH Cygni is a symbiotic star – that is, a close binary comprising a red giant and a hot dwarf star that interact physically, giving rise to outbursts. The system also shows semi-regular oscillations, and sudden fades and rises that may be connected with eclipses.

Observers can follow the changes of these variable stars by using the comparison stars whose magnitudes are given below each chart. Observations of variable stars by amateurs are of scientific value, provided they are collected and made available for analysis. This is done by several organizations, including the British Astronomical Association (see the list of astronomical societies in this volume), the American Association of Variable Star Observers (49 Bay State Road, Cambridge, Massachusetts 02138, USA) and the Royal Astronomical Society of New Zealand (PO Box 3181, Wellington, New Zealand).

Star	RA		Declination		Range	Type	Period	Spectrum
	h	m	°	′			(days)	
R Andromedae	00	24.0	+38	35	5.8–14.9	Mira	409	S
W Andromedae	02	17.6	+44	18	6.7–14.6	Mira	396	S
U Antliae	10	35.2	−39	34	5–6	Irregular	—	C
Theta Apodis	14	05.3	−76	48	5–7	Semi-regular	119	M
R Aquarii	23	43.8	−15	17	5.8–12.4	Symbiotic	387	M+Pec
T Aquarii	20	49.9	−05	09	7.2–14.2	Mira	202	M
R Aquilae	19	06.4	+08	14	5.5–12.0	Mira	284	M
V Aquilae	19	04.4	−05	41	6.6–8.4	Semi-regular	353	C
Eta Aquilae	19	52.5	+01	00	3.5–4.4	Cepheid	7.2	F–G
U Arae	17	53.6	−51	41	7.7–14.1	Mira	225	M
R Arietis	02	16.1	+25	03	7.4–13.7	Mira	187	M
U Arietis	03	11.0	+14	48	7.2–15.2	Mira	371	M
R Aurigae	05	17.3	+53	35	6.7–13.9	Mira	458	M
Epsilon Aurigae	05	02.0	+43	49	2.9–3.8	Algol	9892	F+B
R Boötis	14	37.2	+26	44	6.2–13.1	Mira	223	M
X Camelopardalis	04	45.7	+75	06	7.4–14.2	Mira	144	K–M

Star	RA h	RA m	Declination °	Declination ′	Range	Type	Period (days)	Spectrum
R Cancri	08	16.6	+11	44	6.1–11.8	Mira	362	M
X Cancri	08	55.4	+17	14	5.6–7.5	Semi-regular	195?	C
R Canis Majoris	07	19.5	−16	24	5.7–6.3	Algol	1.1	F
VY Canis Majoris	07	23.0	−25	46	6.5–9.6	Unique	—	M
S Canis Minoris	07	32.7	+08	19	6.6–13.2	Mira	333	M
R Canum Ven.	13	49.0	+39	33	6.5–12.9	Mira	329	M
*V Canum Ven.	13	19.5	+45	32	6.5–8.6	Semi-regular	192	M
R Carinae	09	32.2	−62	47	3.9–10.5	Mira	309	M
S Carinae	10	09.4	−61	33	4.5–9.9	Mira	149	K–M
l Carinae	09	45.2	−62	30	3.3–4.2	Cepheid	35.5	F–K
Eta Carinae	10	45.1	−59	41	−0.8–7.9	Irregular	—	Pec
R Cassiopeiae	23	58.4	+51	24	4.7–13.5	Mira	430	M
S Cassiopeiae	01	19.7	+72	37	7.9–16.1	Mira	612	S
W Cassiopeiae	00	54.9	+58	34	7.8–12.5	Mira	406	C
Gamma Cas.	00	56.7	+60	43	1.6–3.0	Gamma Cas.	—	B
Rho Cassiopeiae	23	54.4	+57	30	4.1–6.2	Semi-regular	—	F–K
R Centauri	14	16.6	−59	55	5.3–11.8	Mira	546	M
S Centauri	12	24.6	−49	26	7–8	Semi-regular	65	C
T Centauri	13	41.8	−33	36	5.5–9.0	Semi-regular	90	K–M
S Cephei	21	35.2	+78	37	7.4–12.9	Mira	487	C
T Cephei	21	09.5	+68	29	5.2–11.3	Mira	388	M
Delta Cephei	22	29.2	+58	25	3.5–4.4	Cepheid	5.4	F–G
Mu Cephei	21	43.5	+58	47	3.4–5.1	Semi-regular	730	M
U Ceti	02	33.7	−13	09	6.8–13.4	Mira	235	M
W Ceti	00	02.1	−14	41	7.1–14.8	Mira	351	S
*Omicron Ceti	02	19.3	−02	59	2.0–10.1	Mira	332	M
R Chamaeleontis	08	21.8	−76	21	7.5–14.2	Mira	335	M
T Columbae	05	19.3	−33	42	6.6–12.7	Mira	226	M
R Comae Ber.	12	04.3	+18	47	7.1–14.6	Mira	363	M
*R Coronae Bor.	15	48.6	+28	09	5.7–14.8	R Coronae Bor.	—	C
S Coronae Bor.	15	21.4	+31	22	5.8–14.1	Mira	360	M
T Coronae Bor.	15	59.6	+25	55	2.0–10.8	Recurrent nova	—	M+Pec
V Coronae Bor.	15	49.5	+39	34	6.9–12.6	Mira	358	C
W Coronae Bor.	16	15.4	+37	48	7.8–14.3	Mira	238	M
R Corvi	12	19.6	−19	15	6.7–14.4	Mira	317	M
R Crucis	12	23.6	−61	38	6.4–7.2	Cepheid	5.8	F–G
R Cygni	19	36.8	+50	12	6.1–14.4	Mira	426	S
U Cygni	20	19.6	+47	54	5.9–12.1	Mira	463	C
W Cygni	21	36.0	+45	22	5.0–7.6	Semi-regular	131	M
RT Cygni	19	43.6	+48	47	6.0–13.1	Mira	190	M

Star	RA		Declination		Range	Type	Period	Spectrum
	h	m	°	′			(days)	
SS Cygni	21	42.7	+43	35	7.7–12.4	Dwarf nova	50±	K+Pec
*CH Cygni	19	24.5	+50	14	5.6–9.0	Symbiotic	—	M+B
Chi Cygni	19	50.6	+32	55	3.3–14.2	Mira	408	S
R Delphini	20	14.9	+09	05	7.6–13.8	Mira	285	M
U Delphini	20	45.5	+18	05	5.6–7.5	Semi-regular	110?	M
EU Delphini	20	37.9	+18	16	5.8–6.9	Semi-regular	60	M
Beta Doradûs	05	33.6	−62	29	3.5–4.1	Cepheid	9.8	F–G
R Draconis	16	32.7	+66	45	6.7–13.2	Mira	246	M
T Eridani	03	55.2	−24	02	7.2–13.2	Mira	252	M
R Fornacis	02	29.3	−26	06	7.5–13.0	Mira	389	C
R Geminorum	07	07.4	+22	42	6.0–14.0	Mira	370	S
U Geminorum	07	55.1	+22	00	8.2–14.9	Dwarf nova	105±	Pec+M
Zeta Geminorum	07	04.1	+20	34	3.6–4.2	Cepheid	10.2	F–G
Eta Geminorum	06	14.9	+22	30	3.2–3.9	Semi-regular	233	M
S Gruis	22	26.1	−48	26	6.0–15.0	Mira	402	M
S Herculis	16	51.9	+14	56	6.4–13.8	Mira	307	M
U Herculis	16	25.8	+18	54	6.4–13.4	Mira	406	M
Alpha Herculis	17	14.6	+14	23	2.7–4.0	Semi-regular	—	M
68, u Herculis	17	17.3	+33	06	4.7–5.4	Algol	2.1	B+B
R Horologii	02	53.9	−49	53	4.7–14.3	Mira	408	M
U Horologii	03	52.8	−45	50	6–14	Mira	348	M
R Hydrae	13	29.7	−23	17	3.5–10.9	Mira	389	M
U Hydrae	10	37.6	−13	23	4.3–6.5	Semi-regular	450?	C
VW Hydri	04	09.1	−71	18	8.4–14.4	Dwarf nova	27±	Pec
R Leonis	09	47.6	+11	26	4.4–11.3	Mira	310	M
R Leonis Minoris	09	45.6	+34	31	6.3–13.2	Mira	372	M
R Leporis	04	59.6	−14	48	5.5–11.7	Mira	427	C
Y Librae	15	11.7	−06	01	7.6–14.7	Mira	276	M
RS Librae	15	24.3	−22	55	7.0–13.0	Mira	218	M
Delta Librae	15	01.0	−08	31	4.9–5.9	Algol	2.3	A
R Lyncis	07	01.3	+55	20	7.2–14.3	Mira	379	S
R Lyrae	18	55.3	+43	57	3.9–5.0	Semi-regular	46?	M
RR Lyrae	19	25.5	+42	47	7.1–8.1	RR Lyrae	0.6	A–F
Beta Lyrae	18	50.1	+33	22	3.3–4.4	Eclipsing	12.9	B
U Microscopii	20	29.2	−40	25	7.0–14.4	Mira	334	M
*U Monocerotis	07	30.8	−09	47	5.9–7.8	RV Tauri	91	F–K
V Monocerotis	06	22.7	−02	12	6.0–13.9	Mira	340	M
R Normae	15	36.0	−49	30	6.5–13.9	Mira	508	M
T Normae	15	44.1	−54	59	6.2–13.6	Mira	241	M
R Octantis	05	26.1	−86	23	6.3–13.2	Mira	405	M

Star	RA h	m	Declination °	'	Range	Type	Period (days)	Spectrum
S Octantis	18	08.7	−86	48	7.2−14.0	Mira	259	M
V Ophiuchi	16	26.7	−12	26	7.3−11.6	Mira	297	C
X Ophiuchi	18	38.3	+08	50	5.9−9.2	Mira	329	M
RS Ophiuchi	17	50.2	−06	43	4.3−12.5	Recurrent nova	—	OB+M
U Orionis	05	55.8	+20	10	4.8−13.0	Mira	368	M
W Orionis	05	05.4	+01	11	5.9−7.7	Semi-regular	212	C
Alpha Orionis	05	55.2	+07	24	0.0−1.3	Semi-regular	2335	M
S Pavonis	19	55.2	−59	12	6.6−10.4	Semi-regular	381	M
Kappa Pavonis	18	56.9	−67	14	3.9−4.8	W Virginis	9.1	G
R Pegasi	23	06.8	+10	33	6.9−13.8	Mira	378	M
X Persei	03	55.4	+31	03	6.0−7.0	Gamma Cas.	—	O9.5
Beta Persei	03	08.2	+40	57	2.1−3.4	Algol	2.9	B
Zeta Phoenicis	01	08.4	−55	15	3.9−4.4	Algol	1.7	B+B
R Pictoris	04	46.2	−49	15	6.4−10.1	Semi-regular	171	M
RS Puppis	08	13.1	−34	35	6.5−7.7	Cepheid	41.4	F−G
L2 Puppis	07	13.5	−44	39	2.6−6.2	Semi-regular	141	M
T Pyxidis	09	04.7	−32	23	6.5−15.3	Recurrent nova	7000±	Pec
U Sagittae	19	18.8	+19	37	6.5−9.3	Algol	3.4	B+G
WZ Sagittae	20	07.6	+17	42	7.0−15.5	Dwarf nova	1900±	A
R Sagittarii	19	16.7	−19	18	6.7−12.8	Mira	270	M
RR Sagittarii	19	55.9	−29	11	5.4−14.0	Mira	336	M
RT Sagittarii	20	17.7	−39	07	6.0−14.1	Mira	306	M
RU Sagittarii	19	58.7	−41	51	6.0−13.8	Mira	240	M
RY Sagittarii	19	16.5	−33	31	5.8−14.0	R Coronae Bor.	—	G
RR Scorpii	16	56.6	−30	35	5.0−12.4	Mira	281	M
RS Scorpii	16	55.6	−45	06	6.2−13.0	Mira	320	M
RT Scorpii	17	03.5	−36	55	7.0−15.2	Mira	449	S
Delta Scorpii	16	00.3	−22	37	1.6−2.3	Irregular	—	B
S Sculptoris	00	15.4	−32	03	5.5−13.6	Mira	363	M
R Scuti	18	47.5	−05	42	4.2−8.6	RV Tauri	146	G−K
R Serpentis	15	50.7	+15	08	5.2−14.4	Mira	356	M
S Serpentis	15	21.7	+14	19	7.0−14.1	Mira	372	M
T Tauri	04	22.0	+19	32	9.3−13.5	T Tauri	—	F−K
SU Tauri	05	49.1	+19	04	9.1−16.9	R Coronae Bor.	—	G
Lambda Tauri	04	00.7	+12	29	3.4−3.9	Algol	4.0	B+A
R Trianguli	02	37.0	+34	16	5.4−12.6	Mira	267	M
R Ursae Majoris	10	44.6	+68	47	6.5−13.7	Mira	302	M
T Ursae Majoris	12	36.4	+59	29	6.6−13.5	Mira	257	M
*Z Ursae Majoris	11	56.5	+57	52	6.2−9.4	Semi-regular	196	M
*RY Ursae Majoris	12	20.5	+61	19	6.7−8.3	Semi-regular	310?	M

Star	RA		Declination		Range	Type	Period (days)	Spectrum
	h	m	°	′				
U Ursae Minoris	14	17.3	+66	48	7.1–13.0	Mira	331	M
R Virginis	12	38.5	+06	59	6.1–12.1	Mira	146	M
S Virginis	13	33.0	−07	12	6.3–13.2	Mira	375	M
SS Virginis	12	25.3	+00	48	6.0–9.6	Semi-regular	364	C
R Vulpeculae	21	04.4	+23	49	7.0–14.3	Mira	137	M
Z Vulpeculae	19	21.7	+25	34	7.3–8.9	Algol	2.5	B+A

V CANUM VENATICORUM   13h 19.5m +45° 32′ (2000)

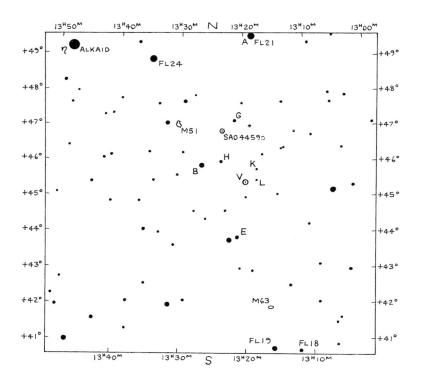

A 5.1   H 7.8
B 5.9   K 8.4
E 6.5   L 8.6
G 7.1

o (MIRA) CETI   02h 19.3m −02° 59′ (2000)

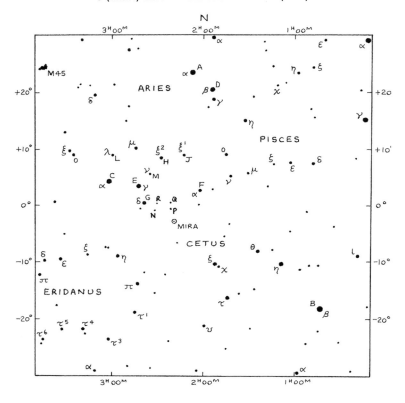

A	2.2	J	4.4
B	2.4	L	4.9
C	2.7	M	5.1
D	3.0	N	5.4
E	3.6	P	5.5
F	3.8	Q	5.7
G	4.1	R	6.1
H	4.3		

R CORONAE BOREALIS   15h 48.6m +28° 09′ (2000)

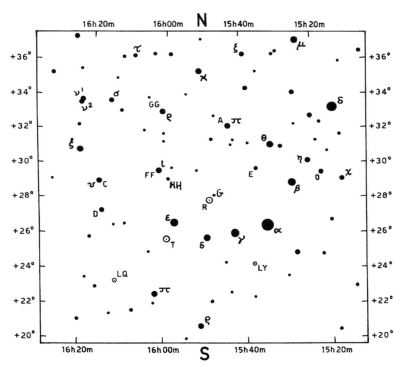

FF 5.0   C 5.8
GG 5.4   D 6.2
A 5.6   E 6.5
HH 7.1
G 7.4

CH CYGNI   19h 24.5m +50° 14' (2000)

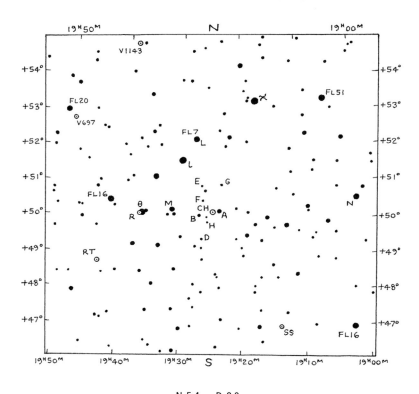

N 5.4	D 8.0
M 5.5	E 8.1
L 5.8	F 8.5
A 6.5	G 8.5
B 7.4	H 9.2

U MONOCEROTIS   07h 30.8m −09° 47′ (2000)

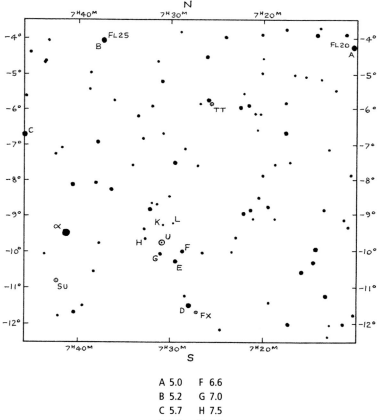

A 5.0	F 6.6
B 5.2	G 7.0
C 5.7	H 7.5
D 5.9	K 7.8
E 6.0	L 8.0

RY URSAE MAJORIS   12h 20.5m +61° 19' (2000)
Z URSAE MAJORIS   11h 56.5m +57° 52' (2000)

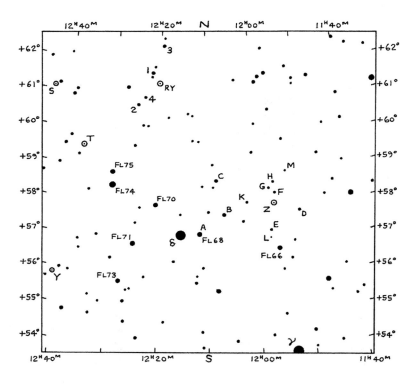

A	6.5	F	8.6	M	9.1
B	7.2	G	8.7	1	6.9
C	7.6	H	8.8	2	7.4
D	8.0	K	8.9	3	7.7
E	8.3	L	9.0	4	7.8

Mira Stars: Maxima, 2011

JOHN ISLES

Below are the predicted dates of maxima for Mira stars that reach magnitude 7.5 or brighter at an average maximum. Individual maxima can in some cases be brighter or fainter than average by a magnitude or more, and all dates are only approximate. The positions, extreme ranges and mean periods of these stars can be found in the preceding list of interesting variable stars.

Star	Mean magnitude at maximum	Dates of maxima
R Andromedae	6.9	19 Nov
W Andromedae	7.4	15 Sep
R Aquarii	6.5	29 Jan
R Aquilae	6.1	16 Feb, 27 Nov
R Bootis	7.2	30 May
R Cancri	6.8	28 Aug
S Canis Minoris	7.5	9 Oct
R Carinae	4.6	22 Sep
S Carinae	5.7	4 Feb, 3 Jul, 29 Nov
R Cassiopeiae	7.0	18 May
R Centauri	5.8	10 Jan (primary maximum), 12 Oct (secondary maximum, mean mag. 6.0)
T Cephei	6.0	3 Mar
U Ceti	7.5	3 Jul
Omicron Ceti	3.4	12 Sep
T Columbae	7.5	9 Jan, 22 Aug
S Coronae Borealis	7.3	16 Sep
V Coronae Borealis	7.5	22 Dec
R Corvi	7.5	10 Sep
R Cygni	7.5	13 Apr
U Cygni	7.2	3 May

Star	Mean magnitude at maximum	Dates of maxima
RT Cygni	7.3	10 Feb, 19 Aug
Chi Cygni	5.2	10 Feb
R Horologii	6.0	20 Mar
R Hydrae	4.5	26 Nov
R Leonis	5.8	21 May
R Leonis Minoris	7.1	6 Feb
R Leporis	6.8	17 Mar
RS Librae	7.5	28 Apr, 2 Dec
V Monocerotis	7.0	26 Mar
R Normae	7.2	18 Jul
T Normae	7.4	22 Aug
V Ophiuchi	7.5	11 Aug
X Ophiuchi	6.8	15 Oct
U Orionis	6.3	4 Mar
R Sagittarii	7.3	29 May
RR Sagittarii	6.8	17 Sep
RT Sagittarii	7.0	1 Mar
RU Sagittarii	7.2	11 Feb, 9 Oct
RR Scorpii	5.9	2 Jul
RS Scorpii	7.0	3 Nov
S Sculptoris	6.7	21 Dec
R Serpentis	6.9	3 Sep
R Trianguli	6.2	17 Feb, 10 Nov
R Ursae Majoris	7.5	22 Sep
R Virginis	6.9	1 Mar, 25 Jul, 17 Dec
S Virginis	7.0	24 Feb

Some Interesting Double Stars

BOB ARGYLE

The positions, angles and separations given below correspond to epoch 2011.0.

No.	RA		Declin-ation	Star	Magni-tudes	Separa-tion	PA	Cata-logue	Comments
	h	m	° ′			arcsec	°		
1	00	31.5	−62 58	β Tuc	4.4,4.8	27.1	169	LCL 119	Both stars again difficult doubles.
2	00	49.1	+57 49	η Cas	3.4,7.5	13.2	322	Σ60	Easy. Creamy, bluish. P = 480 years.
3	00	55.0	+23 38	36 And	6.0,6.4	1.1	325	Σ73	P = 168 years. Both yellow. Slowly opening.
4	01	13.7	+07 35	ζ Psc	5.6,6.5	23.1	63	Σ100	Yellow, reddish-white
5	01	39.8	−56 12	p Eri	5.8,5.8	11.7	188	Δ5	Period = 483 years.
6	01	53.5	+19 18	γ Ari	4.8,4.8	7.5	1	Σ180	Very easy. Both white.
7	02	02.0	+02 46	α Psc	4.2,5.1	1.8	264	Σ202	Binary, period = 933 years.
8	02	03.9	+42 20	γ And	2.3,5.0	9.6	63	Σ205	Yellow, blue. Relatively fixed.
				γ2 And	5.1,6.3	0.2	98	OΣ38	BC. Needs 50 cm. Closing.
9	02	29.1	+67 24	ι Cas AB	4.9,6.9	2.6	230	Σ262	AB is long period binary. P = 620 years.
				ι Cas AC	4.9,8.4	7.2	118		
10	02	33.8	−28 14	ω For	5.0,7.7	10.8	245	HJ 3506	Common proper motion.
11	02	43.3	+03 14	γ Cet	3.5,7.3	2.3	298	Σ299	Not too easy.
12	02	58.3	−40 18	θ Eri	3.4,4.5	8.3	90	PZ 2	Both white.
13	02	59.2	+21 20	ε Ari	5.2,5.5	1.4	208	Σ333	Closing slowly. P=350 years? Both white.

No.	RA	Declin-ation	Star	Magni-tudes	Separa-tion	PA	Cata-logue	Comments
	h m	° ′			arcsec	°		
14	03 00.9	+52 21	Σ331 Per	5.3,6.7	12.0	85	–	Fixed.
15	03 12.1	−28 59	α For	4.0,7.0	5.3	300	HJ 3555	P = 269 years. B variable?
16	03 48.6	−37 37	f Eri	4.8,5.3	8.2	215	Δ16	Pale yellow. Fixed.
17	03 54.3	−02 57	32 Eri	4.8,6.1	6.9	348	Σ470	Fixed.
18	04 32.0	+53 55	1 Cam	5.7,6.8	10.3	308	Σ550	Fixed.
19	04 50.9	−53 28	ι Pic	5.6,6.4	12.4	58	Δ18	Good object for small apertures. Fixed.
20	05 13.2	−12 56	κ Lep	4.5,7.4	2.0	357	Σ661	Visible in 7.5 cm. Slowly closing.
21	05 14.5	−08 12	β Ori	0.1,6.8	9.5	204	Σ668	Companion once thought to be close double
22	05 21.8	−24 46	41 Lep	5.4,6.6	3.4	93	HJ 3752	Deep yellow pair in a rich field.
23	05 24.5	−02 24	η Ori	3.8,4.8	1.7	78	DA 5	Slow-moving binary.
24	05 35.1	+09 56	λ Ori	3.6,5.5	4.3	44	Σ738	Fixed.
25	05 35.3	−05 23	θ Ori AB	6.7,7.9	8.6	32	Σ748	Trapezium in M42.
			θ Ori CD	5.1,6.7	13.4	61		
26	05 40.7	−01 57	ζ Ori	1.9,4.0	2.6	166	Σ774	Can be split in 7.5 cm. Long-period binary.
27	06 14.9	+22 30	η Gem	var,6.5	1.6	254	β1008	Well seen with 20 cm. Primary orange.
28	06 46.2	+59 27	12 Lyn AB	5.4,6.0,	1.8	68	Σ948	AB is binary, P = 706 years.
			12 Lyn AC	5.4,7.3	8.7	309	–	
29	07 08.7	−70 30	γ Vol	3.9,5.8	14.1	298	Δ42	Very slow binary.
30	07 16.6	−23 19	h3945 cMa	4.8,6.8	26.8	51	–	Contrasting colours. Yellow and blue.
31	07 20.1	+21 59	δ Gem	3.5,8.2	5.6	227	Σ1066	Not too easy. Yellow, pale blue.
32	07 34.6	+31 53	α Gem	1.9,2.9	4.7	57	Σ1110	Widening. Easy with 7.5 cm.
33	07 38.8	−26 48	κ Pup	4.5,4.7	9.8	318	H III 27	Both white.

No.	RA h m	Declin- ation ° ′	Star	Magni- tudes	Separa- tion arcsec	PA °	Cata- logue	Comments
34	08 12.2	+17 39	ζ Cnc AB	5.6,6.0	1.1	34	Σ1196	Period (AB)= 60 years. Near maximum separation.
			ζ Cnc AB-C	5.0,6.2	5.9	68	Σ1196	Period (AB C) = 1150 years.
35	08 46.8	+06 25	ε Hyd	3.3,6.8	2.9	306	Σ1273	PA slowly increasing. A is a very close pair.
36	09 18.8	+36 48	38 Lyn	3.9,6.6	2.6	226	Σ1334	Almost fixed.
37	09 47.1	−65 04	υ Car	3.1,6.1	5.0	129	RMK 11	Fixed. Fine in small telescopes.
38	10 20.0	+19 50	γ Leo	2.2,3.5	4.6	126	Σ1424	Binary, period = 510 years. Both orange.
39	10 32.0	−45 04	s Vel	6.2,6.5	13.5	218	PZ 3	Fixed.
40	10 46.8	−49 26	μ Vel	2.7,6.4	2.6	56	R 155	P = 138 years. Near widest separation.
41	10 55.6	+24 45	54 Leo	4.5,6.3	6.6	111	Σ1487	Slowly widening. Pale yellow and white.
42	11 18.2	+31 32	ξ UMa	4.3,4.8	1.6	204	Σ1523	Binary, 60 years. Needs 7.5 cm.
43	11 23.9	+10 32	ι Leo	4.0,6.7	2.0	99	Σ1536	Binary, period = 186 years.
44	11 32.3	−29 16	N Hya	5.8,5.9	9.4	210	H III 96	Fixed.
45	12 14.0	−45 43	D Cen	5.6,6.8	2.8	243	RMK 14	Orange and white. Closing.
46	12 26.6	−63 06	α Cru	1.4,1.9	4.0	114	Δ252	Third star in a low power field.
47	12 41.5	−48 58	γ Cen	2.9,2.9	0.3	315	HJ 4539	Period = 84 years. Closing. Both yellow.
48	12 41.7	−01 27	γ Vir	3.5,3.5	1.6	18	Σ1670	Now widening quickly. Beautiful pair for 10 cm.
49	12 46.3	−68 06	β Mus	3.7,4.0	1.0	54	R 207	Both white. Closing slowly. P = 194 years.
50	12 54.6	−57 11	μ Cru	4.3,5.3	34.9	17	Δ126	Fixed. Both white.

No.	RA	Declin- ation	Star	Magni- tudes	Separa- tion	PA	Cata- logue	Comments
	h m	° ′			arcsec	°		
51	12 56.0	+38 19	α CVn	2.9,5.5	19.3	229	Σ1692	Easy. Yellow, bluish.
52	13 22.6	−60 59	J Cen	4.6,6.5	60.0	343	Δ133	Fixed. A is a close pair.
53	13 24.0	+54 56	ζ UMa	2.3,4.0	14.4	152	Σ1744	Very easy. Naked eye pair with Alcor.
54	13 51.8	−33 00	3 Cen	4.5,6.0	7.7	102	H III 101	Both white. Closing slowly.
55	14 39.6	−60 50	α Cen	0.0,1.2	6.1	250	RHD 1	Finest pair in the sky. P = 80 years. Closing.
56	14 41.1	+13 44	ζ Boo	4.5,4.6	0.5	293	Σ1865	Both white. Closing − highly inclined orbit.
57	14 45.0	+27 04	ε Boo	2.5,4.9	2.9	344	Σ1877	Yellow, blue. Fine pair.
58	14 46.0	−25 27	54 Hya	5.1,7.1	8.3	122	H III 97	Closing slowly.
59	14 49.3	−14 09	μ Lib	5.8,6.7	1.8	6	β106	Becoming wider. Fine in 7.5 cm.
60	14 51.4	+19 06	ξ Boo	4.7,7.0	6.0	307	Σ1888	Fine contrast. Easy.
61	15 03.8	+47 39	44 Boo	5.3,6.2	1.5	60	Σ1909	Period = 206 years. Beginning to close.
62	15 05.1	−47 03	π Lup	4.6,4.7	1.7	66	HJ 4728	Widening.
63	15 18.5	−47 53	μ Lup AB	5.1,5.2	1.1	300	HJ 4753	AB closing. Under observed.
			μ Lup AC	4.4,7.2	22.7	127	Δ180	AC almost fixed
64	15 23.4	−59 19	γ Cir	5.1,5.5	0.7	359	HJ 4757	Closing. Needs 20 cm. Long-period binary.
65	15 34.8	+10 33	δ Ser	4.2,5.2	4.0	173	Σ1954	Long period binary.
66	15 35.1	−41 10	γ Lup	3.5,3.6	0.8	277	HJ 4786	Binary. Period = 190 years. Needs 20 cm.
67	15 56.9	−33 58	γ Lup	5.3,5.8	10.2	49	PZ 4	Fixed.
68	16 14.7	+33 52	σ CrB	5.6,6.6	7.1	238	Σ2032	Long-period binary. Both white.
69	16 29.4	−26 26	α Sco	1.2,5.4	2.6	277	GNT 1	Red, green. Difficult from mid-northern latitudes.

No.	RA		Declin-ation	Star	Magni-tudes	Separa-tion	PA	Cata-logue	Comments
	h	m	° ′			arcsec	°		
70	16	30.9	+01 59	λ Oph	4.2,5.2	1.4	38	Σ2055	P = 129 years. Fairly difficult in small apertures.
71	16	41.3	+31 36	ζ Her	2.9,5.5	1.1	170	Σ2084	Period 34 years. Now widening. Needs 20 cm.
72	17	05.3	+54 28	μ Dra	5.7,5.7	2.4	5	Σ2130	Period 672 years.
73	17	14.6	+14 24	α Her	var,5.4	4.6	103	Σ2140	Red, green. Long period binary.
74	17	15.3	−26 35	36 Oph	5.1,5.1	5.0	142	SHJ 243	Period = 471 years.
75	17	23.7	+37 08	ρ Her	4.6,5.6	4.1	319	Σ2161	Slowly widening.
76	17	26.9	−45 51	HJ 4949 AB	5.6,6.5	2.1	251	HJ 4949	Beautiful coarse triple. All white.
				Δ 216 AC	7.1	105.0	310		
77	18	01.5	+21 36	95 Her	5.0,5.1	6.5	257	Σ2264	Colours thought variable in C19.
78	18	05.5	+02 30	70 Oph	4.2,6.0	5.9	130	Σ2272	Opening. Easy in 7.5 cm.
79	18	06.8	−43 25	HJ 5014 CrA	5.7,5.7	1.7	2	–	Period = 450 years. Needs 10 cm.
80	18	25.4	−20 33	21 Sgr	5.0,7.4	1.7	279	JC 6	Slowly closing binary, orange and green.
81	18	35.9	+16 58	OΣ358 Her	6.8,7.0	1.5	149	–	Period = 380 years.
82	18	44.3	+39 40	ε1 Lyr	5.0,6.1	2.4	347	Σ2382	Quadruple system with epsilon2. Both pairs
83	18	44.3	+39 40	ε2 Lyr	5.2,5.5	2.4	78	Σ2383	visible in 7.5 cm.
84	18	56.2	+04 12	θ Ser	4.5,5.4	22.4	104	Σ2417	Fixed. Very easy
85	19	06.4	−37 04	γ CrA	4.8,5.1	1.4	8	HJ 5084	Beautiful pair. Period = 122 years.
86	19	30.7	+27 58	β Cyg AB	3.1,5.1	34.3	54	Σ I 43	Glorious. Yellow, blue-greenish.
				β Cyg Aa	3.1,5.2	0.4	95	MCA 55	Aa. Period = 214 years. Needs 40 cm.

No.	RA		Declin-ation	Star	Magni-tudes	Separa-tion	PA	Cata-logue	Comments
	h	m	° ′			arcsec	°		
87	19	45.0	+45 08	δ Cyg	2.9,6.3	2.7	219	Σ2579	Slowly widening. Period = 780 years.
88	19	48.2	+70 16	ε Dra	3.8,7.4	3.3	20	Σ2603	Slow binary.
89	19	54.6	−08 14	57 Aql	5.7,6.4	36.0	170	Σ2594	Easy pair. Contrasting colours.
90	20	46.7	+16 07	γ Del	4.5,5.5	9.1	265	Σ2727	Easy. Yellowish. Long period binary.
91	20	59.1	+04 18	ε Equ AB	6.0,6.3	0.5	283	Σ2737	Fine triple. AB is closing, P = 101.5 years
				ε Equ AC	6.0,7.1	10.3	66		
92	21	06.9	+38 45	61 Cyg	5.2,6.0	31.3	151	Σ2758	Nearby binary. Both orange. Period = 659 years.
93	21	19.9	−53 27	θ Ind	4.5,7.0	7.0	271	HJ 5258	Pale yellow and reddish. Long-period binary.
94	21	44.1	+28 45	μ Cyg	4.8,6.1	1.6	317	Σ2822	Period = 789 years.
95	22	03.8	+64 37	ξ Cep	4.4,6.5	8.4	274	Σ2863	White and blue. Long-period binary.
96	22	14.3	−21 04	41 Aqr	5.6,6.7	5.1	113	H N 56	Yellowish and purple?
97	22	26.6	−16 45	53 Aqr	6.4,6.6	1.3	43	SHJ 345	Long period binary; periastron in 2023.
98	22	28.8	−00 01	ζ Aqr	4.3,4.5	2.3	172	Σ2909	Period = 587 years. Slowly widening.
99	23	19.1	−13 28	94 Aqr	5.3,7.0	12.3	351	Σ2988	Yellow and orange. Probable binary.
100	23	59.5	+33 43	Σ3050 And	6.6,6.6	2.1	337	–	Period = 320 years.

Some Interesting Nebulae, Clusters and Galaxies

Object	RA		Declina-tion		Remarks
	h	m	°	′	
M31 Andromedae	00	40.7	+41	05	Andromeda Galaxy, visible to naked eye.
H VIII 78 Cassiopeiae	00	41.3	+61	36	Fine cluster, between Gamma and Kappa Cassiopeiae.
M33 Trianguli	01	31.8	+30	28	Spiral. Difficult with small apertures.
H VI 33–4 Persei, C14	02	18.3	+56	59	Double cluster; Sword-handle.
Δ142 Doradûs	05	39.1	−69	09	Looped nebula round 30 Doradus. Naked eye. In Large Magellanic Cloud.
M1 Tauri	05	32.3	+22	00	Crab Nebula, near Zeta Tauri.
M42 Orionis	05	33.4	−05	24	Orion Nebula. Contains the famous Trapezium, Theta Orionis.
M35 Geminorum	06	06.5	+24	21	Open cluster near Eta Geminorum.
H VII 2 Monocerotis, C50	06	30.7	+04	53	Open cluster, just visible to naked eye.
M41 Canis Majoris	06	45.5	−20	42	Open cluster, just visible to naked eye.
M47 Puppis	07	34.3	−14	22	Mag. 5.2. Loose cluster.
H IV 64 Puppis	07	39.6	−18	05	Bright planetary in rich neighbourhood.
M46 Puppis	07	39.5	−14	42	Open cluster.
M44 Cancri	08	38	+20	07	Praesepe. Open cluster near Delta Cancri. Visible to naked eye.
M97 Ursae Majoris	11	12.6	+55	13	Owl Nebula, diameter 3′. Planetary.
Kappa Crucis, C94	12	50.7	−60	05	'Jewel Box'; open cluster, with stars of contrasting colours.
M3 Can. Ven.	13	40.6	+28	34	Bright globular.
Omega Centauri, C80	13	23.7	−47	03	Finest of all globulars. Easy with naked eye.
M80 Scorpii	16	14.9	−22	53	Globular, between Antares and Beta Scorpii.
M4 Scorpii	16	21.5	−26	26	Open cluster close to Antares.

Object	RA		Declina-tion		Remarks
	h	m	°	′	
M13 Herculis	16	40	+36	31	Globular. Just visible to naked eye.
M92 Herculis	16	16.1	+43	11	Globular. Between Iota and Eta Herculis.
M6 Scorpii	17	36.8	−32	11	Open cluster; naked eye.
M7 Scorpii	17	50.6	−34	48	Very bright open cluster; naked eye.
M23 Sagittarii	17	54.8	−19	01	Open cluster nearly 50′ in diameter.
H IV 37 Draconis, C6	17	58.6	+66	38	Bright planetary.
M8 Sagittarii	18	01.4	−24	23	Lagoon Nebula. Gaseous. Just visible with naked eye.
NGC 6572 Ophiuchi	18	10.9	+06	50	Bright planetary, between Beta Ophiuchi and Zeta Aquilae.
M17 Sagittarii	18	18.8	−16	12	Omega Nebula. Gaseous. Large and bright.
M11 Scuti	18	49.0	−06	19	Wild Duck. Bright open cluster.
M57 Lyrae	18	52.6	+32	59	Ring Nebula. Brightest of planetaries.
M27 Vulpeculae	19	58.1	+22	37	Dumb-bell Nebula, near Gamma Sagittae.
H IV 1 Aquarii, C55	21	02.1	−11	31	Bright planetary, near Nu Aquarii.
M15 Pegasi	21	28.3	+12	01	Bright globular, near Epsilon Pegasi.
M39 Cygni	21	31.0	+48	17	Open cluster between Deneb and Alpha Lacertae. Well seen with low powers.

(M = Messier number; NGC = New General Catalogue number; C = Caldwell number.)

Our Contributors

Dr David M. Harland gained his BSc in astronomy in 1977 and a doctorate in computational science. Subsequently, he has taught computer science, worked in industry and managed academic research. In 1995 he 'retired' and has since published many books on space themes.

Richard Myer Baum is a former Director of the Mercury and Venus Section of the British Astronomical Association, an amateur astronomer and an independent scholar. He is author of *The Planets: Some Myths and Realities* (1973), (with W. Sheehan) *In Search of Planet Vulcan; the Ghost in Newton's Clockwork Universe* (1997) and *The Haunted Observatory* (2007). He has contributed to the *Journal of the British Astronomical Association*, *Journal for the History of Astronomy*, *Sky and Telescope* and many other publications including *The Dictionary of Nineteenth-Century British Scientists* (2004) and *The Biographical Encyclopedia of Astronomers* (2007).

Martin Mobberley is one of the UK's most active imagers of comets, planets, asteroids, variable stars, novae and supernovae and served as President of the British Astronomical Association from 1997 to 1999. In 2000 he was awarded the Association's Walter Goodacre Award. He is the sole author of seven popular astronomy books published by Springer as well as three children's 'Space Exploration' books published by Top That Publishing. In addition he has authored hundreds of articles in *Astronomy Now* and numerous other astronomical publications.

Professor Fred Watson is Astronomer-in-Charge of the Australian Astronomical Observatory at Coonabarabran in north-western New South Wales, and one of Australia's best-known science communicators.

He is a regular contributor to the *Yearbook of Astronomy*, and his recent books include *Universe* (for which he was chief consultant), *Stargazer – the Life and Times of the Telescope* and *Why is Uranus Upside Down – and Other Questions About the Universe*. In 2006 he was awarded the Australian Government Eureka Prize for Promoting Understanding of Science. In 2010 he was appointed a Member of the Order of Australia. Visit Fred's website at http://fredwatson.com.au/.

Jack Wickings joined the Sidmouth Astronomical Society in 1988. He became its Chairman in 1992 remaining in the post until 2005. During his tenure he saw the membership of the society rise from 40–50 to well over 200. He also saw the coming together of the Sidmouth Astronomical Society and Sidmouth Amateur Radio Society to form the Norman Lockyer Observatory Society, a company limited by guarantee and a registered charity. His time also saw a major expansion to the facilities at the observatory, a process which continues with the soon-to-be commissioned 20-inch telescope. None of this would have been possible without a large and enthusiastic membership.

Dr John Mason is co-editor of the *Yearbook of Astronomy*. He is a past President of the British Astronomical Association and Acting Director of the BAA's Meteor Section. He is currently Principal Lecturer at the South Downs Planetarium and Science Centre in Chichester. He is a frequent broadcaster on radio and television and has appeared many times with Sir Patrick Moore on BBC TV's *The Sky at Night*. For over twenty-five years he has been leading overseas expeditions to observe and record annular and total solar eclipses, the polar aurora and major meteor showers. He was made an MBE in the 2009 New Year's Honours List for his services to science education.

Paul G. Abel is a lunar and planetary amateur astronomer who makes all of his observations visually using drawings to capture the details of the Moon and planets. Paul is a reporter on the BBC's *Sky at Night* TV programme and is currently Assistant Director of the Saturn Section of the British Astronomical Association. By profession Paul is a theoretical physicist whose research interests lie in general relativity, Hawking radiation and quantum field theory in curved space-times. He currently teaches mathematics in the Department of Physics and Astronomy at the University of Leicester.

Dr Allan Chapman, of Wadham College, Oxford, is probably Britain's leading authority on the history of astronomy. He has published many research papers and several books, as well as numerous popular accounts. He is a frequent and welcome contributor to the *Yearbook*.

Astronomical Societies in the British Isles

Association for Astronomy Education
Secretary: Teresa Grafton, The Association for Astronomy Education, c/o The Royal Astronomical Society, Burlington House, Piccadilly, London W1V 0NL.

Astronomical Society of Edinburgh
Secretary: Graham Rule, 105/19 Causewayside, Edinburgh EH9 1QG.
Website: www.roe.ac.uk/asewww/; *Email:* asewww@roe.ac.uk
Meetings: City Observatory, Calton Hill, Edinburgh. 1st Friday each month, 8 p.m.

Astronomical Society of Glasgow
Secretary: Mr David Degan, 5 Hillside Avenue, Alexandria, Dunbartonshire G83 0BB.
Website: www.astronomicalsocietyofglasgow.org.uk
Meetings: Royal College, University of Strathclyde, Montrose Street, Glasgow. 3rd Thursday each month, Sept.–Apr., 7.30 p.m.

Astronomical Society of Haringey
Secretary: Jerry Workman, 91 Greenslade Road, Barking, Essex IG11 9XF.
Meetings: Palm Court, Alexandra Palace, 3rd Wednesday each month, 8 p.m.

Astronomy Ireland
Secretary: Tony Ryan, PO Box 2888, Dublin 1, Eire.
Website: www.astronomy.ie; *Email:* info@astronomy.ie
Meetings: 2nd Monday of each month. Telescope meetings every clear Saturday.

British Astronomical Association
Assistant Secretary: Burlington House, Piccadilly, London W1V 9AG.
Meetings: Lecture Hall of Scientific Societies, Civil Service Commission Building, 23 Savile Row, London W1. Last Wednesday each month (Oct.–June), 5 p.m. and some Saturday afternoons.

Federation of Astronomical Societies
Secretary: Clive Down, 10 Glan-y-Llyn, North Cornelly, Bridgend, County Borough CF33 4EF.
Email: clivedown@btinternet.com

Junior Astronomical Society of Ireland
Secretary: K. Nolan, 5 St Patrick's Crescent, Rathcoole, Co. Dublin.
Meetings: The Royal Dublin Society, Ballsbridge, Dublin 4. Monthly.

Society for Popular Astronomy
Secretary: Guy Fennimore, 36 Fairway, Keyworth, Nottingham NG12 5DU.
Website: www.popastro.com; *Email:* SPAstronomy@aol.com
Meetings: Last Saturday in Jan., Apr., July, Oct., 2.30 p.m. in London.

Webb Society
Treasurer/Membership Secretary: Steve Rayner, 10 Meon Close, Tadley RG26 4HN.

Aberdeen and District Astronomical Society
Secretary: Ian C. Giddings, 95 Brentfield Circle, Ellon, Aberdeenshire AB41 9DB.
Meetings: Robert Gordon's Institute of Technology, St Andrew's Street, Aberdeen.
Fridays, 7.30 p.m.

Abingdon Astronomical Society (was **Fitzharry's Astronomical Society**)
Secretary: Chris Holt, 9 Rutherford Close, Abingdon, Oxon OX14 2AT.
Website: www.abingdonastro.org.uk; *Email:* info@abingdonastro.co.uk
Meetings: All Saints' Methodist Church Hall, Dorchester Crescent, Abingdon, Oxon.
2nd Monday Sept.–June, 8 p.m. and additional beginners' meetings and observing
evenings as advertised.

Altrincham and District Astronomical Society
Secretary: Derek McComiskey, 33 Tottenham Drive, Manchester M23 9WH.
Meetings: Timperley Village Club. 1st Friday Sept.–June, 8 p.m.

Andover Astronomical Society
Secretary: Mrs S. Fisher, Staddlestones, Aughton, Kingston, Marlborough, Wiltshire
SN8 3SA.
Meetings: Grately Village Hall. 3rd Thursday each month, 7.30 p.m.

Astra Astronomy Section
Secretary: c/o Duncan Lunan, Flat 65, Dalraida House, 56 Blythswood Court,
Anderston, Glasgow G2 7PE.
Meetings: Airdrie Arts Centre, Anderson Street, Airdrie. Weekly.

Astrodome Mobile School Planetarium
Contact: Peter J. Golding, 53 City Way, Rochester, Kent ME1 2AX.
Website: www.astrodome.clara.co.uk; *Email:* astrodome@clara.co.uk

Aylesbury Astronomical Society
Secretary: Alan Smith, 182 Marley Fields, Leighton Buzzard, Bedfordshire LU7 8WN.
Meetings: 1st Monday in month at 8 p.m., venue in Aylesbury area. Details from
Secretary.

Bassetlaw Astronomical Society
Secretary: Andrew Patton, 58 Holding, Worksop, Notts S81 0TD.
Meetings: Rhodesia Village Hall, Rhodesia, Worksop, Notts. 2nd and 4th Tuesdays of
month at 7.45 p.m.

Batley & Spenborough Astronomical Society
Secretary: Robert Morton, 22 Links Avenue, Cleckheaton, West Yorks BD19 4EG.
Meetings: Milner K. Ford Observatory, Wilton Park, Batley. Every Thursday, 8 p.m.

Bedford Astronomical Society
Secretary: Mrs L. Harrington, 24 Swallowfield, Wyboston, Bedfordshire MK44 3AE.
Website: www.observer1.freeserve.co.uk/bashome.html
Meetings: Bedford School, Burnaby Rd, Bedford. Last Wednesday each month.

Bingham & Brooks Space Organization
Secretary: N. Bingham, 15 Hickmore's Lane, Lindfield, West Sussex.

Birmingham Astronomical Society
Contact: P. Bolas, 4 Moat Bank, Bretby, Burton-on-Trent DE15 0QJ.
Website: www.birmingham-astronomical.co.uk; *Email:* pbolas@aol.com
Meetings: Room 146, Aston University. Last Tuesday of month. Sept.–June (except
Dec., moved to 1st week in Jan.).

Blackburn Leisure Astronomy Section
Secretary: Mr H. Murphy, 20 Princess Way, Beverley, East Yorkshire HU17 8PD.
Meetings: Blackburn Leisure Welfare. Mondays, 8 p.m.

348 | 2011 YEARBOOK OF ASTRONOMY

Blackpool & District Astronomical Society
Secretary: Terry Devon, 30 Victory Road, Blackpool, Lancashire FY1 3JT.
Website: www.blackpoolastronomy.org.uk; *Email:* info@blackpoolastronomy.org.uk
Meetings: St Kentigern's Social Centre, Blackpool. 1st Wednesday of the month,
7.45 p.m.

Bolton Astronomical Society
Secretary: Peter Miskiw, 9 Hedley Street, Bolton, Lancashire BL1 3LE.
Meetings: Ladybridge Community Centre, Bolton. 1st and 3rd Tuesdays Sept.–May,
7.30 p.m.

Border Astronomy Society
Secretary: David Pettitt, 14 Sharp Grove, Carlisle, Cumbria CA2 5QR.
Website: www.members.aol.com/P3pub/page8.html
Email: davidpettitt@supanet.com
Meetings: The Observatory, Trinity School, Carlisle. Alternate Thursdays, 7.30 p.m.,
Sept.–May.

Boston Astronomers
Secretary: Mrs Lorraine Money, 18 College Park, Horncastle, Lincolnshire LN9 6RE.
Meetings: Blackfriars Arts Centre, Boston. 2nd Monday each month, 7.30 p.m.

Bradford Astronomical Society
Contact: Mrs J. Hilary Knaggs, 6 Meadow View, Wyke, Bradford BD12 9LA.
Website: www.bradford-astro.freeserve.co.uk/index.htm
Meetings: Eccleshill Library, Bradford. Alternate Mondays, 7.30 p.m.

Braintree, Halstead & District Astronomical Society
Secretary: Mr J. R. Green, 70 Dorothy Sayers Drive, Witham, Essex CM8 2LU.
Meetings: BT Social Club Hall, Witham Telephone Exchange. 3rd Thursday each
month, 8 p.m.

Breckland Astronomical Society (was **Great Ellingham and District Astronomy Club**)
Contact: Martin Wolton, Willowbeck House, Pulham St Mary, Norfolk IP21 4QS.
Meetings: Great Ellingham Recreation Centre, Watton Road (B1077), Great
Ellingham, 2nd Friday each month, 7.15 p.m.

Bridgend Astronomical Society
Secretary: Clive Down, 10 Glan-y-Llyn, Broadlands, North Cornelly, Bridgend
County CF33 4EF.
Email: clivedown@btinternet.com
Meetings: Bridgend Bowls Centre, Bridgend. 2nd Friday, monthly, 7.30 p.m.

Bridgwater Astronomical Society
Secretary: Mr G. MacKenzie, Watergore Cottage, Watergore, South Petherton,
Somerset TA13 5JQ.
Website: www.ourworld.compuserve.com/hompages/dbown/Bwastro.htm
Meetings: Room D10, Bridgwater College, Bath Road Centre, Bridgwater. 2nd
Wednesday each month, Sept.–June.

Bridport Astronomical Society
Secretary: Mr G.J. Lodder, 3 The Green, Walditch, Bridport, Dorset DT6 4LB.
Meetings: Walditch Village Hall, Bridport. 1st Sunday each month, 7.30 p.m.

Brighton Astronomical and Scientific Society
Secretary: Ms T. Fearn, 38 Woodlands Close, Peacehaven, East Sussex BN10 7SF.
Meetings: St John's Church Hall, Hove. 1st Tuesday each month, 7.30 p.m.

Bristol Astronomical Society
Secretary: Dr John Pickard, 'Fielding', Easter Compton, Bristol BS35 5SJ.
Meetings: Frank Lecture Theatre, University of Bristol Physics Dept., alternate
Fridays in term time, and Westbury Park Methodist Church Rooms, North View,
other Fridays.

Callington Community Astronomy Group
Secretary: Beccy Watson. *Tel:* 07891 573786
Email: enquiries@callington-astro.org.uk
Website: www.callington-astro.org.uk
Meetings: Callington Space Centre, Callington Community College, Launceston
Road, Callington, Cornwall PL17 7DR. 1st Friday of each month, 7.30 p.m.,
Sept.–June.

Cambridge Astronomical Society
Secretary: Brian Lister, 80 Ramsden Square, Cambridge CB4 2BL.
Meetings: Institute of Astronomy, Madingley Road. 3rd Friday each month.

Cardiff Astronomical Society
Secretary: D.W.S. Powell, 1 Tal-y-Bont Road, Ely, Cardiff CF5 5EU.
Meetings: Dept. of Physics and Astronomy, University of Wales, Newport Road,
Cardiff. Alternate Thursdays, 8 p.m.

Castle Point Astronomy Club
Secretary: Andrew Turner, 3 Canewdon Hall Close, Canewdon, Rochford, Essex
SS4 3PY.
Meetings: St Michael's Church Hall, Daws Heath. Wednesdays, 8 p.m.

Chelmsford Astronomers
Secretary: Brendan Clark, 5 Borda Close, Chelmsford, Essex.
Meetings: Once a month.

Chester Astronomical Society
Secretary: John Gilmour, 2 Thomas Brassey Close, Chester CH2 3AE.
Tel.: 07974 948278
Email: john_gilmour@ouvip.com
Website: www.manastro.co.uk/nwgas/chester/
Meetings: Burley Memorial Hall, Waverton, near Chester. Last Wednesday of each
month except August and December at 7.30 p.m.

Chester Society of Natural Science, Literature and Art
Secretary: Paul Braid, 'White Wing', 38 Bryn Avenue, Old Colwyn, Colwyn Bay
LL29 8AH.
Email: p.braid@virgin.net
Meetings: Once a month.

Chesterfield Astronomical Society
President: Mr D. Blackburn, 71 Middlecroft Road, Stavely, Chesterfield, Derbyshire
S41 3XG. Tel: 07909 570754.
Website: www.chesterfield-as.org.uk
Meetings: Barnet Observatory, Newbold, each Friday.

Clacton & District Astronomical Society
Secretary: C. L. Haskell, 105 London Road, Clacton-on-Sea, Essex.

Cleethorpes & District Astronomical Society
Secretary: C. Illingworth, 38 Shaw Drive, Grimsby, South Humberside.
Meetings: Beacon Hill Observatory, Cleethorpes. 1st Wednesday each month.

Cleveland & Darlington Astronomical Society
Contact: Dr John McCue, 40 Bradbury Rd., Stockton-on-Tees, Cleveland TS20 1LE.
Meetings: Grindon Parish Hall, Thorpe Thewles, near Stockton-on-Tees. 2nd Friday, monthly.

Cork Astronomy Club
Secretary: Charles Coughlan, 12 Forest Ridge Crescent, Wilton, Cork, Eire.
Meetings: 1st Monday, Sept.–May (except bank holidays).

Cornwall Astronomical Society
Secretary: J.M. Harvey, 1 Tregunna Close, Porthleven, Cornwall TR13 9LW.
Meetings: Godolphin Club, Wendron Street, Helston, Cornwall. 2nd and 4th Thursday of each month, 7.30 for 8 p.m.

Cotswold Astronomical Society
Secretary: Rod Salisbury, Grove House, Christchurch Road, Cheltenham, Gloucestershire GL50 2PN.
Website: www.members.nbci.com/CotswoldAS
Meetings: Shurdington Church Hall, School Lane, Shurdington, Cheltenham. 2nd Saturday each month, 8 p.m.

Coventry & Warwickshire Astronomical Society
Secretary: Steve Payne, 68 Stonebury Avenue, Eastern Green, Coventry CV5 7FW.
Website: www.cawas.freeserve.co.uk; *Email:* sjp2000@thefarside57.freeserve.co.uk
Meetings: The Earlsdon Church Hall, Albany Road, Earlsdon, Coventry. 2nd Friday, monthly, Sept.–June.

Crawley Astronomical Society
Secretary: Ron Gamer, 1 Pevensey Close, Pound Hill, Crawley, West Sussex RH10 7BL.
Meetings: Ifield Community Centre, Ifield Road, Crawley. 3rd Friday each month, 7.30 p.m.

Crayford Manor House Astronomical Society
Secretary: Roger Pickard, 28 Appletons, Hadlow, Kent TM1 0DT.
Meetings: Manor House Centre, Crayford. Monthly during term time.

Crewkerne and District Astronomical Society (CADAS)
Chairman: Kevin Dodgson, 46 Hermitage Street, Crewkerne, Somerset TA18 8ET.
Email: crewastra@aol.com

Croydon Astronomical Society
Secretary: John Murrell, 17 Dalmeny Road, Carshalton, Surrey.
Meetings: Lecture Theatre, Royal Russell School, Combe Lane, South Croydon. Alternate Fridays, 7.45 p.m.

Derby & District Astronomical Society
Secretary: Ian Bennett, Freers Cottage, Sutton Lane, Etwall.
Website: www.derby-astro-soc.fsnet/index.html;
Email: bennett.lovatt@btinternet.com
Meetings: Friends Meeting House, Derby. 1st Friday each month, 7.30 p.m.

Doncaster Astronomical Society
Secretary: A. Anson, 15 Cusworth House, St James Street, Doncaster DN1 3AY
Website: www.donastro.freeserve.co.uk; *Email:* space@donastro.freeserve.co.uk
Meetings: St George's Church House, St George's Church, Church Way, Doncaster. 2nd and 4th Thursday of each month, commencing at 7.30 p.m.

Dumfries Astronomical Society
Secretary: Klaus Schiller, lesley.burrell@btinternet.com.
Website: www.astronomers.ukscientists.com
Meetings: George St Church Hall, George St, Dumfries. 2nd Tuesday of each month,
Sept.–May.

Dundee Astronomical Society
Secretary: G. Young, 37 Polepark Road, Dundee, Tayside DD1 5QT.
Meetings: Mills Observatory, Balgay Park, Dundee. 1st Friday each month, 7.30 p.m.
Sept.–Apr.

Easington and District Astronomical Society
Secretary: T. Bradley, 52 Jameson Road, Hartlepool, Co. Durham.
Meetings: Easington Comprehensive School, Easington Colliery. Every 3rd Thursday
throughout the year, 7.30 p.m.

East Antrim Astronomical Society
Secretary: Stephen Beasant
Website: www.eaas.co.uk
Meetings: Ballyclare High School, Ballyclare, County Antrim. First Monday each
month.

Eastbourne Astronomical Society
Secretary: Peter Gill, 18 Selwyn House, Selwyn Road, Eastbourne, East Sussex
BN21 2LF.
Meetings: Willingdon Memorial Hall, Church Street, Willingdon. One Saturday per
month, Sept.–July, 7.30 p.m.

East Riding Astronomers
Secretary: Tony Scaife, 15 Beech Road, Elloughton, Brough, North Humberside
HU15 1JX.
Meetings: As arranged.

East Sussex Astronomical Society
Secretary: Marcus Croft, 12 St Mary's Cottages, Ninfield Road, Bexhill-on-Sea, East
Sussex.
Website: www.esas.org.uk
Meetings: St Mary's School, Wrestwood Road, Bexhill. 1st Thursday of each month,
8 p.m.

Edinburgh University Astronomical Society
Secretary: c/o Dept. of Astronomy, Royal Observatory, Blackford Hill, Edinburgh.

Ewell Astronomical Society
Secretary: Richard Gledhill, 80 Abinger Avenue, Cheam SM2 7LW.
Website: www.ewell-as.co.uk
Meetings: St Mary's Church Hall, London Road, Ewell. 2nd Friday of each month
except August, 7.45 p.m.

Exeter Astronomical Society
Secretary: Tim Sedgwick, Old Dower House, Half Moon, Newton St Cyres, Exeter,
Devon EX5 5AE.
Meetings: The Meeting Room, Wynards, Magdalen Street, Exeter. 1st Thursday of
month.

Farnham Astronomical Society
Secretary: Laurence Anslow, 'Asterion', 18 Wellington Lane, Farnham, Surrey
GU9 9BA.
Meetings: Central Club, South Street, Farnham. 2nd Thursday each month, 8 p.m.

Foredown Tower Astronomy Group
Secretary: M. Feist, Foredown Tower Camera Obscura, Foredown Road, Portslade, East Sussex BN41 2EW.
Meetings: At the above address, 3rd Tuesday each month. 7 p.m. (winter), 8 p.m. (summer).

Greenock Astronomical Society
Secretary: Carl Hempsey, 49 Brisbane Street, Greenock.
Meetings: Greenock Arts Guild, 3 Campbell Street, Greenock.

Grimsby Astronomical Society
Secretary: R. Williams, 14 Richmond Close, Grimsby, South Humberside.
Meetings: Secretary's home. 2nd Thursday each month, 7.30 p.m.

Guernsey: La Société Guernesiasie Astronomy Section
Secretary: Debby Quertier, Lamorna, Route Charles, St Peter Port, Guernsey GY1 1QS. and Jessica Harris, Keanda, Les Sauvagees, St Sampson's, Guernsey GY2 4XT.
Meetings: Observatory, Rue du Lorier, St Peter's. Tuesdays, 8 p.m.

Guildford Astronomical Society
Secretary: A. Langmaid, 22 West Mount, The Mount, Guildford, Surrey GU2 5HL.
Meetings: Guildford Institute, Ward Street, Guildford. 1st Thursday each month except Aug., 7.30 p.m.

Gwynedd Astronomical Society
Secretary: Mr Ernie Greenwood, 18 Twrcelyn Street, Llanerchymedd, Anglesey LL74 8TL.
Meetings: Dept. of Electronic Engineering, Bangor University. 1st Thursday each month except Aug., 7.30 p.m.

The Hampshire Astronomical Group
Secretary: Geoff Mann, 10 Marie Court, 348 London Road, Waterlooville, Hampshire PO7 7SR.
Website: www.hantsastro.demon.co.uk; *Email:* Geoff.Mann@hazleton97.fsnet.co.uk
Meetings: 2nd Friday, Clanfield Memorial Hall, all other Fridays Clanfield Observatory.

Hanney & District Astronomical Society
Secretary: Bob Church, 47 Upthorpe Drive, Wantage, Oxfordshire OX12 7DG.
Meetings: Last Thursday each month, 8 p.m.

Harrogate Astronomical Society
Secretary: Brian Bonser, 114 Main Street, Little Ouseburn TO5 9TG.
Meetings: National Power HQ, Beckwith Knowle, Harrogate. Last Friday each month.

Havering Astronomical Society
Secretary: Frances Ridgley, 133 Severn Drive, Upminster, Essex RM14 1PP.
Meetings: Cranham Community Centre, Marlborough Gardens, Upminster, Essex. 3rd Wednesday each month except July and Aug., 7.30 p.m.

Heart of England Astronomical Society
Secretary: John Williams, 100 Stanway Road, Shirley, Solihull B90 3JG.
Website: www.members.aol.com/hoeas/home.html; *Email:* hoeas@aol.com
Meetings: Furnace End Village, over Whitacre, Warwickshire. Last Thursday each month, except June, July & Aug., 8 p.m.

Hebden Bridge Literary & Scientific Society, Astronomical Section
Secretary: Peter Jackson, 44 Gilstead Lane, Bingley, West Yorkshire BD16 3NP.
Meetings: Hebden Bridge Information Centre. Last Wednesday, Sept.–May.

Herefordshire Astronomical Society
Secretary: Paul Olver, The Buttridge, Wellington Lane, Canon Pyon, Hereford HR4 8NL.
Email: info@hsastro.org.uk
Meetings: The Kindle Centre, ASDA Supermarket, Hereford. 1st Thursday of every month (except August) 7 p.m.

Herschel Astronomy Society
Secretary: Kevin Bishop, 106 Holmsdale, Crown Wood, Bracknell, Berkshire RG12 3TB.
Meetings: Eton College. 2nd Friday each month, 7.30 p.m.

Highlands Astronomical Society
Secretary: Richard Green, 11 Drumossie Avenue, Culcabock, Inverness IV2 3SJ.
Meetings: The Spectrum Centre, Inverness. 1st Tuesday each month, 7.30 p.m.

Hinckley & District Astronomical Society
Secretary: Mr S. Albrighton, 4 Walnut Close, The Bridleways, Hartshill, Nuneaton, Warwickshire CV10 0XH.
Meetings: Burbage Common Visitors Centre, Hinckley. 1st Tuesday Sept.–May, 7.30 p.m.

Horsham Astronomy Group (was **Forest Astronomical Society**)
Secretary: Dan White, 32 Burns Close, Horsham, West Sussex RH12 5PF.
Email: secretary@horshamastronomy.com
Meetings: 1st Wednesday each month.

Howards Astronomy Club
Secretary: H. Ilett, 22 St George's Avenue, Warblington, Havant, Hampshire.
Meetings: To be notified.

Huddersfield Astronomical and Philosophical Society
Secretary: Lisa B. Jeffries, 58 Beaumont Street, Netherton, Huddersfield, West Yorkshire HD4 7HE.
Email: l.b.jeffries@hud.ac.uk
Meetings: 4a Railway Street, Huddersfield. Every Wednesday and Friday, 7.30 p.m.

Hull and East Riding Astronomical Society
President: Sharon E. Long
Email: charon@charon.karoo.co.uk
Website: http://www.heras.org.uk
Meetings: The Wilberforce Building, Room S25, University of Hull, Cottingham Road, Hull. 2nd Monday each month, Sept.–May, 7.30–9.30 p.m.

Ilkeston & District Astronomical Society
Secretary: Mark Thomas, 2 Elm Avenue, Sandiacre, Nottingham NG10 5EJ.
Meetings: The Function Room, Erewash Museum, Anchor Row, Ilkeston. 2nd Tuesday monthly, 7.30 p.m.

Ipswich, Orwell Astronomical Society
Secretary: R. Gooding, 168 Ashcroft Road, Ipswich.
Meetings: Orwell Park Observatory, Nacton, Ipswich. Wednesdays, 8 p.m.

Irish Astronomical Association
President: Terry Moseley, 31 Sunderland Road, Belfast BT6 9LY, Northern Ireland.
Email: terrymosel@aol.com
Meetings: Ashby Building, Stranmillis Road, Belfast. Alternate Wednesdays, 7.30 p.m.

Irish Astronomical Society
Secretary: James O'Connor, PO Box 2547, Dublin 15, Eire.
Meetings: Ely House, 8 Ely Place, Dublin 2. 1st and 3rd Monday each month.
Isle of Man Astronomical Society
Secretary: James Martin, Ballaterson Farm, Peel, Isle of Man IM5 3AB.
Email: ballaterson@manx.net
Meetings: Isle of Man Observatory, Foxdale. 1st Thursday of each month, 8 p.m.
Isle of Wight Astronomical Society
Secretary: J. W. Feakins, 1 Hilltop Cottages, High Street, Freshwater, Isle of Wight.
Meetings: Unitarian Church Hall, Newport, Isle of Wight. Monthly.
Keele Astronomical Society
Secretary: Natalie Webb, Department of Physics, University of Keele, Keele,
Staffordshire ST5 5BG.
Meetings: As arranged during term time.
Kettering and District Astronomical Society
Asst. Secretary: Steve Williams, 120 Brickhill Road, Wellingborough,
Northamptonshire.
Meetings: Quaker Meeting Hall, Northall Street, Kettering, Northamptonshire.
1st Tuesday each month, 7.45 p.m.
King's Lynn Amateur Astronomical Association
Secretary: P. Twynman, 17 Poplar Avenue, RAF Marham, King's Lynn.
Meetings: As arranged.
Lancaster and Morecambe Astronomical Society
Secretary: Mrs E. Robinson, 4 Bedford Place, Lancaster LA1 4EB.
Email: ehelenerob@btinternet.com
Meetings: Church of the Ascension, Torrisholme. 1st Wednesday each month except
July and Aug.
Knowle Astronomical Society
Secretary: Nigel Foster, 21 Speedwell Drive, Balsall Common, Coventry,
West Midlands CV7 7AU.
Meetings: St George & St Theresa's Parish Centre, 337 Station Road, Dorridge,
Solihull, West Midlands B93 8TZ. 1st Monday of each month (+/− 1 week for Bank
Holidays) except August.
Lancaster University Astronomical Society
Secretary: c/o Students' Union, Alexandra Square, University of Lancaster.
Meetings: As arranged.
Layman's Astronomical Society
Secretary: John Evans, 10 Arkwright Walk, The Meadows, Nottingham.
Meetings: The Popular, Bath Street, Ilkeston, Derbyshire. Monthly.
Leeds Astronomical Society
Secretary: Mark A. Simpson, 37 Roper Avenue, Gledhow, Leeds LS8 1LG.
Meetings: Centenary House, North Street. 2nd Wednesday each month, 7.30 p.m.
Leicester Astronomical Society
Secretary: Dr P. J. Scott, 21 Rembridge Close, Leicester LE3 9AP.
Meetings: Judgemeadow Community College, Marydene Drive, Evington, Leicester.
2nd and 4th Tuesdays each month, 7.30 p.m.
Letchworth and District Astronomical Society
Secretary: Eric Hutton, 14 Folly Close, Hitchin, Hertfordshire.
Meetings: As arranged.

Lewes Amateur Astronomers
Secretary: Christa Sutton, 8 Tower Road, Lancing, West Sussex BN15 9HT.
Meetings: The Bakehouse Studio, Lewes. Last Wednesday each month.
Limerick Astronomy Club
Secretary: Tony O'Hanlon, 26 Ballycannon Heights, Meelick, Co. Clare, Eire.
Meetings: Limerick Senior College, Limerick. Monthly (except June and Aug.), 8 p.m.
Lincoln Astronomical Society
Secretary: David Swaey, 'Everglades', 13 Beaufort Close, Lincoln LN2 4SF.
Meetings: The Lecture Hall, off Westcliffe Street, Lincoln. 1st Tuesday each month.
Liverpool Astronomical Society
Secretary: Mr K. Clark, 31 Sandymount Drive, Wallasey, Merseyside L45 0LJ.
Meetings: Lecture Theatre, Liverpool Museum. 3rd Friday each month, 7 p.m.
Norman Lockyer Observatory Society
Secretary: G. E. White, PO Box 9, Sidmouth EX10 0YQ.
Website: www.ex.ac.uk/nlo/; *Email:* g.e.white@ex.ac.uk
Meetings: Norman Lockyer Observatory, Sidmouth. Fridays and 2nd Monday each month, 7.30 p.m.
Loughton Astronomical Society
Secretary: Charles Munton, 14a Manor Road, Wood Green, London N22 4YJ.
Meetings: 1st Theydon Bois Scout Hall, Loughton Lane, Theydon Bois. Weekly.
Lowestoft and Great Yarmouth Regional Astronomers (LYRA) Society
Secretary: Simon Briggs, 28 Sussex Road, Lowestoft, Suffolk.
Meetings: Community Wing, Kirkley High School, Kirkley Run, Lowestoft. 3rd Thursday each month, 7.30 p.m.
Luton Astronomical Society
Secretary: Mr G. Mitchell, Putteridge Bury, University of Luton, Hitchin Road, Luton.
Website: www.lutonastrosoc.org.uk; *Email:* user998491@aol.com
Meetings: Univ. of Luton, Putteridge Bury (except June, July and August), or Someries Junior School, Wigmore Lane, Luton (July and August only), last Thursday each month, 7.30–9.00 p.m.
Lytham St Anne's Astronomical Association
Secretary: K. J. Porter, 141 Blackpool Road, Ansdell, Lytham St Anne's, Lancashire.
Meetings: College of Further Education, Clifton Drive South, Lytham St Anne's. 2nd Wednesday monthly Oct.–June.
Macclesfield Astronomical Society
Secretary: Mr John H. Thomson, 27 Woodbourne Road, Sale, Cheshire M33 3SY
Website: www.maccastro.com; *Email:* jhandlc@yahoo.com
Meetings: Jodrell Bank Science Centre, Goostrey, Cheshire. 1st Tuesday of every month, 7 p.m.
Maidenhead Astronomical Society
Secretary: Tim Haymes, Hill Rise, Knowl Hill Common, Knowl Hill, Reading RG10 9YD.
Meetings: Stubbings Church Hall, near Maidenhead. 1st Friday Sept.–June.
Maidstone Astronomical Society
Secretary: Stephen James, 4 The Cherry Orchard, Haddow, Tonbridge, Kent.
Meetings: Nettlestead Village Hall. 1st Tuesday in the month except July and Aug., 7.30 p.m.

Manchester Astronomical Society
Secretary: Mr Kevin J. Kilburn FRAS, Godlee Observatory, UMIST, Sackville Street, Manchester M60 1QD.
Website: www.u-net.com/ph/mas/; *Email:* kkilburn@globalnet.co.uk
Meetings: At the Godlee Observatory. Thursdays, 7 p.m., except below.
Free Public Lectures: Renold Building UMIST, third Thursday Sept.–Mar., 7.30 p.m.

Mansfield and Sutton Astronomical Society
Secretary: Angus Wright, Sherwood Observatory, Coxmoor Road, Sutton-in-Ashfield, Nottinghamshire NG17 5LF.
Meetings: Sherwood Observatory, Coxmoor Road. Last Tuesday each month, 7.30 p.m.

Mexborough and Swinton Astronomical Society
Secretary: Mark R. Benton, 14 Sandalwood Rise, Swinton, Mexborough, South Yorkshire S64 8PN.
Website: www.msas.org.uk; *Email:* mark@masas.f9.co.uk
Meetings: Swinton WMC. Thursdays, 7.30 p.m.

Mid-Kent Astronomical Society
Secretary: Peter Parish, 30 Wooldeys Road, Rainham, Kent ME8 7NU.
Meetings: Bredhurst Village Hall, Hurstwood Road, Bredhurst, Kent. 2nd and last Fridays each month except August, 7.45 p.m.
Website: www.mkas-site.co.uk

Milton Keynes Astronomical Society
Secretary: Mike Leggett, 19 Matilda Gardens, Shenley Church End, Milton Keynes MK5 6HT.
Website: www.mkas.org.uk; *Email:* mike-pat-leggett@shenley9.fsnet.co.uk
Meetings: Rectory Cottage, Bletchley. Alternate Fridays.

Moray Astronomical Society
Secretary: Richard Pearce, 1 Forsyth Street, Hopeman, Elgin, Moray, Scotland.
Meetings: Village Hall Close, Co. Elgin.

Newbury Amateur Astronomical Society (NAAS)
Secretary: Mrs Monica Balstone, 37 Mount Pleasant, Tadley RG26 4BG.
Meetings: United Reformed Church Hall, Cromwell Place, Newbury. 1st Friday of month, Sept.–June.

Newcastle-on-Tyne Astronomical Society
Secretary: C. E. Willits, 24 Acomb Avenue, Seaton Delaval, Tyne and Wear.
Meetings: Zoology Lecture Theatre, Newcastle University. Monthly.

North Aston Space & Astronomical Club
Secretary: W. R. Chadburn, 14 Oakdale Road, North Aston, Sheffield.
Meetings: To be notified.

Northamptonshire Natural History Society (Astronomy Section)
Secretary: R. A. Marriott, 24 Thirlestane Road, Northampton NN4 8HD.
Email: ram@hamal.demon.co.uk
Meetings: Humfrey Rooms, Castilian Terrace, Northampton. 2nd and last Mondays, most months, 7.30 p.m.

Northants Amateur Astronomers
Secretary: Mervyn Lloyd, 76 Havelock Street, Kettering, Northamptonshire.
Meetings: 1st and 3rd Tuesdays each month, 7.30 p.m.

North Devon Astronomical Society
Secretary: P. G. Vickery, 12 Broad Park Crescent, Ilfracombe, Devon EX34 8DX.
Meetings: Methodist Hall, Rhododendron Avenue, Sticklepath, Barnstaple. 1st
Wednesday each month, 7.15 p.m.

North Dorset Astronomical Society
Secretary: J. E. M. Coward, The Pharmacy, Stalbridge, Dorset.
Meetings: Charterhay, Stourton, Caundle, Dorset. 2nd Wednesday each month.

North Downs Astronomical Society
Secretary: Martin Akers, 36 Timber Tops, Lordswood, Chatham, Kent ME5 8XQ.
Meetings: Vigo Village Hall. 3rd Thursday each month. 7.30 p.m.

North-East London Astronomical Society
Secretary: Mr B. Beeston, 38 Abbey Road, Bush Hill Park, Enfield EN1 2QN.
Meetings: Wanstead House, The Green, Wanstead. 3rd Sunday each month (except
Aug.), 3 p.m.

North Gwent and District Astronomical Society
Secretary: Jonathan Powell, 14 Lancaster Drive, Gilwern, nr Abergavenny,
Monmouthshire NP7 0AA.
Meetings: Gilwern Community Centre. 15th of each month, 7.30 p.m.

North Staffordshire Astronomical Society
Secretary: Duncan Richardson, Halmerend Hall Farm, Halmerend, Stoke-on-Trent,
Staffordshire ST7 8AW.
Email: dwr@enterprise.net
Meetings: 21st Hartstill Scout Group HQ, Mount Pleasant, Newcastle-under-Lyme
ST5 1DR. 1st Tuesday each month (except July and Aug.), 7–9.30 p.m.

Northumberland Astronomical Society
Contact: Dr Adrian Jametta, 1 Lake Road, Hadston, Morpeth, Northumberland
NE65 9TF.
Email: adrian@themoon.co.uk
Website: www.nastro.org.uk
Meetings: Hauxley Nature Reserve (near Amble). Last Thursday of every month
(except December), 7.30 pm. Additional meetings and observing sessions listed
on website.
Tel: 07984 154904

North Western Association of Variable Star Observers
Secretary: Jeremy Bullivant, 2 Beaminster Road, Heaton Mersey, Stockport,
Cheshire.
Meetings: Four annually.

Norwich Astronomical Society
Secretary: Dave Balcombe, 52 Folly Road, Wymondham, Norfolk NR18 0QR.
Website: www.norwich.astronomical.society.org.uk
Meetings: Seething Observatory, Toad Lane, Thwaite St Mary, Norfolk. Every Friday,
7.30 p.m.

Nottingham Astronomical Society
Secretary: C. Brennan, 40 Swindon Close, The Vale, Giltbrook, Nottingham
NG16 2WD.
Meetings: Djanogly City Technology College, Sherwood Rise (B682). 1st and 3rd
Thursdays each month, 7.30 p.m.

Oldham Astronomical Society
Secretary: P. J. Collins, 25 Park Crescent, Chadderton, Oldham.
Meetings: Werneth Park Study Centre, Frederick Street, Oldham. Fortnightly, Friday.

Open University Astronomical Society
Secretary: Dr Andrew Norton, Department of Physics and Astronomy, The Open University, Walton Hall, Milton Keynes MK7 6AA.
Website: www.physics.open.ac.uk/research/astro/a_club.html
Meetings: Open University, Milton Keynes. 1st Tuesday of every month, 7.30 p.m.

Orpington Astronomical Society
Secretary: Dr Ian Carstairs, 38 Brabourne Rise, Beckenham, Kent BR3 2SG.
Meetings: High Elms Nature Centre, High Elms Country Park, High Elms Road, Farnborough, Kent. 4th Thursday each month, Sept.–July, 7.30 p.m.

Papworth Astronomy Club
Contact: Keith Tritton, Magpie Cottage, Fox Street, Great Gransden, Sandy, Bedfordshire SG19 3AA.
Email: kpt2@tutor.open.ac.uk
Meetings: Bradbury Progression Centre, Church Lane, Papworth Everard, nr Huntingdon. 1st Wednesday each month, 7 p.m.

Peterborough Astronomical Society
Secretary: Sheila Thorpe, 6 Cypress Close, Longthorpe, Peterborough.
Meetings: 1st Thursday every month, 7.30 p.m.

Plymouth Astronomical Society
Secretary: Alan G. Penman, 12 St Maurice View, Plympton, Plymouth, Devon PL7 1FQ.
Email: oakmount12@aol.com
Meetings: Glynis Kingham Centre, YMCA Annex, Lockyer Street, Plymouth. 2nd Friday each month, 7.30 p.m.

PONLAF
Secretary: Matthew Hepburn, 6 Court Road, Caterham, Surrey CR3 5RD.
Meetings: Room 5, 6th floor, Tower Block, University of North London. Last Friday each month during term time, 6.30 p.m.

Port Talbot Astronomical Society (formerly **Astronomical Society of Wales**)
Secretary: Mr J. Hawes, 15 Lodge Drive, Baglan, Port Talbot, West Glamorgan SA12 8UD.
Meetings: Port Talbot Arts Centre. 1st Tuesday each month, 7.15 p.m.

Preston & District Astronomical Society
Secretary: P. Sloane, 77 Ribby Road, Wrea Green, Kirkham, Preston, Lancashire.
Meetings: Moor Park (Jeremiah Horrocks) Observatory, Preston. 2nd Wednesday, last Friday each month, 7.30 p.m.

Reading Astronomical Society
Secretary: Mrs Ruth Sumner, 22 Anson Crescent, Shinfield, Reading RG2 8JT.
Meetings: St Peter's Church Hall, Church Road, Earley. 3rd Friday each month, 7 p.m.

Renfrewshire Astronomical Society
Secretary: Ian Martin, 10 Aitken Road, Hamilton, South Lanarkshire ML3 7YA.
Website: www.renfrewshire-as.co.uk; *Email:* RenfrewAS@aol.com
Meetings: Coats Observatory, Oakshaw Street, Paisley. Fridays, 7.30 p.m.

Rower Astronomical Society
Secretary: Mary Kelly, Knockatore, The Rower, Thomastown, Co. Kilkenny, Eire.

St Helens Amateur Astronomical Society
Secretary: Carl Dingsdale, 125 Canberra Avenue, Thatto Heath, St Helens, Merseyside WA9 5RT.
Meetings: As arranged.

Salford Astronomical Society
Secretary: Mrs Kath Redford, 2 Albermarle Road, Swinton, Manchester M27 5ST.
Meetings: The Observatory, Chaseley Road, Salford. Wednesdays.

Salisbury Astronomical Society
Secretary: Mrs R. Collins, 3 Fairview Road, Salisbury, Wiltshire SP1 1JX.
Meetings: Glebe Hall, Winterbourne Earls, Salisbury. 1st Tuesday each month.

Sandbach Astronomical Society
Secretary: Phil Benson, 8 Gawsworth Drive, Sandbach, Cheshire.
Meetings: Sandbach School, as arranged.

Sawtry & District Astronomical Society
Secretary: Brooke Norton, 2 Newton Road, Sawtry, Huntingdon, Cambridgeshire PE17 5UT.
Meetings: Greenfields Cricket Pavilion, Sawtry Fen. Last Friday each month.

Scarborough & District Astronomical Society
Secretary: Mrs S. Anderson, Basin House Farm, Sawdon, Scarborough, North Yorkshire.
Meetings: Scarborough Public Library. Last Saturday each month, 7–9 p.m.

Scottish Astronomers Group
Secretary: Dr Ken Mackay, Hayford House, Cambusbarron, Stirling FK7 9PR.
Meetings: North of Hadrian's Wall, twice yearly.

Sheffield Astronomical Society
Secretary: Darren Swindels, 102 Sheffield Road, Woodhouse, Sheffield, South Yorkshire S13 7EU.
Website: www.sheffieldastro.org.uk; *Email:* info@sheffieldastro.org.uk
Meetings: Twice monthly at Mayfield Environmental Education Centre, David Lane, Fulwood, Sheffield S10, 7.30–10 p.m.

Shetland Astronomical Society
Secretary: Peter Kelly, The Glebe, Fetlar, Shetland ZE2 9DJ.
Email: theglebe@zetnet.co.uk
Meetings: Fetlar, Fridays, Oct.–Mar.

Shropshire Astronomical Society
Contact: Mr David Woodward, 20 Station Road, Condover, Shrewsbury, Shropshire SY5 7BQ.
Website: http://www.shropshire-astro.com; *Email:* jacquidodds@ntlworld.com
Meetings: Quarterly talks at the Gateway Arts and Education Centre, Chester Street, Shrewsbury and monthly observing meetings at Rodington Village Hall.

Sidmouth and District Astronomical Society
Secretary: M. Grant, Salters Meadow, Sidmouth, Devon.
Meetings: Norman Lockyer Observatory, Salcombe Hill. 1st Monday in each month.

Solent Amateur Astronomers
Secretary: Ken Medway, 443 Burgess Road, Swaythling, Southampton SO16 3BL.
Website: www.delscope.demon.co.uk;
Email: ken@medway1875.freeserve.co.uk
Meetings: Communications Room 2 Oasis Academy, Fairisle Road, Lordshill, Southampton, SO16 8BY. 3rd Tuesday each month, 7.30 p.m.

Southampton Astronomical Society
Secretary: John Thompson, 4 Heathfield, Hythe, Southampton SO45 5BJ.
Website: www.home.clara.net/lmhobbs/sas.html;
Email: John.G.Thompson@Tesco.net
Meetings: Conference Room 3, The Civic Centre, Southampton. 2nd Thursday each month (except Aug.), 7.30 p.m.

South Downs Astronomical Society
Secretary: J. Green, 46 Central Avenue, Bognor Regis, West Sussex PO21 5HH.
Website: www.southdowns.org.uk
Meetings: Chichester High School for Boys. 1st Friday in each month (except Aug.).

South-East Essex Astronomical Society
Secretary: C. P. Jones, 29 Buller Road, Laindon, Essex.
Website: www.seeas.dabsol.co.uk/; *Email:* cpj@cix.co.uk
Meetings: Lecture Theatre, Central Library, Victoria Avenue, Southend-on-Sea. Generally 1st Thursday in month, Sept.–May, 7.30 p.m.

South-East Kent Astronomical Society
Secretary: Andrew McCarthy, 25 St Paul's Way, Sandgate, near Folkestone, Kent CT20 3NT.
Meetings: Monthly.

South Lincolnshire Astronomical & Geophysical Society
Secretary: Ian Farley, 12 West Road, Bourne, Lincolnshire PE10 9PS.
Meetings: Adult Education Study Centre, Pinchbeck. 3rd Wednesday each month, 7.30 p.m.

Southport Astronomical Society
Secretary: Patrick Brannon, Willow Cottage, 90 Jacksmere Lane, Scarisbrick, Ormskirk, Lancashire L40 9RS.
Meetings: Monthly Sept.–May, plus observing sessions.

Southport, Ormskirk and District Astronomical Society
Secretary: J. T. Harrison, 92 Cottage Lane, Ormskirk, Lancashire L39 3NJ.
Meetings: Saturday evenings, monthly, as arranged.

South Shields Astronomical Society
Secretary: c/o South Tyneside College, St George's Avenue, South Shields.
Meetings: Marine and Technical College. Each Thursday, 7.30 p.m.

South Somerset Astronomical Society
Secretary: G. McNelly, 11 Laxton Close, Taunton, Somerset.
Meetings: Victoria Inn, Skittle Alley, East Reach, Taunton, Somerset. Last Saturday each month, 7.30 p.m.

South-West Hertfordshire Astronomical Society
Secretary: Tom Walsh, 'Finches', Coleshill Lane, Winchmore Hill, Amersham, Buckinghamshire HP7 0NP.
Meetings: Rickmansworth. Last Friday each month, Sept.–May.

Stafford and District Astronomical Society
Secretary: Miss L. Hodkinson, 6 Elm Walk, Penkridge, Staffordshire ST19 5NL.
Meetings: Weston Road High School, Stafford. Every 3rd Thursday, Sept.–May, 7.15 p.m.

Stirling Astronomical Society
Secretary: Hamish MacPhee, 10 Causewayhead Road, Stirling FK9 5ER.
Meetings: Smith Museum & Art Gallery, Dumbarton Road, Stirling. 2nd Friday each month, 7.30 p.m.

Stoke-on-Trent Astronomical Society
Secretary: M. Pace, Sundale, Dunnocksfold, Alsager, Stoke-on-Trent.
Meetings: Cartwright House, Broad Street, Hanley. Monthly.

Stratford-upon-Avon Astronomical Society
Secretary: Robin Swinbourne, 18 Old Milverton, Leamington Spa, Warwickshire CV32 6SA.
Meetings: Tiddington Home Guard Club. 4th Tuesday each month, 7.30 p.m.

Sunderland Astronomical Society
Contact: Don Simpson, 78 Stratford Avenue, Grangetown, Sunderland SR2 8RZ.
Meetings: Friends Meeting House, Roker. 1st, 2nd and 3rd Sundays each month.

Sussex Astronomical Society
Secretary: Mrs C. G. Sutton, 75 Vale Road, Portslade, Sussex.
Meetings: English Language Centre, Third Avenue, Hove. Every Wednesday, 7.30–9.30 p.m., Sept.–May.

Swansea Astronomical Society
Secretary: Dr Michael Morales, 238 Heol Dulais, Birch Grove, Swansea SA7 9LH.
Website: www.crysania.co.uk/sas/astro/star
Meetings: Lecture Room C, Science Tower, University of Swansea. 2nd and 4th Thursday each month from Sept.–June, 7 p.m.

Tavistock Astronomical Society
Secretary: Mrs Ellie Coombes, Rosemount, Under Road, Gunnislake, Cornwall PL18 9JL.
Meetings: Science Laboratory, Kelly College, Tavistock. 1st Wednesday each month, 7.30 p.m.

Thames Valley Astronomical Group
Secretary: K. J. Pallet, 82a Tennyson Street, South Lambeth, London SW8 3TH.
Meetings: As arranged.

Thanet Amateur Astronomical Society
Secretary: P. F. Jordan, 85 Crescent Road, Ramsgate.
Meetings: Hilderstone House, Broadstairs, Kent. Monthly.

Torbay Astronomical Society
Secretary: Tim Moffat, 31 Netley Road, Newton Abbot, Devon TQ12 2LL.
Meetings: Torquay Boys' Grammar School, 1st Thursday in month; and Town Hall, Torquay, 3rd Thursday in month, Oct.–May, 7.30 p.m.

Tullamore Astronomical Society
Secretary: Tom Walsh, 25 Harbour Walk, Tullamore, Co. Offaly, Eire.
Website: www.iol.ie/seanmck/tas.htm; *Email:* tcwalsh25@yahoo.co.uk
Meetings: Order of Malta Lecture Hall, Tanyard, Tullamore, Co. Offaly, Eire. Mondays at 8 p.m., every fortnight.

Tyrone Astronomical Society
Secretary: John Ryan, 105 Coolnafranky Park, Cookstown, Co. Tyrone, Northern Ireland.
Meetings: Contact Secretary.

Usk Astronomical Society
Secretary: Bob Wright, 'Llwyn Celyn', 75 Woodland Road, Croesyceiliog, Cwmbran NP44 2OX.
Meetings: Usk Community Education Centre, Maryport Street, Usk. Every Thursday during school term, 7 p.m.

Vectis Astronomical Society
Secretary: Rosemary Pears, 1 Rockmount Cottages, Undercliff Drive, St Lawrence, Ventnor, Isle of Wight PO38 1XG.
Website: www.wightskies.fsnet.co.uk/main.html;
Email: may@tatemma.freeserve.co.uk
Meetings: Lord Louis Library Meeting Room, Newport. 4th Friday each month except Dec., 7.30 p.m.

Vigo Astronomical Society
Secretary: Robert Wilson, 43 Admers Wood, Vigo Village, Meopham, Kent DA13 0SP.
Meetings: Vigo Village Hall. As arranged.

Walsall Astronomical Society
Secretary: Bob Cleverley, 40 Mayfield Road, Sutton Coldfield B74 3PZ.
Meetings: Freetrade Inn, Wood Lane, Pelsall North Common. Every Thursday.

Wealden Astronomical Society
Secretary: K.A. Woodcock, 24 Emmanuel Road, Hastings, East Sussex TN34 3LB.
Email: wealdenas@hotmail.co.uk
Meetings: Herstmonceux Science Centre. Dates, as arranged.

Wellingborough District Astronomical Society
Secretary: S. M. Williams, 120 Brickhill Road, Wellingborough, Northamptonshire.
Meetings: Gloucester Hall, Church Street, Wellingborough. 2nd Wednesday each month, 7.30 p.m.

Wessex Astronomical Society
Secretary: Leslie Fry, 14 Hanhum Road, Corfe Mullen, Dorset.
Meetings: Allendale Centre, Wimborne, Dorset. 1st Tuesday of each month.

West Cornwall Astronomical Society
Secretary: Dr R. Waddling, The Pines, Pennance Road, Falmouth, Cornwall TR11 4ED.
Meetings: Helston Football Club, 3rd Thursday each month, and St Michall's Hotel, 1st Wednesday each month, 7.30 p.m.

West of London Astronomical Society
Secretary: Duncan Radbourne, 28 Tavistock Road, Edgware, Middlesex HA8 6DA.
Website: www.wocas.org.uk
Meetings: Monthly, alternately in Uxbridge and North Harrow. 2nd Monday in month, except Aug.

West Midlands Astronomical Association
Secretary: Miss S. Bundy, 93 Greenridge Road, Handsworth Wood, Birmingham.
Meetings: Dr Johnson House, Bull Street, Birmingham. As arranged.

West Yorkshire Astronomical Society
Secretary: Pete Lunn, 21 Crawford Drive, Wakefield, West Yorkshire.
Meetings: Rosse Observatory, Carleton Community Centre, Carleton Road, Pontefract. Each Tuesday, 7.15 p.m.

Whitby and District Astronomical Society
Secretary: Rosemary Bowman, The Cottage, Larpool Drive, Whitby, North Yorkshire YO22 4ND.
Meetings: Whitby Mission, Seafarers' Centre, Haggersgate, Whitby. 1st Tuesday of the month, 7.30 p.m.

Whittington Astronomical Society
Secretary: Peter Williamson, The Observatory, Top Street, Whittington, Shropshire.
Meetings: The Observatory. Every month.
Wiltshire Astronomical Society
Chair: Mr Andrew J. Burns, The Knoll, Lowden Hill, Chippenham, SN15 2BT;
01249 654541
Website: www.wasnet.co.uk; *Email:* angleburns@hotmail.com
Secretary: Simon Barnes, 25 Woodcombe, Melksham, Wiltshire SN12 6HA.
Meetings: The Field Pavilion, Rusty Lane, Seend, Nr Devizes, Wiltshire. 1st Tuesday
each month, Sept.–June. Viewing evenings 4th Friday plus special events, Lacock
Playing Fields, Lacock, Wilsthire.
Wolverhampton Astronomical Society
Secretary: Mr M. Bryce, Iona, 16 Yellowhammer Court, Kidderminster,
Worcestershire DY10 4RR.
Website: www.wolvas.org.uk; *Email:* michaelbryce@wolvas.org.uk
Meetings: Beckminster Methodist Church Hall, Birches Barn Road, Wolverhampton.
Alternate Mondays, Sept.–Apr., extra dates in summer, 7.30 p.m.
Worcester Astronomical Society
Secretary: Mr S. Bateman, 12 Bozward Street, Worcester WR2 5DE.
Meetings: Room 117, Worcester College of Higher Education, Henwick Grove,
Worcester. 2nd Thursday each month, 8 p.m.
Worthing Astronomical Society
Contact: G. Boots, 101 Ardingly Drive, Worthing, West Sussex BN12 4TW.
Website: www.worthingastro.freeserve.co.uk;
Email: gboots@observatory99.freeserve.co.uk
Meetings: Heene Church Rooms, Heene Road, Worthing. 1st Wednesday each
month (except Aug.), 7.30 p.m.
Wycombe Astronomical Society
Secretary: Mr P. Treherne, 34 Honeysuckle Road, Widmer End, High Wycombe,
Buckinghamshire HP15 6BW.
Meetings: Woodrow High House, Amersham. 3rd Wednesday each month, 7.45 p.m.
The York Astronomical Society
Contact: Hazel Collett, Public Relations Officer
Tel: 07944 751277
Website: www.yorkastro.freeserve.co.uk; *Email:* info@yorkastro.co.uk
Meetings: The Knavesmire Room, York Priory Street Centre, Priory Street, York.
1st and 3rd Friday of each month (except Aug.), 8 p.m.

Any society wishing to be included in this list of local societies or to
update details, including any website addresses, is invited to write to
the Editor (c/o Pan Macmillan, 20 New Wharf Road, London N1 9RR
or astronomy@macmillan.co.uk), so that the relevant information may
be included in the next edition of the *Yearbook*.

The William Herschel Society maintains the museum established at 19 New King Street, Bath BA1 2BL – the only surviving Herschel House. It also undertakes activities of various kinds. New members would be welcome; those interested are asked to contact the Membership Secretary at the museum.

The South Downs Planetarium (Kingsham Farm, Kingsham Road, Chichester, West Sussex PO19 8RP) is now fully operational. For further information, visit www.southdowns.org.uk/sdpt or telephone (01243) 774400